SILICONES AND THEIR USES

Distillation towers used in silicone preparation.

SILICONES AND THEIR USES

ROB ROY McGREGOR

Administrative Fellow

Mellon Institute, Pittsburgh, Pa.

McGraw-Hill Book Company, Inc.

NEW YORK · TORONTO · LONDON

Library of Congress Catalog Card Number: 53-6046

IV

THE MAPLE PRESS COMPANY, YORK, PA.

What Are Silicones?

Silicones may be defined briefly, for the purposes of this book, as synthetic compounds containing the elements silicon and oxygen, and organic groups, the silicon being present in sufficient amount to affect the properties measurably.

As commercial products silicones assume many different forms: fluids, greases, resins, rubbers. They find application in practically all industries: aircraft manufacture, baking of bread, electrical insulation, lubrication, masonry protection, paint formulation, pharmaceutical preparations, textile finishing, to mention only a few.

Some of the properties that account for their wide variety of uses are small change of properties over a wide temperature range [−70°C (−94°F) to 250°C (482°F)], water repellency, good dielectric properties, low surface tension, nonstick properties, and lack of toxicity.

Preface

Few developments in technology in recent years have seemed so confusing to the average reader as that of the silicones. We can visualize a new metal alloy with distinctive properties, or a new textile that may be put to unaccustomed uses. But the silicones are not some particular material. They are a class of materials. The individual members of the class may be oils or resins or rubbers, or they may take still other forms. The very multiplicity of forms and uses seems to be the stumbling block in getting an understanding of what is meant when one says "silicones."

Many articles and at least two books have been published describing the properties and chemistry of these materials. Taken together they present a good description of the chemistry and fields of usefulness of the silicones. But the average reader has neither the time nor the facilities to bring all these writings together. He finds something in one place and something in another and may end up by being more confused than enlightened.

Recognition of this difficulty was the spur to preparation of a small volume that would correlate the available information.

What was wanted was a statement in as nontechnical language as possible that would give an over-all picture of what silicones are and what they can be used for. The literature and commercial bulletins have been combed to find illustrative material, and many specialists have contributed both information and criticism. Thus the book is really the work of many. But as water is said to pick up a flavor from the pump by which it is obtained, so the way in which these facts are presented must be charged to the author.

As the book was originated by a suggestion from the Dow Corning Corporation, it should not be surprising that many members of that organization have made helpful contributions. The valuable tabulation of uses of silicones in various industries (Chapter Four) was compiled by L. S. Putnam and James B. Davidson. T. A. Kauppi has been helpful in reading the entire manuscript and in giving both information and criticism. Dr. M. J. Hunter and C. C. Currie, after reviewing many of the sections, have suggested useful alterations. Dr. W. R. Collings and Dr. S. L. Bass have also provided advice and encouragement.

Dr. E. C. Sullivan has provided background information and has proposed changes in the sequence of chapters that have resulted in more logical presentation and in greater readability.

Dr. E. L. Warrick and Dr. J. L. Speier of the Multiple Fellowship on Silicones at the Mellon Institute have been of the greatest help through their willingness to discuss specific points and methods of presentation.

Dr. W. A. Hamor, Director of Research, Mellon Institute, has given thoughtful advice concerning methods of presentation and is responsible for numerous valuable suggestions.

The history of early organosilicon work has had the benefit of criticism from Dr. John W. Oliver, Head, Department of History, University of Pittsburgh.

It is a pleasure to acknowledge the kindness of the following individuals in providing literature and information concerning silicone products prepared by their companies: Mr. J. W. Raynolds, Silicone Department, General Electric Company; Dr. J. K. Simons, Plaskon Division, Libbey-Owens-Ford Glass Company; and Dr. C. O. Strother, Linde Air Products Company.

Special thanks are due to Eileen Messmer for her patience in typing repeated revisions and for her industry in seeing that the manuscript reached the completed stage.

Rob Roy McGregor

Contents

Introduction

This book is intended to serve as a practical manual on silicones for engineers, designers, and others who wish to use these products. It is not intended primarily for the chemist, and accordingly an attempt has been made to use nonchemical language in so far as possible. The larger part of it is given over to descriptions of the available commercial products, their properties, and how they can be used.

The book is divided into five chapters in the following order:

1. History of Silicones
2. Commercial Silicones
3. Physiological Response to Silicones
4. Applications of Silicones to Specific Industries and Cost Considerations
5. Chemistry of Silicone Preparation

History of Silicones (Chapter One) is divided into two sections: (1) the story of the early academic investigations; (2) the steps leading to commercial development.

The story of the early history explains how the materials first became of interest and serves as an introduction to the general chemistry involved.

The "commercial history" describes the steps by which the silicones grew from a few materials with specialized uses to a wide variety of products serving a multitude of industries.

Commercial Silicones (Chapter Two) commences with a condensed statement of the principles used in silicone preparation. It should be helpful to those who do not care to study the more complete description of the chemistry that appears in the last chapter.

The major portion of Chapter Two describes the physical properties and the applications of the commercial products. There is no doubt that many applications have been overlooked, for new uses are constantly being developed. The principal ways, however, in which silicones are being employed and the techniques of application are pointed out. These examples will suggest many others.

Most of the information given concerning these products may be found in industrial catalogues and other literature issued by the Dow Corning Corporation, Midland, Mich.; General Electric Company, Silicone Division, Waterford, N.Y.; Linde Air Products Company, Tonawanda, N.Y., and the Plaskon Division of the Libbey-Owens-Ford Glass Company, Toledo, Ohio. This volume summarizes much of this information and puts it in convenient form.

No apology need be made for the fact that many of the products are identified as being produced by the Dow Corning Corporation. Most of them are prepared by other manufacturers as well, but, because of his personal connection, the writer has had more complete access to Dow Corning records. The object has been to describe silicone products in general.

Chapter Three, a discussion of the physiological response to silicones, draws attention to an aspect of these materials that is only beginning to be investigated. Silicones appear to be without effect from a toxicological point of view, and suggestions have come from many quarters as to how they might be usefully employed in both pharmacy and medicine. These suggestions are pointed out in the hope that they may stimulate further investigations by workers in these fields.

Chapter Four shows a tabulation of representative industries and the applications they have made of silicones. A short discussion of the price situation with regard to silicones is included.

Chemistry of Silicone Preparation (Chapter Five) describes the preparation of silicones from the raw materials to the finished products. The reactions and techniques for forming the intermediates are described. A section on polymerization tells of the methods used to prepare fluid and resinous products.

This chapter will prove of more interest to the chemist, but should also be informative to the nonchemist who wishes more than a superficial knowledge of silicones. No attempt is made to give more than the fundamental reactions in the formation of silicones, but this information provides a basis for supplemental study. The chemist who wishes a more complete statement of the chemistry involved should consult Rochow's "Introduction to the Chemistry of the Silicones" (Wiley) or the bibliography compiled by Post in his "Silicones and Other Organic Silicon Compounds" (Reinhold).

CHAPTER ONE

History of Silicones

Section 1:

Early Studies in Organosilicon Chemistry

The basic material from which the silicones are formed is quartz, *i.e.*, silica or silicon dioxide, SiO_2. It is the main constituent of ordinary white sand. In the form of large crystals or fine grains it has been known since man first trod the earth. But for thousands of years its true nature was unknown. It was known simply as a hard, transparent, and colorless material that could be melted only by the application of intense heat. It was unaffected by any acids but it could be melted at a lower temperature if mixed with wood ashes or potash. One of the earliest uses of silica was in the manufacture of glass. Silica was used simply because it gave a desired result, but the nature of it was a complete mystery. One of the earliest recorded guesses as to the nature of silica was made by the Roman scholar Pliny, about the beginning of the Christian era, when he suggested that it was a form of ice resulting from excessive freezing.[1]*

* Superscript numbers denote references, which are listed in Literature Cited, at the back of the book.

Throughout the years following Pliny's statement men busied themselves in a search after the philosopher's stone, the transmutation of base elements into gold or some universal medicine that would cure all ills. They were to discover in their search a great deal about mercury, sulfur, iron, lead, and other metals. These investigators were the alchemists who groped their way about in the early dawn of chemical knowledge, some seeking truth and others seeking notoriety. Silica or sand did not appear to have any glamour for them, for they did little to improve on Pliny's idea that silica was a special form of ice. So the years and the centuries rolled by while this form of matter, put to use in one way or another, remained a complete enigma.

Johann van Helmont (1577–1644), son of a wealthy and noble family of Brussels, studied the various arts and sciences taught in his time but came to the conclusion that much of what he learned was based on false premises. Of an independent turn of mind, he decided to determine some facts by direct experiment. What is of interest to us is that he tried to find out something about silica. A definite weight of silica was heated with soda ash, forming a soluble glass or "water glass." When this was dissolved in water and the solution acidified, a solid material precipitated. The weight of the precipitate was the same as that of the sand he had used in the first place.[2] That may seem little to find as a result of his experiment, but he could do little more than note the fact and hope that it might be of interest to someone later.

About this time a new attitude became evident in investigations of this type, for a more inquiring spirit was abroad and there were questionings of some of the pontifical statements of the elders. There appeared men like Robert Boyle (1627–1691) who reasoned independently and who wanted to obtain their information by experiment and observation. Stahl (1660–1734), Cavendish (1731–1810), Priestley (1733–1804), and Scheele (1742–1786) are names familiar to the history of science, for one by one they arose to throw off the shackles of black magic and alchemy.

Although the techniques of the experimental method were limited, these men devised, by one means or another, to get firsthand information and to reason on the basis of observed results.

Scheele was a Swedish apothecary, poor but filled with an insatiable curiosity. He was not a profound thinker but was a brilliant and tireless technician. He was the first to isolate chlorine, discovered many of the inorganic and organic acids, and investigated glycerin, borax, and graphite as well as a multitude of other compounds. Following his discovery of hydrofluoric acid, HF, in 1771, he believed that he had learned the composition of silica. He produced the acid by heating fluorspar, CaF_2, in the presence of sulfuric acid. The reaction was carried out in a glass vessel, and when the gas (HF) was passed into water, a precipitate was formed which proved to be silica. Scheele made the natural deduction from this that silica was the reaction product of hydrofluoric acid and water.[3] But his triumph was short-lived, for it was shown that if the acid was generated in a lead vessel no silica was formed. The silica had come from the glass. While this result showed that his original deduction was wrong, it did demonstrate that silica could be formed from a volatile compound.

So by the year 1800 little more was known about silica than that it was hard, transparent, and high-melting, that it would react with alkalies, and that one of the essential constituents could appear as part of a volatile compound.

In the latter part of the eighteenth century Lavoisier had successfully combatted the old "phlogiston" theory and had shown that when metals and other substances are heated to a high temperature they combine with oxygen. The old nomenclature of "metallic calx" gave place to "metallic oxide." Lavoisier even went so far as to hint that the caustic alkalies, up to then regarded as elements, might be the oxides of unknown metals. Sir Humphry Davy (1778–1829) in England was intrigued with this notion. He had seen the great power of decomposition exhibited by the voltaic battery and decided to try its effect on the alkalies. By this means in 1807 he was able to isolate potassium and later sodium as well. This success led him to the opinion that silica, similarly, might be the oxide of some unknown element. But in spite of his best efforts he could effect no change in the silica.[4]

The idea that removal of oxygen from various compounds would reveal the presence of new elements was not held by Davy alone. Johann Berzelius (1779–1848) in Stockholm held such ideas. He was a stocky Swede who became a member of the nobility but maintained the study of chemistry as his prime interest. Laboratory assistants were apparently not easy to find, for his cook was given the double duty of preparing meals and cleaning laboratory ware. Berzelius was a prodigious worker, and, in addition to doing experimental work, expressed his opinions on the new chemical ideas being promulgated. He was responsible for originating our present method of chemical notation. Berzelius was acquainted with Davy's unsuccessful attempts to isolate a new element from silica and decided to try chemical means. He decided to start with potassium fluosilicate, K_2SiF_6, and flux this with an excess of Davy's newly discovered potassium metal. He was excited to find that the mixture melted well together and that when cooled it could be extracted with water. A black powdery residue was left. This was the long-sought unknown element which had been locked up in the structure of quartz. This was reported in the year 1824.[5]

Thus culminated the apparently hopeless quest for a knowledge of the constitution of silica, the most abundant compound in the crust of the earth.

One could imagine the jubilation such a result would cause in the mind of the discoverer. He would surely take some time out to gloat over his success and to notify scientifically minded individuals that he had accomplished the impossible. To read Berzelius's account of his results is to dispel any such illusions. Instead of slowing up momentarily, he appeared to attack further work with something amounting to fury. He examined the new element for its reaction to heat, acids, and alkalies. His most surprising result came when he led a stream of chlorine through his new product. As stated in his article, "If silicon is heated in a stream of chlorine it ignites and burns vigorously . . . the product from this burning may be condensed to a liquid with a yellow color from the excess of chlorine. Freed from chlorine, the liquid is colorless. It has a suffocating odor."[6]

The liquid product from the reaction of chlorine and silicon was silicon tetrachloride, $SiCl_4$. This is produced commercially today by methods similar to that used by Berzelius and is one of the basic materials used in the preparation of silicones.

Silicon in the form of the chloride was found to be much more reactive than the oxide. The first investigators could do little more than try various reactions to see what would happen, for there was no previous experience to guide them. And a fund of knowledge could be built up only by treating it with various reagents and observing what happened.

In 1830 a French chemist by the name of Persoz reported that he had treated the "chloride of silicon" with ammonia and obtained a white solid product which was extremely resistant to heat.[7] He did not present it as a monumental discovery, but just as something he had observed—in case anyone was interested.

About fifteen years later another French chemist, Ebelman, no doubt realizing that there was an acid characteristic to "the chloride of silicon," treated it with ethyl alcohol. If an organic acid were treated with ethyl alcohol there would be a reaction resulting in the formation of an ester. He noted that the alcohol reacted with the silicon compound, for hydrochloric acid was given off, and the final product was a liquid of not unpleasant odor. The reaction[8] was

$$SiCl_4 + 4C_2H_5OH \rightarrow Si(OC_2H_5)_4 + 4HCl$$

This simply meant that the chlorine on silicon had been replaced by the alcohol. The final product is known as ethyl silicate and is made today in commercial quantities by exactly the same method.

One of the outstanding names in the history of chemistry is that of Friedrich Wöhler (1800–1882). Here was another of those men who spent his life doing what he enjoyed most—solving the puzzles of chemistry. He was a student of Gmelin at Heidelberg, spent a year with Berzelius at Stockholm, and did a great deal of his later work in collaboration with Liebig at Giessen. He was not a great theorist but he was a keen observer. He is best known because of his synthesis of urea in 1824, the first time that an "organic" substance had been prepared from materials that were not of animal or plant origin. His interests ranged over all chemistry. One of his "firsts" was the preparation of metallic aluminum. He used metallic aluminum in various experiments, and in describing (in 1857) an electrolytic experiment in which he used an aluminum rod he states, "We were therefore surprised to see in a cell with an immersed aluminum rod strong gas evolution from the surface, followed by a solution; and our interest was further increased when some of the rising bubbles exploded in the air, burning with a white flame and leaving a white residue."[9] The answer to this was not readily apparent, but it became evident that the aluminum rod contained silicon and that compounds containing silicon and hydrogen had been formed. This was something entirely new, and Wöhler could not rest until he knew more about it. So he mixed some elemental silicon with carbon, heated the mixture, and then passed hydrochloric acid over it. On cooling the gases he found a low-boiling liquid (28°C). This contained not only silicon and hydrogen, but chlorine as well.[10] Wöhler was not able to determine the exact composition, but later work showed that the compound had the formula $SiHCl_3$. As the organic compound $CHCl_3$ is known as chloroform, the silicon analogue is now known as "silicochloroform." Here we have another compound which made its appearance almost 100 years ago as a scientific curiosity and is now a commercial product used in the preparation of silicones. Indeed, had Wöhler gone just one step farther and used an organic chloride, RCl, instead of hydrogen chloride, HCl, he would have anticipated by nearly a century a useful development in silicone chemistry. It all looks so simple in retrospect; but it must be remembered that this was a virgin field and only those with keen observation and insatiable curiosity could note the unusual reactions or muster the patience to follow the results to some definite conclusion.

It was becoming evident that silicon was capable of many unexpected reactions. Deville and Wöhler announced in 1859 that they had heated crystalline silicon in oxygen-depleted air and obtained a compound which gave off ammonia on the addition of water.[11] In the discussion of this reaction they indulged in the "geological phantasy" that perhaps in the building period of the earth silicon nitrides were formed. When water appeared, ammonia was formed, which allowed nitrogen to be incorporated into organic compounds. One might call this the "inorganic nitrogen cycle."

In 1863 Wöhler reported a continuation of his work on silicon.[12] He had made a compound containing silicon and calcium, $SiCa_2$, and also some containing silicon, oxygen, and hydrogen. The latter appeared to puzzle him, for he could get no consistent analytical results from them. Nevertheless he felt sure they were definite compounds. After discussing these results, he went on to say that the compounds prepared suggested a certain analogy to carbon compounds. No doubt there were complete series of compounds in which silicon played the same dominant role as carbon does in the carbon compounds.[13] Silicon was beginning to be regarded by the chemist as a base material in synthesis rather than an enigmatic unknown locked in rocks and stone.

The work just referred to was being done about the time of the Civil War in America; Mark Twain was just beginning his literary career; it was the heyday of the Victorian era in England. To the present-day historian these events seem rather recent; but when the present-day chemist realizes that the atomic weight of silicon was not a matter of general agreement and considers the great amount of knowledge that has been built up since that time, he wonders if this work was not done in the Dark Ages. But work goes slowly when the background of information is small, and men like Berzelius, Ebelman, and Wöhler had little background on which to rely. To build these foundations was a task only for men of the keenest insight and the utmost determination.

While Wöhler in Giessen was stating his conjecture about the chemistry of silicon, two men in Paris were making preparations for a further study. One of these was Charles Friedel, later Professor of Mineralogy at the Sorbonne, and C. M. Crafts, a Bostonian who had come to Paris to study under Wurtz at the Ecole des Mines. In a short series of papers dating from 1863 to 1866 they greatly enlarged the knowledge of the chemistry of silicon and made the first contribution to organosilicon chemistry, as contrasted with the chemistry of silicon itself. It is possible to find reports in the present-day literature which were anticipated nearly a century ago in these papers by Friedel and Crafts. Their first contribution reported the atomic weight of silicon as 28. Although Schiel in 1861 had reported an atomic weight of 28.01,[14] this was the first time that the work had been repeated. They checked on Ebelman's work concerning the preparation of the "silicon ethers," but the most outstanding work was that of preparing compounds in which an organic radical was attached to silicon. No such compounds had ever been made before. The union of silicon and carbon is one of the essential points in the constitution of a silicone, and for this reason, if for no other, this synthesis by Friedel and Crafts must be considered a most important step in the history of silicone development.[15]

The methods that were available at that time to bring about this reaction were cumbersome and difficult of control. It was necessary to prepare the reagent diethyl zinc, $(C_2H_5)_2Zn$, which is highly inflammable, mix that with silicon tetrachloride, and then hold the mixture for some hours in a sealed tube at 160°C. From this they obtained tetraethyl silicon, $(C_2H_5)_4Si$, or tetraethyl silane, as it is now called, a mobile, colorless liquid, boiling at 153°C. What they had done, of course, was to exchange the ethyl groups on the zinc for the chlorines on the silicon:

$$2Zn(C_2H_5)_2 + SiCl_4 \rightarrow 2ZnCl_2 + Si(C_2H_5)_4$$

They then repeated the preparation using dimethyl zinc, $(CH_3)_2Zn$, and obtained tetramethyl silane, $(CH_3)_4Si$.[16] It, too, was not attacked by strong acids or alkalies. These compounds are commercially available today but are made by simpler methods.

Having prepared the compounds from silicon tetrachloride they decided to learn what would happen if they subjected the final product to the action of chlorine. They found that the silicon-carbon bond was not affected but that the chlorine took the place of one or more hydrogens in the organic group:

$$2(C_2H_5)_4Si + 3Cl_2 \rightarrow (C_2H_5)_3SiC_2H_4Cl + (C_2H_5)_3SiC_2H_3Cl_2 + 3HCl$$

The final products of this reaction were not unlike organic compounds (such as ethyl chloride, C_2H_5Cl), so they proceeded to treat them as such. It is possible to make ethyl alcohol, C_2H_5OH, from ethyl chloride by exchanging the chlorine for a hydroxyl (—OH) group. In the silicon compound with one chlorine the reaction went smoothly, but if two chlorines were present the entire organic group split off from silicon and was replaced by oxygen.[17] This was an entirely unexpected result and was recognized only because of careful observation.

With the completion of this work Crafts returned to America where he became the first head of the chemistry department at Cornell University. Although he returned to France some ten years later and collaborated with Friedel in highly important researches, he did not continue any further work on organosilicon chemistry. In 1891 he again returned to his native America to accept the presidency of Massachusetts Institute of Technology.

Friedel was primarily a mineralogist and this no doubt is part of the reason why he wished to continue the study of silicon. After Crafts' departure Friedel was joined by a promising young German chemist by the name of Ladenburg. Friedel's influence, at the start of their work at least, is seen in their credo which concludes their first joint paper:

> Many are of the opinion that the new theories and methods of approach are useless and confusing for inorganic chemists. We believe we have shown through these results that the so-called inorganic elements are capable of forming compounds which are analogous to those of carbon, or are at least of that general type. We hope, by continuing the way we have started, to be able to broaden considerably the chemistry of silicon. The future will tell us whether our opinions are correct and our efforts successful.

Their first investigation comprised an examination of Wöhler's "silicochloroform." Although Wöhler had isolated this some ten years earlier, the exact composition was not known. Friedel and Ladenburg showed that this was the same as silicon tetrachloride except that one of the chlorines had been replaced by hydrogen: $SiHCl_3$. It was of great interest to know the relative activities of the chlorines as compared with those of the hydrogen. This was determined by treating the compound with alcohol, just as Ebelman had done with silicon tetrachloride 30 years before. When the final product was recovered it was found that all the chlorines had reacted but that the hydrogen remained unaffected.[18] This is another piece of information which, as we shall see, is of value in the preparation of silicones.

Of course, it must be remembered that these men were primarily interested in learning more about the chemistry of silicon per se. If the preparation of compounds containing carbon could shed any light on this, they would attempt to make them, but otherwise they were not particularly interested. They considered that the chemistry of silicon was probably analogous in some way to that of carbon, and they wanted to find out in what respect this was true.

One of the obvious facts about organic compounds was that, in most cases, carbon was linked directly to carbon. In many cases the number of carbons so linked together was quite large. Now if the chemistry of silicon were to be similar to that of carbon, compounds should be found, or should be able to be synthesized, in which many silicons were linked together. Friedel and Ladenburg decided to attempt the preparation of such compounds. They transformed silicon tetrachloride, $SiCl_4$, into silicon tetraiodide, SiI_4, because the iodide should be more reactive than the chloride. Then they heated this with finely divided silver in the hope that iodine would be removed to form silver iodide and the silicons would have no choice but that of joining with themselves.

$$2SiI_4 + 2Ag \rightarrow I_3Si - SiI_3 + 2AgI$$

This is precisely what happened, and here they had two silicons linked together in a way that was analogous to a C—C linkage.[19] This seems to be rather flimsy evidence for any analogy with carbon, but they felt that it was a step in the right direction. Later work, however, was to show that the

Si—Si bond could be readily broken, and that the analogy to a C—C bond could not be carried very far.

So far, in nearly all the organosilicon compounds prepared there were either four organic radicals attached to silicon, or none. Friedel and Ladenburg by a slight modification of the zinc ethyl method were able to substitute one, two, three, and four ethyl ($—C_2H_5$) groups for the ethoxy ($—OC_2H_5$) groups in ethyl silicate.[20] This enlarged the types of compounds that could be prepared and widened the range of future study.

It will be noted that the date of this last publication was 1871. The Franco-Prussian War was fought in 1870; and Friedel, the Frenchman, and Ladenburg, the German, held conflicting political and religious opinions. Ladenburg returned to Heidelberg. It should be interpolated that their common interests in science were sufficient for a continued friendship and deep personal regard, and upon Friedel's death in 1898 Ladenburg expressed his sense of personal loss.

With the departure from Paris of Ladenburg, the chemist, Friedel, the mineralogist, maintained little more than a passive interest in investigations of the type described. It would seem that in the silicon work with both Crafts and Ladenburg, Friedel must have been the actuating force or the catalyst because of his interest in mineralogy. Although Crafts was not without interest in mineralogy too, he was more the chemist. Ladenburg was an organic chemist. So while one would guess that Crafts and Ladenburg did most of the actual work of synthesis, neither of them would have continued with such zeal had it not been for the urging and encouragement of Friedel.

Upon his return to Germany, Ladenburg continued for a short time in the work he had been doing with Friedel. He had worked out a method, as just described, of substituting different numbers of ethyl groups for the ethoxyl groups in ethyl silicate. He noted that if the product contained two ethyl groups and two ethoxy groups [$(C_2H_5)_2Si—(OC_2H_5)_2$]

it would react with acidified water, giving off alcohol and forming a very viscous oil that decomposed only at extremely high temperature and did not freeze at $-15°C$.[21] Here, in the year 1872, was the forerunner of the present silicone fluids of commerce. What had happened was that, although the ethyl groups were unaffected, the ethoxy groups had been hydrolyzed or split off by the acidified water, and oxygen had taken their place. The oxygen was capable of acting as a bridge between silicons, just as it does in silica. And as each silicon was bridged to the next one, very large molecules were formed. But the presence of the unaffected ethyl groups prevented the compound from reverting all the way to silica. This is the basic reaction in the preparation of silicones. Subsequent work over the years has served to control the reaction, but fundamentally it is the one that Ladenburg noted.

Both Crafts and Ladenburg, working with Friedel, had been successful in preparing compounds in which carbon was joined to silicon. But the organic groups used had been the two simplest ones, methyl ($—CH_3$) and ethyl ($—C_2H_5$). Ladenburg, now the chemist not influenced by the mineralogist, was curious to know what the effect of another type of group would be. Kekule had shown in 1866 that benzene should be described structurally not as a chain of carbon atoms but as a short chain of six carbon atoms in which one end had combined with the other, making a closed ring. Such a molecule, attached to silicon, might result in different properties than resulted where the straight chain compounds were used. So he prepared a compound in which three ethyl groups and one phenyl (benzene) group were attached to silicon. He found that the phenyl group was split off from the silicon by acids and alkalies more readily than the ethyl groups were.[22] This seems like a simple enough matter to note, but if it were not known in these days that such is the case, there would be great difficulty in explaining some of the reactions of silicones.

Without the inspiration of Friedel, Ladenburg then turned

his attention completely to organic chemistry. His work in that field is notable and all but swallowed up his interest in organosilicon chemistry. It is true that a few of his students were encouraged to complete theses in work of this type, but while their work was creditable, it seems as though they simply went through with it to meet academic requirements. Some isolated facts were discovered but they were largely extensions of Ladenburg's earlier work rather than the development of fundamentally new techniques or ideas.

We find little more of high interest until almost the close of the century. It seems that Friedel still maintained some interest in Wöhler's "silicochloroform," $SiHCl_3$, for in 1896 he presented to the Academy of Science a paper by one of his students, C. Combes, in which a more efficient method of generating this product was described. It differed from Wöhler's method only in that some copper powder was added to the silicon, the mixture then being heated and treated with hydrochloric acid as before.[23] Here is another finding that is usefully incorporated, as we shall see, in present-day manufacture of the base material for silicones.

So far neither the organic nor the inorganic chemists seem to have closed in on this subject with any definite conclusions. Silicon had been freed from its prison in quartz and silicate rocks. Its properties bore more similarity to those of carbon than other elements did, for its compounds could be reacted in some ways like organic compounds. And yet it changed somewhat the nature of the organic materials with which it was combined. The final product was more heat-resistant than analogous organic compounds, but in some cases it would fall apart when treated with acids or alkalies. There might be special rules governing the chemistry of silicon compounds, but there had been no success in preparing compounds in which more than a couple of silicons were joined to one another. Altogether, it was quite confusing.

As we consider how the studies continued through the first

half of the next century, we find that the number of investigators increased and their interests became wider. Some contributed individual items of value while others planned and carried through definite programs with specific ends in view. The purpose of this story will be served if we consider the work of only a few of those who worked in the period from 1900 to 1940.

One who contributed, although in a specialized direction, was Alfred Stock of Breslau. In 1912 he reported that when studying compounds in which hydrogen was attached to boron, he found an impurity to be present which he identified as a compound in which hydrogen was attached to silicon. This was the hydride of silicon, SiH_4, or silane.[24] He tried to find information about such compounds and was plainly irritated to discover that no one had ever investigated them. There was no alternative but to get the information himself. His study was carried out with great care, and as a result we know much about these rather unstable materials.[25] Among other things, Stock wanted to know how a chain of silicon atoms surrounded by hydrogens

$$\begin{array}{ccccccccc} & \mathrm{H} & & \mathrm{H} & & \mathrm{H} & & \mathrm{H} & \\ & | & & | & & | & & | & \\ - & \mathrm{Si} & - & \mathrm{Si} & - & \mathrm{Si} & - & \mathrm{Si} & - \\ & | & & | & & | & & | & \\ & \mathrm{H} & & \mathrm{H} & & \mathrm{H} & & \mathrm{H} & \end{array}$$

would compare with an analogous carbon chain

$$\begin{array}{ccccccccc} & \mathrm{H} & & \mathrm{H} & & \mathrm{H} & & \mathrm{H} & \\ & | & & | & & | & & | & \\ - & \mathrm{C} & - & \mathrm{C} & - & \mathrm{C} & - & \mathrm{C} & - \\ & | & & | & & | & & | & \\ & \mathrm{H} & & \mathrm{H} & & \mathrm{H} & & \mathrm{H} & \end{array}$$

It will be recalled that Friedel and Ladenburg in 1869 had tried to prepare similar compounds but got no farther than two silicons tied together, and these were surrounded by iodine atoms or by ethyl ($—C_2H_5$) groups.

Carbon chains surrounded by hydrogens are quite stable, the longer chains being oils. But Stock found that any analogy with silicon was on paper only. The chemical formulas of the carbon and silicon compounds looked similar, but the properties had little in common. Stock prepared the silicon compounds by first preparing magnesium silicide, Mg_2Si, and then dropping acid on this solid:

$$Mg_2Si + HCl \rightarrow SiH_4 + Si_2H_6 + Si_3H_8 + \cdot \cdot \cdot + MgCl_2$$

The volatile silicon hydrides were condensed and then separated by fractional distillation. The first member of the silicon series, SiH_4 (silane), is analogous to CH_4 (methane) in chemical structure, but, whereas the hydrogens in methane are stable against aqueous alkali, those in silane are readily removed by this reagent. Silane has the reputation of being explosive upon exposure to air, but Moisson and Smiles indicate that the explosibility is due to the presence of higher homologues.[26] The longer chains are less and less stable; in fact Stock could not isolate any pure compounds larger than Si_4H_{10}. This was startling evidence of the fact that the chemistries of carbon and of silicon are highly dissimilar, for the higher homologues of methane are important constituents of the stable lubricating oils on the market today.

In addition to the pure hydrides, Stock prepared compounds containing both hydrogen and halogen, *e.g.*, SiH_2Br_2, using Wöhler's method[27] of heating powdered silicon and passing the halo acid through the mass:

$$Si + 2HBr \rightarrow SiH_2Br_2$$

This latter compound, he thought, might be useful in the synthesis of other materials, for the bromines could be preferentially reacted with water or by other means. He actually did replace the halogens with methyl groups[28] and by treatment of the resulting product with aqueous alkali obtained an oily product similar to that obtained by Ladenburg from the hydrolysis of diethyl diethoxysilane, $(C_2H_5)_2Si(OC_2H_5)_2$. Again modern silicone preparation had been anticipated but in such a hazy fashion that only a prophet of the first order could have been expected to see what the future had in store.

Although Stock's silicon hydrides were highly unstable toward oxidation, we shall see that much later work demonstrated ways of stabilizing them partially. Silicochloroform, $SiHCl_3$, is reasonably stable. If the chlorines are replaced by organic groups, the stability remains; and the number of stable hydrogens may be increased if the organic groups are large enough. If one phenyl ($—C_6H_5$) group is present, we may have as many as three hydrogens on the silicon and still have some stability.[29] It was also shown later by Schumb[30] that the groups attached to silicon affected the possible chain length in compounds having the Si—Si bonding. Stock was not acquainted with all these facts, but his studies opened the door to their discovery.

One should not neglect to mention Bygden's excellent publications in 1911 and 1912 in which he made a comparison of the physical properties of certain carbon compounds and their silicon analogues.[31] Blix in Berlin reported the preparation of silicon sulfobromide, $SiSBr_2$, which upon contact with water decomposed with almost explosive violence.[32] Schlenk, Renning, and Racky asked whether it was possible to prepare triphenylsilane, $(C_6H_5)_3Si$, which would be analogous to the free radical triphenylmethyl $[(C_6H_5)_3C]$. They answered the question in the negative and then let the whole subject drop.[33]

In the 1930s there was the beginning of a number of papers by Russian investigators.[34] They sensed that there might be some industrial value in various types of resinous compounds that could be prepared through the use of organosilicon intermediates. They were able to show that these products were remarkably heat stable, but they did not seem able to convince anyone of their value. It is true that the products they made would not now be considered particularly desirable commercial products, but in view of the encouraging results obtained, one wonders why they were not pushed more energetically. In a conversation with the author, Dr. Kreshkov of the Mendeleef Institute (Moscow) attributed this in part to the lack of magnesium in Russia to operate the Grignard method. It is difficult to think that this could be a controlling factor, but whatever the reason, their promising start was not vigorously followed up as far as we can tell from the literature. Some new work is reported from time to time, but in the main their articles are reviews of previous work or reports of developments in America.

While in the period of 1900–1940 these somewhat sporadic investigations were being carried out, there was one man who made a firm resolve to determine what the common factors were in the chemistries of carbon and silicon. This man was Prof. F. S. Kipping of the University of Nottingham in England. In the period from 1899 until 1944 he published 54 papers on this subject. As may be surmised from this long period of intensive work, he was one in whom the British tenacity of purpose was evident to a superlative degree. He had one end in view and refused to be diverted from his target. He was confronted with failures that were difficult to explain, and at times his products transformed themselves into unidentifiable oils and glues which, with typical British understatement, he frequently described as "uninviting." He was uncompromisingly interested in the *chemistry* of compounds containing silicon, and even in his later years, when shown some of the first commercial silicones, he could scarcely bring himself to take more than a passive interest in them. After all, they demonstrated little that was new about the *chemistry* of silicon, so why should they be of particular interest to him?

Kipping really had two aims in mind, one developing from the work on the other. First of all, he realized that there was still no demonstration that the chemistry of silicon was really similar to that of carbon. One of the points of interest in carbon chemistry is that if a carbon atom is surrounded by four different units it will rotate the plane of polarized light. An analogy between carbon and silicon would be demonstrated if silicon behaved similarly. It took Kipping 8 years of careful work before he was able to show that this was the case. Second, having prepared compounds that showed this phenomenon, he found that the general chemistry of silicon itself was not too well known and stated that "our knowledge of the chemistry of silicon is more likely to be extended by a study of the organic derivatives of this element than by that of its mineral compounds."[35] This statement is reminiscent of that of Friedel and Ladenburg at the conclusion of their first joint publication (see page 10).

In attempting to prepare a silicon-containing compound that would rotate the plane of polarized light, Kipping showed that a phenyl ($-C_6H_5$) group attached to silicon was split off if treated with a strong acid, although it was stable to alkalies. If a benzyl ($-CH_2C_6H_5$) group was attached to silicon, it was stable to acids but unstable to alkalies.[36]

The oils and glues with which Kipping was at times confronted did not, in spite of their "uninviting" appearance, escape some investigation. He was able to show that these were large molecules formed from the union of a number of small molecules. He was able to demonstrate not only that the formation of these bodies was due to the reaction

$$-\overset{|}{\underset{|}{\mathrm{Si}}}\mathrm{OH} + \mathrm{HO}\overset{|}{\underset{|}{\mathrm{Si}}}- \rightarrow -\overset{|}{\underset{|}{\mathrm{Si}}}-\mathrm{O}-\overset{|}{\underset{|}{\mathrm{Si}}}- + \mathrm{H_2O}$$

but that the reaction

$$-\overset{|}{\underset{|}{\mathrm{Si}}}(\mathrm{OH})_2 \rightarrow -\overset{|}{\underset{|}{\mathrm{Si}}}=\mathrm{O} + \mathrm{H_2O}$$

does not occur.[37] In other words, although $-OH$ groups on silicon atoms may condense readily to form water, no two groups on the same silicon ever react with one another. This is a fundamental tenet in the study of all silicon compounds (organic or inorganic) and became clear only after long investigation. He was also able to show that in addition to the lack of a double bond between silicon and oxygen a double bond never occurred between silicon and carbon. Indeed, silicon has not yet been found united to any element by a double bond. These facts are among the most fundamental in the understanding of the chemistry of silicon whether this element is in an organic or inorganic system.

Very early in his work Kipping found that the recently discovered Grignard reaction (described in Chapter Five) was a most effective means of attaching organic groups to silicon.[36] By pointing out the method, he made it simpler for others to work in this field and so was indirectly responsible for more work being done in other quarters. He showed not only that this reagent could be used to substitute organic groups for halogens attached to silicon, but that it could break the

$$\begin{array}{c} | \quad\quad | \\ -Si-O-Si- \\ | \quad\quad | \end{array}$$

bonding under certain circumstances.[38] He also repeated previous work on the use of sodium for substituting organic groups for halogens attached to silicon. He found, as others had, that in this type of reaction it was difficult to replace a limited number of the halogens. Either all the halogens were replaced or none was. He did find, however, that in some cases a halogen was replaced by another silicon, resulting in a

$$\begin{array}{c} | \quad | \\ -Si-Si- \\ | \quad | \end{array}$$

bonding. This bonding was somewhat unstable in the presence of oxygen and under some conditions quite unstable to alkalies. He found that "the Si—Si bonding is not necessarily unstable toward alkalies, and whether the silicon atoms become separated or not is determined by the nature of the atoms or groups with which they are combined."[39] Kipping was never satisfied that he understood the nature of the reaction, and in his Bakerian lecture in 1937 he pointed out that these reactions "are of an unexpected nature, a fact which indicates the possibility of interesting developments in this particular direction."[40]

No attempt has been made to do more than point out a few of the facts Kipping brought to light. A reading of all Kipping's papers is a "must" for those who would like a full understanding of the chemistry of organosilicon compounds.

We have now completed a survey of the more important developments in the study of silicon and its organic compounds up to the year 1940.

It will be noted that there was little or no interest evidenced in the high-molecular-weight compounds now known as "silicones." It is true that on a few occasions some viscous oils had been prepared, but they had been prepared more or less by accident and had not been studied with any care. There appeared to be three points of interest in these investigations:

1. A better understanding of the reactions of silicon
2. A demonstration that there is a separate chemistry of silicon somewhat analogous to that of carbon
3. An understanding of why the substitution of silicon for carbon in an organic compound affects the reactivity of the compound

While these investigations developed information of the highest importance, none of them was directed toward the formation of high-molecular-weight materials in any way comparable to the present-day silicones. Indeed, the commercial development of silicones would have been impossible without still further fundamental knowledge from an entirely different direction.

To understand the source of this newer knowledge, we must retrace our steps to the times when chemists were trying to find the nature of some natural products. There is no need to follow this story in great detail, but we can take as an example the study of natural rubber. Although rubber was in rather common use by 1850, no one had any reasonable idea about its composition or structure. In 1860 Williams in England reported that if rubber were heated in absence of air, a liquid distilled out that was identified as isoprene, C_5H_8. He also noted that if isoprene was left in a bottle for some months, it lost its original liquid form and became sticky.[41] In 1879 a French chemist, Bouchardat, noted that when isoprene was treated with cold aqueous hydrochloric acid, a product formed which possessed some of the properties of india rubber. Although a great deal continued to be done on the study of rubber, the next step we may note is that of Pickles' suggestion in 1910 that rubber was composed of eight isoprene units whose ends joined to form a ring.[42] These eight-unit rings were recognized as "polymers." How these units were held together to form rubber was not explained too satisfactorily, but it seemed that some sort of subsidiary forces must be operating. Staudinger in Zurich was studying natural products (including rubber), and in 1920 he stated it as his belief "that the most varied polymerization products can be satisfactorily represented by formulas with normal valences without the necessity of assuming that they are molecular compounds in which the components are held together by subsidiary valences."[43] This idea of macromolecules, or giant molecules, was new; and Staudinger applied it to many products, showing that the properties of these giant molecules were not due simply to a summation of the properties of the individual units, but that, actually, the properties of the whole were greater than those of the parts. In 1926 Staudinger applied this idea to rubber, suggesting that the giant-chain molecules of rubber may vary in length according to the treatment to which rubber is subjected.[44] This proved to be a most fruitful suggestion and the study and technology of rubber have benefited from it ever since. Much of Staudinger's finest work was directed toward a study of these giant molecules or "high polymers" and much of the information we have about them and the techniques for studying them are due to his untiring efforts.

We should return for a moment to the 1890s when one of the masters of organic chemistry was studying the constitution of sugars. This man was Emil Fischer (1850–1919). He was one of the leaders in organic chemistry in Germany at the time of Germany's preeminence in work of that type. In the 1890s he was able to show that there was no fundamental difference between simple and complex sugars. They differed in properties largely as a result of differences in molecular size. In 1901 he commenced a study of albumin. He knew that albumin was made up of a certain type of acids known as "amino acids." He prepared these acids and then coupled them. He was able to show that the larger the molecule was made the more the product resembled the natural albumins. So while others were to find by a breaking-down process that natural products were large polymers, Fischer was demonstrating the same fact by a building-up process.

These results, informative as they were about natural products, must have been of the greatest help to Staudinger in his attempts to explain and obtain acceptance of his idea of giant molecules.

While Staudinger in Switzerland was successfully pushing his work on the properties of high polymers, a worker of equal stature in America began a study of the principles underlying the preparation of high polymers and the laws governing the formation of various types. This man was W. H. Carothers (1896–1937) who in 1928 in the laboratories of the E. I. du Pont de Nemours & Company began a series of studies that have proved to be classics. Carothers was a brilliant experimentalist and a sound thinker. He was responsible for a clarification of the subject and a statement of the laws governing the formation of polymers of varied structures. Although Carothers's studies formed the basis of the development of nylon and Neoprene, it may be considered remarkable that these possibilities were of less interest to him than the elucidation of the chemistry involved.

The conclusions reached and the principles laid down are given broadly in the section on Polymerization. For our immediate purposes it may be sufficient to point out that by the early 1930s the principles of polymerization had been developed and that it was now possible for those interested in "high polymers" to proceed with some assurance in the development of products of high molecular weight with possible new and useful properties.

It would not be correct to leave the impression that Staudinger and Carothers were alone responsible for all the ideas developed concerning high polymers up to 1935. The other contributors are numerous but in such an account as this the attempt must be to give the over-all picture rather than to paint individual portraits. This is another case in which it is unfortunate that all men who contribute to the sum of knowledge do not win individual recognition at all times. It is still true, however, that for many of the aristocrats of science the excitement of the search is its own reward.

The stage was at last set for the appearance of silicones. And it is only right that we should recognize who was responsible for the setting. Long years of earnest work by scientists who were curious about natural phenomena had been rewarded by a wide knowledge of the peculiarities of silicon chemistry. Others who were curious about large molecules, how they were formed naturally and how they could be produced synthetically, had learned fundamental truths about them and had shown principles governing their formation. It was not too much to expect that these two lines of activity should be brought together, that the knowledge of silicon-containing compounds and the knowledge of the principles governing the formation of large molecules should result in the synthesis of large molecules containing silicon. What the properties of such compounds would be one could only guess, but the fact that the two necessary lines of information had been developed assured the appearance of the joint product. Now it was simply a matter of time.

The manner in which these studies were used to bring about the commercial development of silicones is described in the next section on Commercial Development of Silicones.

But it should not be assumed that the beginning of "applied" research marked the end of "pure" research. Although the importance of the commercial applications of silicones had become recognized by industry the intriguing nature of their chemistry was being attested by numerous academic publications. Work that had been started as a result of scientific curiosity a century earlier was now bearing fruit that had not been foreseen. It had been assumed originally that results would show silicon to be simply an analogue of carbon. While this proved to be the case in a limited sense, the differences were much more evident than the similarities. What had been started as a search for further knowledge proved to be the groundwork for technological advance that has proved helpful to industry and in so doing has contributed its part to improving our standard of living.

It would be a mistake to consider this the end of the story from the standpoint of either pure or applied science. While industry is naturally doing a great deal to further its knowledge of these compounds and to develop more economical methods of preparing them, the centers of pure research are doing their share to clarify points in organosilicon chemistry that are still obscure. The number of papers of this latter type appearing between the years 1945 and 1950 have been about 100 times as great as in the century preceding. Industry has recognized the fact that it has eaten up in 10 years the pure research of

100 years. Without this type of research, technology would wither. Thus we see a greater and greater overlapping of the fields of pure and applied research, the only point of distinction between the two being the motivation of the individual who does the work. And who shall say that the mental satisfaction of the one is any less real than the material satisfaction of the other?

Section 2:

Commercial Development of Silicones

In view of the wide background of knowledge just described the question may be asked: Why was the commercial development of silicones so long delayed? The previous history provides some of the answers. The classical chemists had long been schooled in investigational methods that called for the separation, by distillation or crystallization, of pure compounds. Large, poorly definable polymeric bodies did not lend themselves to this method of approach. No doubt Kipping expressed the sentiments of many other chemists of his day when he described such products as "uninviting glues." There was little commercial background at the time to suggest that these "glues" had any practical significance. Further, those interested in chemical research had few, if any, connections with industry. Without the backing which industry could furnish there was great difficulty and little incentive in embarking on a study of such indefinable products.

The word "polymer" had been in common use for years, but it was not until Staudinger voiced his concept of "macromolecules" in the 1920s that there was a major interest in the study of them. The recognition that these undistillable and non-crystallizable bodies were built up by known chemical reactions and could be considered simply as very large molecules opened up the enormous field of polymer research. This heralded the beginning of the "plastic age," and high polymers of many types began to appear as commercial products. Some of these products were transparent and could be used, with more or less success, in the place of glass.

The possibility of a hybrid polymer—a cross between the organic polymers (plastics) and the inorganic polymers (glasses)—appealed to some glass manufacturers as a desirable possibility. Dr. E. C. Sullivan, then Director of Research for the Corning Glass Works of Corning, N.Y., engaged Dr. J. F. Hyde, an organic chemist, to investigate this matter.

Hyde was acquainted with the literature describing organosilicon research, and he had the advantage of the rapidly accumulating knowledge of large polymers. By using knowledge from both these fields he was able to prepare large polymers containing both organic and inorganic constituents.

At this point there arose one of those coincidences that often direct a course of action. The Corning Glass Works had just begun the development of glass fibers and was on the lookout for appropriate markets. One of the most promising outlets for this product appeared to be as a woven tape for use in electrical insulation. Cotton, impregnated with a resinous dielectric, had been used but it would char at elevated temperature. This difficulty could be overcome by the use of glass tape in place of the cotton, but it was found that the resin impregnant would stand only slightly more heat than the cotton would. Thus there was but little advantage in using the glass. To realize the full value of the glass tape there was needed a resinous dielectric that was considerably more heat stable than the organic materials in common use.

Hyde was able to point out that the organosilicon polymers he had been developing could be made in resinous form and that certain types were unusually heat stable. The work then turned toward resinous compounds that would be of use as a heat-stable dielectric in tapes made of glass fiber.

Studies and experimental work were then conducted along these lines. When sufficient progress had been made to justify a demonstration, the products were shown to officials of the General Electric Company in the hope that glass-fiber tapes would be recognized as the basis of high-temperature insulation. This approach to high-temperature electrical insulation was recognized as fundamentally correct, and the study of these organosilicon insulating resins was then taken up in the General Electric laboratories as well, under the capable guidance of Dr. E. G. Rochow and Dr. W. I. Patnode. About this time the Corning Glass Works Fellowship at Mellon Institute, Pittsburgh, under the headship of the author, undertook similar work, aimed not only at the production of insulating resins but also at a general survey of the chemistry of the materials and the engineering required for their production.

The knowledge of this work catalyzed similar investigations by other industrial laboratories, and soon the technical literature showed that ever-increasing attention was being given to organosilicon compounds.

By 1942 work had progressed with the Corning group to the point where commercial production could be considered. As the manufacture of these materials was in the nature of an organic synthesis rather than a glassmaking operation, the Corning Glass Works approached the Dow Chemical Company with a view to obtaining engineering and research assistance. The result was that in 1943 the formation of the Dow Corning Corporation, financed jointly by the Dow Chemical Company and the Corning Glass Works, was announced. The fury of World War II was then at its peak and high priority was granted to Dow Corning for the erection of a factory and procurement of equipment, as Dow Corning was the only source of several organosilicon products demanded by the military forces. While these materials were being produced in commercial quantities, research on their improvement continued, and it was inevitable that new and valuable products would be found. With the close of the war it was therefore possible to offer to industry commercial quantities of a wide range of products with properties that had not been known previously.

Meanwhile other companies, though not actually producing, had been conducting vigorous research. In 1946 the General Electric Company announced the opening of its plant for the production of silicones. In 1949 the Plaskon Division of the Libbey-Owens-Ford Glass Company advertised silicone products for sale, directing attention largely to materials useful with alkyd coatings. About this time The Linde Air Products Company, a division of Union Carbide and Carbon Corporation, commenced pilot-plant work in Tonawanda, N.Y. At this writing they are planning for full-scale production of a broad line of silicone products.

Although the original aim of the investigations carried out had been to develop electrical insulating resins, the first materials to be made commercially were the silicone fluids.

The limited amounts of fluids that were first available restricted their use to applications such as damping fluids in sensitive instruments used by the Air Force. The stability of the fluids and their small change of viscosity with temperature were the properties that proved of most value here. As production increased the fluids were formulated into a greaselike material that proved to be of great value as an ignition sealing compound for use in the spark-plug wells of military aircraft engines. The resins had by this time reached the point of development where it was possible to use them, in conjunction with glass-fiber tapes, as the insulating medium in motors. Cooperative work with the armed forces helped in their development and appraisal.

The usefulness of the fluids as antifoam agents in petroleum oils had been demonstrated and some military specifications demanded their addition to many types of oils.

In 1945 both the Dow Corning Corporation and the General Electric Company announced the development of a silicone rubber that was useful at temperatures too high for the functioning of organic rubber.

All these products were so necessary for military requirements that little or none of them was available for civilian use. When hostilities concluded in the summer of 1945 the military demands ceased and silicones were left without a market. But the versatility of these materials was such that energy and ingenuity soon showed how they could be adapted to a peacetime economy.

The fluids were found to be excellent mold-release agents in the molding of rubber tires and other rubber goods, as well as of many types of plastics. Polishes and lubricants were developed, and the damping fluids were adapted to peacetime requirements. The resins were improved and developed into high-temperature coatings and laminating materials. The silicone rubber was given improved physical properties and was formulated to maintain its properties at extremely low temperatures while still retaining its high-temperature stability. Application to the waterproofing of textiles was developed.

Evidence accumulated that the silicones in one form or another could be profitably applied in almost any industry one could name. Demand for peacetime applications soon surpassed the requirements for earlier military use, and expansion of facilities became necessary for all producers.

The pattern of growth is familiar, for as production has been increased prices have dropped. This allows application to a greater variety of industries and products; more production is then required and the cycle is repeated. The conclusion of the matter appears to be still far distant, and nobody short of a professional soothsayer is willing to hazard a guess as to the position of silicones in the industries of the future.

CHAPTER TWO

Commercial Silicones

Introduction

The commercial preparation of silicones involves a synthesis of intermediates followed by a polymerization to form the required products.

A statement of the chemistry and of the polymerization procedures used is necessarily a somewhat lengthy story, and it is considered that some readers would be content with a general description, stripped of details. For this reason a highly condensed account is given here. Those interested in more exact details will find them in Chapter Five, Chemistry of Silicone Preparation.

The starting material for the preparation of silicones is silicon tetrachloride, $SiCl_4$. This is prepared by treating sand with chlorine gas at a temperature of about 1,000°C. The product is a liquid, boiling at 57.6°C. If this liquid is dripped into water, hydrochloric acid is given off copiously:

$$SiCl_4 + 4H_2O \rightarrow Si(OH)_4 + 4HCl$$

The silicon-containing product, $Si(OH)_4$, which is known as orthosilicic acid, readily splits out water, and the silica or sand is regenerated (see Chapter Five):

$$Si(OH)_4 \rightarrow SiO_2 + 2H_2O$$

Now, the silicon tetrachloride may be reacted by a number of different procedures (see Chapter Five, page 244) in such a way that one of the chlorines or more is replaced by carbon-containing groups such as methyl ($-CH_3$) or ethyl ($-C_2H_5$) or phenyl ($-C_6H_5$) or, in fact, by almost any group one chooses. The symbol R is commonly used to designate an organic group. Thus if two organic groups replace as many chlorines in silicon tetrachloride we have a compound that may be represented as

$$\begin{array}{c} R \\ | \\ Cl-Si-Cl \\ | \\ R \end{array}$$

As the carbon-silicon bonding is not affected by water it is evident that dripping this compound into water will not regenerate silica, whatever else it may do. Actually, it generates a "silicone":

$$\begin{array}{c} R \\ | \\ Cl-Si-Cl \\ | \\ R \end{array} + 2H_2O \rightarrow \begin{array}{c} R \\ | \\ HO-Si-OH \\ | \\ R \end{array} + 2HCl$$

In most cases the —OH groups that are formed on silicon act just as those in orthosilicic acid did. They split out water:

$$\begin{array}{c} R \\ | \\ HO-Si-OH \\ | \\ R \end{array} + \begin{array}{c} R \\ | \\ HO-Si-OH \\ | \\ R \end{array} \rightarrow \begin{array}{c} R \quad\quad\quad R \\ | \quad\quad\quad\;\; | \\ HOSi-O-SiOH \\ | \quad\quad\quad\;\; | \\ R \quad\quad\quad R \end{array} + H_2O$$

This splitting out of water continues, forming long-chain molecules. If each silicon has two R groups the usual result will be that an oily layer will appear on the surface of the water. This is a liquid silicone and may be used for various purposes, depending on the nature of the R groups.

If each silicon has only one R group

```
       R
       |
  Cl—Si—Cl
       |
      Cl
```

it is obvious that treatment with water will give

```
        R
        |
  HO—Si—OH
        |
       OH
```

The long-chain molecule can grow as before, but we now have an additional —OH that can reach out and react with a similar additional —OH on another chain. The final result will be a highly complicated network, and a sandlike precipitate will be formed. This is not silica, for each silicon still has an R group attached to it. When the precipitate is removed and dried it may have a rosinlike feel. It is actually a very brittle silicone resin.

The brittleness of the resin may be avoided by first adding to the starting material a certain amount of a compound having two groups. By a proper adjustment of the amounts of reagents containing both one and two R groups, resins can be prepared that will vary in properties from brittle to soft.

The properties of the fluids and of the resins vary with the proportions of the one and two R-group compounds used and with the nature of the R groups themselves.

The silicone fluids and resins are the starting materials used in preparing the greases, compounds, and rubbers. Methods of preparing these latter materials are described in the text.

As with practically all synthetic materials, the properties of silicones can be altered within certain limits by changes in composition and in methods of preparation so that the product will meet the requirements for specific applications. So it happens, for instance, that many types of silicone fluids can be prepared, and the properties may be varied to obtain a product best suited for a particular use. To emphasize one property it is often necessary to sacrifice some other property and a compromise may be required. This applies not only to the silicone fluids, but to lubricants, resins, rubbers, and to substantially all the types of silicones offered for commercial use.

It would be impossible to describe in a book of this size each different product that is made. Even if it were possible it would be inadvisable. Each application will most likely be best served by some particular material, and the silicone manufacturer should be consulted. New materials are constantly being developed, and the best material of today may be superceded by a better one tomorrow.

To date there are in this country two companies producing a wide variety of silicone products: the Dow Corning Corporation, Midland, Mich., and the General Electric Company, Silicone Department, Waterford, N.Y. In addition to these the Plaskon Division of the Libbey-Owens-Ford Glass Co., Toledo, Ohio, and the Linde Air Products Company, Tonawanda, N.Y., are producing organosilicon chlorides of several types. These various products are listed here, together with an account of their properties, potentialities, and limitations, in the hope of creating a better understanding of the place of silicones in commerce and industry.

COMMERCIAL SILICONES

CLASSES OF COMMERCIAL PRODUCTS

Silicone commercial products may be divided convenient into five classes:

Fluids

The fluids are heat-stable liquids that are obtainable in a wide range of viscosities. Most of them have low vapor pressure and high flash points. They find use as lubricants, damping fluids, water repellents, defoamers, release agents, and have many other applications that will be discussed specifically.

Compounds

The compounds are petrolatum-like materials formulated from the fluids by the addition of small amounts of very finely divided silica.

They do not flow with heat, and they have excellent water repellency and good dielectric properties.

They are used as valve lubricants and for impregnation of pump packing, particularly for high-temperature or corrosive conditions, for a release agent for heat-sealing devices, and as a moistureproof seal in electrical connectors.

Lubricants (Greases and Fluids)

The greases are prepared from the fluids by the addition of carbon black or special soaps. They are nonflowing lubricants intended for use at abnormally high or low temperature as so-called "lifetime" lubricants of sealed bearings.

Resins

These products have found specialized uses in electrical insulation, in the preparation of laminates, in paint formulations, as release agents, and as water repellents. They are

…ion-resistant and water repellent, and they are good …etrics.

Rubbers

Although there is little chemical similarity between organic rubbers and silicone rubbers, there is a great similarity in physical properties. Both show the properties of stretch and retraction, bounce, and great flexibility. The silicone rubbers do not have as great tensile strength or abrasion resistance as the organic rubbers, but they are useful over a much broader temperature span. They are applied where the temperature is either too low or too high for conventional rubbers. They are also resistant to many chemicals that affect the organic rubbers adversely.

Section 1:

Silicone Fluids

Industry uses many types of fluids and the particular fluid used depends on how well its properties conform to the demands of the process or product. Thus, ether may be used because it has a low boiling point, alcohols may be used because of their solvent power, water is a good cooling medium, petroleum oils are good lubricants, and certain high-boiling organic liquids are useful for heat-transfer purposes. No one fluid meets all requirements, and selection must, therefore, be made.

The silicone fluids have found a place for themselves among the great variety of fluids available because they show combinations of properties not found in other fluids. They are clear liquids with an oily feel and are available in viscosities between 0.65 centistokes and 1,000,000 centistokes or even higher. They are lubricants having a very small change of viscosity with temperature; they are very stable at elevated temperatures but have low freezing points. Although they are extremely inert chemically, they are effective in some cases when used in only very small amounts, as in the improvement of paint and in the elimination of foam in many processes. They are nontoxic. Many other distinctive properties are present which make them of value in particular applications. The properties and the applications are discussed in the present chapter.

There are several types of silicone fluids which may be conveniently described under two headings:

A. Dimethyl Silicone Fluids

B. Fluids Other than Dimethyl

The dimethyl silicone fluids are, of course, those in which the polymer is made up of units having two methyl groups and two oxygens attached to each silicon atom. The fluids other than dimethyl are those in which the polymer has some units which have either one or both of the methyl groups replaced by some other organic group—generally phenyl. The properties of the fluids in the two classes differ sufficiently to justify considering them separately.

A. Dimethyl Silicone Fluids

These fluids, having the chemical formula

$$\left(\begin{matrix} CH_3 \\ -Si-O \\ CH_3 \end{matrix}\right)_x$$

are prepared in viscosities from 0.65 centistokes to over 1,000,000 centistokes. They are available from the Dow Corning Corporation who list them as "200 Fluids" or from the General Electric Company as "G. E. Silicone Oils." Either of these terms, coupled with a statement of the desired viscosity, is a complete identification. They have an oily or waxy feel,

TABLE 1 Physical Properties of DC 200 Fluids

Viscosity: Cs at 25°C	Viscosity: SSU at 100°F	Viscosity-Temperature Coefficient[a]	Dielectric Constant[b]	Freezing Point °C	Freezing Point °F	Boiling Point Temperature °C	Boiling Point Temperature °F	Boiling Point Pressure, mm Hg	Flash Point[c] Minimum °F	Thermal Conductivity[d]	Specific Gravity 25°C/25°C	Refractive Index at 25°C	Lb per Gal at 25°C
0.65	28	0.31	2.18	−68	−90	99.5	211	760	30	0.00024	0.761	1.375	6.35
1.0	29	0.37	2.32	−86	−123	152	305	760	110	0.00024	0.818	1.382	6.84
1.5	30	0.46	2.40	−76	−105	192	377	760	160	0.00025	0.852	1.387	7.11
2.0	31	0.48	2.46	−84	−119	230	446	760	175	0.00026	0.871	1.390	7.27
				Pour Point[e] °C	Pour Point[e] °F								
3.0	33	0.51	2.52	−65	−85	70–100	158–212	0.5	215	0.00027	0.896	1.394	7.48
5.0	39	0.55	2.58	−65	−85	120–160	248–320	0.5	275	0.00028	0.918	1.397	7.67
10	52	0.57	2.65	−65	−85	>200	>392	0.5	325	0.00032	0.940	1.399	7.85
20	80	0.59	2.68	−60	−76	>200	>392	0.5	520	0.00034	0.950	1.400	7.93
50	185	0.59	2.72	−55	−67	>250	>482	0.5	525	0.00036	0.955	1.402	7.93
						Volatility[f] after 48 hr: At °C	At °F	%					
100	350	0.60	2.74	−55	−67	200	392	<2	600	0.00037	0.968	1.4030	8.08
200	720	0.62	2.74	−53	−63	200	392	<2	600	0.00037	0.971	1.4031	8.10
350	1250	0.62	2.75	−50	−58	200	392	<2	600	0.00038	0.972	1.4032	8.11
500	1750	0.62	2.75	−50	−58	200	392	<2	600	0.00038	0.972	1.4033	8.11
1000	3500	0.62	2.76	−50	−58	200	392	<2	600	0.00038	0.973	1.4035	8.12
				Solidification Temperature °C	Solidification Temperature °F								
12,500	45,000	0.58	2.82	−46	−51	200	392	<2	600	0.00038	0.973	1.4035	8.12
30,000	115,000	0.61	2.77	−44	−47	200	392	<2	600		0.973	1.4035	8.12

[a] $1 - \frac{V210°F}{V100°F}$

[b] At 1,000 cycles and 25°C Schering bridge was used to determine dielectric constant according to ASTM D-150-45T.

[c] Open cup. ASTM D-92-33.

[d] $\frac{\text{G-cal} \times \text{cm}}{\text{sec} \times \text{sq cm} \times °\text{C}}$ at 50°C.

[e] Pour point ASTM D97-39, sections 5 to 7.

[f] Per cent weight loss of a 35- to 40-g sample after heating 48 hr at 200°C in a 150-ml beaker having a bottom area of about 3 sq in.

depending on viscosity. The physical properties vary somewhat depending on the viscosity, as shown by Table 1.

1. Chemical and Physical Behavior

CHEMICAL BEHAVIOR

Stability in Air

The nonvolatile dimethyl fluids are stable over very long periods when held in contact with air at 150°C (302°F). At 200°C (390°F) they are equally stable if protected from the atmosphere. At 250°C (482°F), in contact with air, the viscosity shows an increase within 12 hr, and within 48 hr a tough rubbery gel is formed.

The viscosity is delayed if an antioxidant is added to the fluid.[45]

Resistance to oxygen is usually determined by holding the test material in an oxygen bomb and noting the drop in pressure with time. This test shows negligible pressure drop with the dimethyl silicones. With an oxygen pressure of 2,000 psi there was no evidence of silica formation after 1 hr at 150°C (302°F) or after ½ hr at 250°C (482°F). In spite of these results this material should be specified for use in oxygen systems only after complete test under the exact operating conditions involved.

The change of viscosity of these fluids at temperatures from 175°C (350°F) to 250°C (482°F) in the presence of air, oxygen, nitrogen, and helium has been reported by Atkins.[46]

Heat and Flame Resistance

The effect of heat in the absence of oxygen is to bring about a breakdown to smaller polymers, an action that is somewhat akin to the cracking of petroleum oils. This action commences somewhat above 250°C (482°F) and is quite rapid at 350°C (662°F).

These polymers can be made to burn, but external heat must be constantly supplied. In other words, a flash point can be determined, but there is no true flame point. Another way of putting it is to say that only the low polymers will burn. If the heat supplied is not sufficient to cause depolymerization combustion will not take place.

Behavior in Presence of Chemicals

The chemical inertness of these fluids is one reason for their interest to industry. They are not stable to all chemicals but they are resistant to many that affect most organic materials.

Among the chemicals that have little or no effect on these fluids may be listed: fatty acids, molten sulfur, sulfur dioxide, 3 per cent hydrogen peroxide, aqueous solutions of metallic salts, 5 per cent citric acid, phenol, liquid ammonia and ammonium hydroxide, paraffin hydrocarbons, aqueous solutions of hydrochloric, nitric, and sulfuric acids. In general, aqueous solutions do not affect these fluids.

They are affected by solid salts such as ferric chloride and aluminum chloride. These bring about increase in viscosity and finally gelation.

Concentrated sulfuric acid will bring about depolymerization and finally complete solution, although the addition of small amounts up to 1 per cent may result in increased viscosity.

Concentrated phosphoric acid is similar to sulfuric acid in its action.

Concentrated nitric acid results in oxidation of the polymer on continued exposure at elevated temperature.

Continued exposure to dry hydrochloric acid results in splitting of the siloxane bond and a lowering of the viscosity.

Dry chlorine chlorinates the organic groups on silicon. Viscosity is increased and instability of the organic groups develops.

The reactivities described assume the application of severe

conditions such as agitation and elevated temperature. If agitation is limited and the temperature kept low, reaction may be slow enough to allow uses that would be impossible under more severe conditions.

Effect on Organic Rubbers

The dimethyl silicone fluids differ from many of the organic fluids in their effect on rubber. Instead of a softening and tackifying effect there is a mild leaching of plasticizer and some shrinkage if the rubber is immersed in the fluid. Nevertheless, used as a surface treatment for natural or synthetic rubbers these fluids increase surface resistivity, impart water repellency, and reduce the adhesion of ice to rubber surfaces. They also act as lubricants for moving parts made of rubber.

When these fluids are incorporated in rubber stocks, particularly Neoprene and GRS, there is a beneficial effect on the abrasion resistance, temperature stability, and weather resistance.[47] (See also page 72.)

Solubility of Gases in Dimethyl Silicones

Air, nitrogen, and carbon dioxide are soluble in dimethyl silicones. If the fluid is to be used in a closed system it may be advisable to degas it before use. Table 2 shows the order of magnitude of the solubility at 25°C.

TABLE 2

Gas	*Cc of Gas Soluble in 1 cc of Fluid*
Air	0.168–0.190
Nitrogen	0.163–0.172
Carbon dioxide	1.00

Solubilities

The solubility of these fluids varies somewhat with their viscosity, the low-viscosity ones being more completely soluble in solvents with which the higher members are only partially miscible. The following listing shows the solubility in some of the more commonly used solvents:

Solvents		Partial solvents	Nonsolvents
Amyl acetate	Methylene chloride	Acetone	Carbitol
Benzene	Methyl ether	Butanol	Cellosolve
Carbon tetrachloride	Methyl ethyl ketone	Dioxane	Cyclohexanol
Chloroform	Mineral seal oil	Ethanol	Dimethyl phthalate
Cyclohexane	Naphtha, V. M. and P.	Heptadecanol	Ethylene glycol
Ethylene dichloride	Perchloroethylene	Isopropanol	Methanol
Ethyl ether	Stoddard solvent	Orthodichlorobenzene	Paraffin oil (liquid)
2-Ethyl hexanol	Toluene		Water
Gasoline	Trichloroethylene		
Hexyl ether	Turpentine		
Kerosene	Xylene		

The fluids show no action on organic lacquers, coatings, or plastics. They are more soluble in naphthenic petroleum oils than in the paraffinic oils. They are not soluble in vegetable oils.

The complete insolubility in water results in excellent water-repellent properties of even very thin films. But this repellency applies to liquid water and not to water vapor. They allow the passage of water vapor and hence do not act as rust preventives over metal surfaces.

Effects with Metals

These fluids are noncorrosive to metals and are generally unaffected by them. Atkins, Murphy, and Saunders[46] have determined the viscosity change on holding the silicone fluid in contact with 10 different metals for 168 hr at 200°C (392°F). The largest viscosity increase occurred in the presence of lead and tellurium. No effect was noted from the presence of duralumin, cadmium, silver, cold-rolled steel, tin, or zinc.

Copper and selenium acted as inhibitors, for at the end of the test the viscosity of the fluid was somewhat lower than at the start.

Physiological Response

The dimethyl silicones are practically inert physiologically. Many studies indicate that they are not irritating to the skin of laboratory test animals in doses as high as 2 per cent of their body weights. These silicone fluids cause no corneal damage when dropped into the eyes but they may cause a delayed and transitory irritation of the conjunctival membranes of some individuals. This irritation, like that resulting from continually facing a strong wind, may persist for a few hours but disappears after a night's sleep. Since all except the lowest members of the series have negligible vapor pressure at room temperatures, no discomfort is likely to be experienced unless the fluid is rubbed by hand into the eyes. Ordinary cleanliness should be observed in handling these materials.

The studies referred to are described in more detail in Chapter Three.

PHYSICAL BEHAVIOR

Boiling Point

In the lower viscosities there are two types of dimethyl silicones: (1) cyclic compounds; (2) linear compounds that are end-blocked by monofunctional groups (see pages 275–276). The physical properties differ for molecules containing the same number of silicon atoms, depending on whether the molecule is cyclic or linear. It should be pointed out that although the number of silicon atoms may be the same in both types the molecular weight will differ as a result of the monofunctional end groups terminating the linear compounds. The difference in molecular weight carries more responsibility for the difference in boiling point than the difference in shape does. A comparison of boiling points is given in Table 3.

TABLE 3 Boiling Points of Dimethyl Silicones (°C)

	Number of Silicon Atoms per Molecule						
	2	3	4	5	6	7	8
Cyclic[48]	....	133	170.9	204.5	236.0	147/20[a]	168/20
Linear (trimethyl end-blocked)[49]	100.1/757	151.7/747	194/761	229/760	141.4/20	165.2/20	185.6/20

[a] 147° at 20 mm Hg.

As the molecular weight and viscosity increase the difference in boiling point between the successive members of either type becomes less and the difficulties of separation become greater. Different cuts are then referred to according to their viscosity rather than their boiling point. Above 50 centistokes viscosity, these materials are substantially undistillable at any pressure. Of course, if they are heated long enough at a high enough temperature they will depolymerize and distill. But the temperature of distillation is then that of the cyclic compounds formed and has no relation to that of the original fluid.

Freezing Point

As with the boiling points, there is a difference in freezing point between cyclics and linears having the same number of silicon atoms. But the differences in freezing points are due to the differences in molecular shape rather than to difference in molecular weight. There is no regularity of change in freezing point from one member of a series to the succeeding ones, as shown by Table 4.

An exact determination of freezing point is difficult because most of these compounds show a marked tendency to super-

TABLE 4 Freezing Points of Dimethyl Silicones (°C)

	Number of Silicon Atoms per Molecule						
	2	3	4	5	6	7	8
Cyclic[48]	....	64.5	17.4	−44.0	−3.0	−32.0	31.5
Linear (trimethyl end-blocked)[50]	−68	−86	−76	−84	−59	−78	−63

cool. Table 1, page 38, shows the freezing point, pour point, and solidification temperature of the higher-molecular-weight fluids. As the viscosity increases, the solidification temperature rises to −44°C (−47°F). About this point there is an extremely sharp rise in viscosity, indicating true freezing. Consequently, all these fluids have practical application as low as −40°, for they maintain good fluidity down to the freezing point.

Viscosity-Temperature Slope

All fluids show some change in viscosity with changing temperatures, but the degree of change differs widely in various liquids. No series of organic liquids shows as little change in this respect as the dimethyl silicone fluids.

Figure 1 shows the viscosity-temperature slope graphically. Included, for comparison, are petroleum oils of three different viscosities, all of which are high-grade products having a viscosity index of over 100.

Table 5 shows the viscosities in centistokes of an SAE 30 oil at three temperatures, compared with those of a dimethyl silicone.

The lowest-molecular-weight fluids show the least change of viscosity with temperature. As the molecular weight increases there is a greater change of viscosity with temperature, but all these fluids are greatly superior to petroleum fluids in this respect.

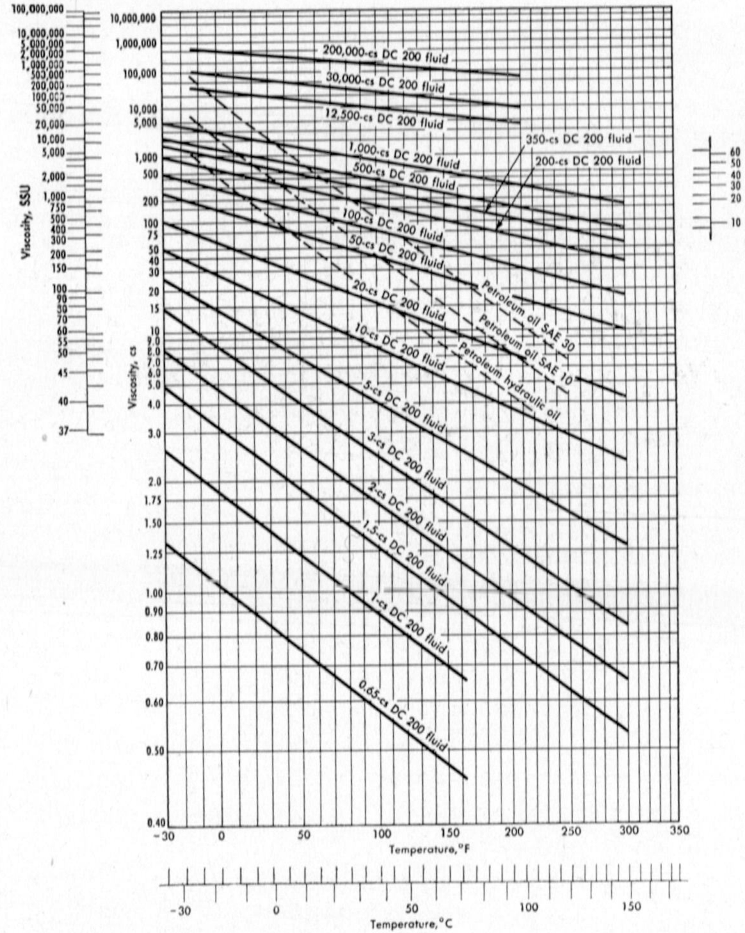

FIGURE 1 Viscosity-temperature slopes of dimethyl polysiloxane fluids and several petroleum oils.

TABLE 5 Viscosities in Centistokes

	120°C (248°F)	25°C (75°F)	−25°C (−13°F)
SAE 30	6.6	250	70,000
Dimethyl silicone	75	350	1,300

Viscosity Stability

The good resistance to oxidation and the chemical inertness of the dimethyl silicones are the reasons for good viscosity stability. In commercial products the change after 16 hr at 200°C (392°F) is held to a maximum of 10 per cent. As noted earlier, higher temperatures or the presence of certain metals accelerate the rate of viscosity change, but this can be controlled to a considerable degree by the addition of inhibitors.[45]

Although the viscosity is relatively insensible to temperature changes it is affected quite remarkably by pressure. Bridgman has studied the effect of pressure on the viscosity of low-molecular-weight dimethyl silicones. His results show that the viscosity of a dimethyl silicone fluid of 100 centistokes increases with pressure according to Table 6.[51]

TABLE 6

Pressure		
Kg per sq cm	*Psi*	*Viscosity, cs*
0	0	100
2,000	28,400	1,120
4,000	56,800	17,600
5,000	71,000	74,200

Shear Stability

Many liquids show permanent drop in viscosity on being passed through small orifices under pressure. This is known as "shear breakdown" and is important in the specification for damping media, hydraulic fluids, or lubricants.

Figure 2, taken from Currie and Smith,[52] shows the transitory drop in viscosity with rate of shear as determined by a pressure viscometer. It will be noted that dimethyl silicone fluids of 1,000 centipoises or less show no determinable effect with increasing rates of shear. With higher-viscosity silicone fluids the effect of shear becomes noticeable, and it becomes greater with increasing viscosity. The loss of viscosity with shear is transitory, for the fluids return to their original viscosity on cessation of shear.

A practical test of dimethyl silicones of approximately 70 centistokes in a standard aircraft-type Pesco gear pump has been described by Zisman *et al.* The test resulted in the conclusion:

> There was no significant viscosity change (less than 2 per cent) in the silicone fluid after having been pumped for as long as 500 hours (or 105,000 cycles). For comparison, the petroleum fluid O.S. 2943 decreased in viscosity to less than 50 per cent of its original value after 18,000 cycles.[53]

The petroleum fluid referred to is a polymer-bodied oil, the polymer having been added to improve the viscosity index.

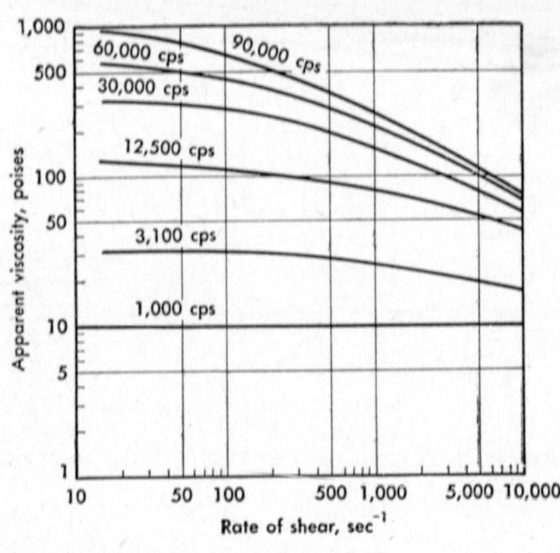

FIGURE 2

Variation of log of apparent viscosity with log of rate of shear for several methyl polysiloxane fluids.

There is no doubt that breakdown was due to degradation of the polymer rather than to the petroleum oil.

Lubricating Properties

The dimethyl silicones are good lubricants for plastic and rubber bearings. They are good lubricants for certain combinations of metal bearings. They are not good lubricants for steel on steel unless "break-in" techniques are used. An excellent listing of good and poor metal combination for these fluids is given by Zisman *et al.* Break-in methods for steel on steel are also described.[53]

The lubricating properties of these fluids are described in more detail in Sec. 3, page 96.

Dielectric Properties

The *dielectric constant* of the dimethyl silicones varies with viscosity or molecular weight, covering the range of approximately 2.2 to 2.8. The graph of Fig. 3 shows the rate of change.

The effect of both temperature and frequency on a dimethyl silicone of 1,000-centistoke viscosity is shown in Fig. 4. The small variation with either of these factors is notable.

The *power factor* is scarcely affected by temperature and remains extremely low up to frequencies of 10^8. Beyond frequencies of 10^8 there is a sharp rise. These effects are shown graphically in Fig. 5.

Dielectric strength measured at 10 mils is in the order of 250 to 300 volts per mil. At 100 mils dielectric strength is in the range of 500 volts per mil.

Volume resistivity is about 10^{14} ohm-cm and remains relatively constant at temperatures up to 200°C (392°F).

Water Repellency

These fluids are insoluble in water and are highly water-repellent. Measurement of the contact angle between a drop of water and a silicone-treated glass surface gives a figure of 90 to 110° which may be compared with the figure of 105 to 106° which is commonly accepted for paraffin.

In spite of this high repellency for liquid water these thin

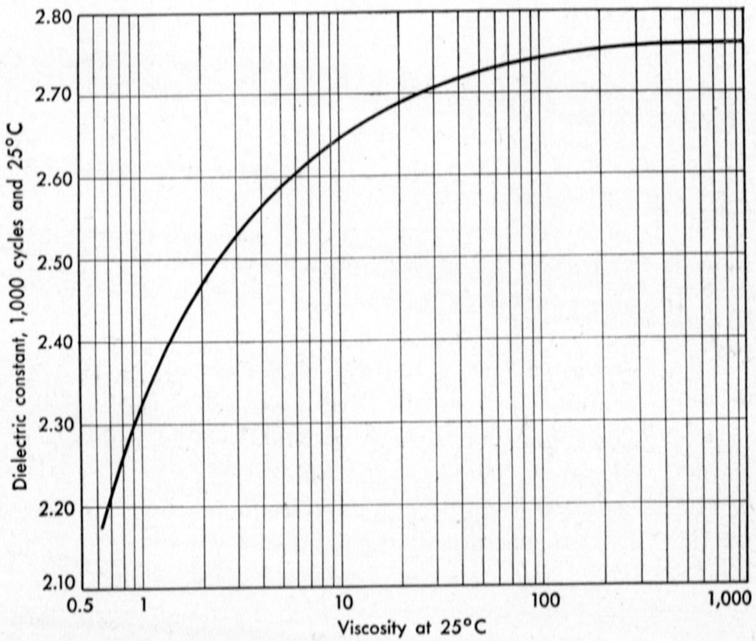

FIGURE 3 Variation of dielectric constant with viscosity of dimethyl polysiloxane fluids.

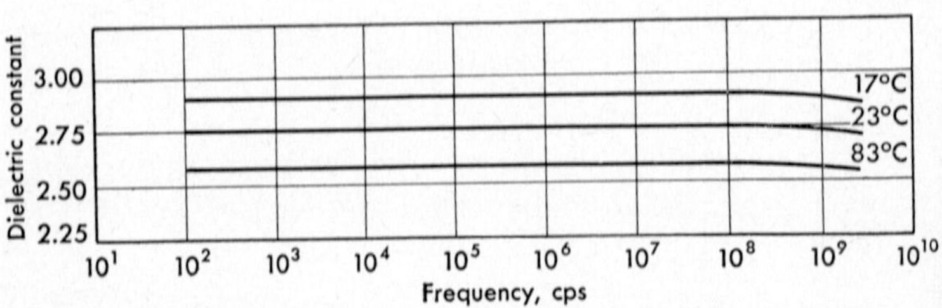

FIGURE 4 Effect of frequency on dielectric constant of 1,000-centistoke dimethyl polysiloxane fluid.

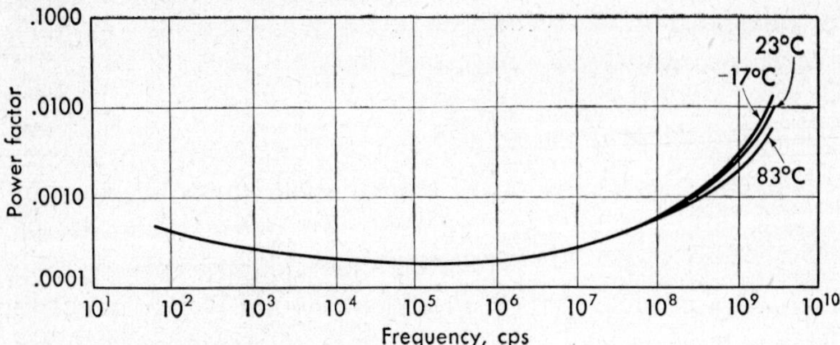

FIGURE 5 Effect of frequency on power factor of 1,000-centistoke dimethyl polysiloxane fluid.

liquid films are not particularly useful in preventing corrosion on metal surfaces. Water vapor can pass through them and attack metal. Protective paints can be prepared with other types of silicone materials, but the dimethyl silicone films are not recommended for such purposes.

Surface Tension

The surface tension of the dimethyl silicones varies with the viscosity but is relatively low for all members of the series. Figure 6 shows the relation between surface tension and viscosity.

Low surface tension indicates high surface activity and a number of useful applications stem from this property. It is

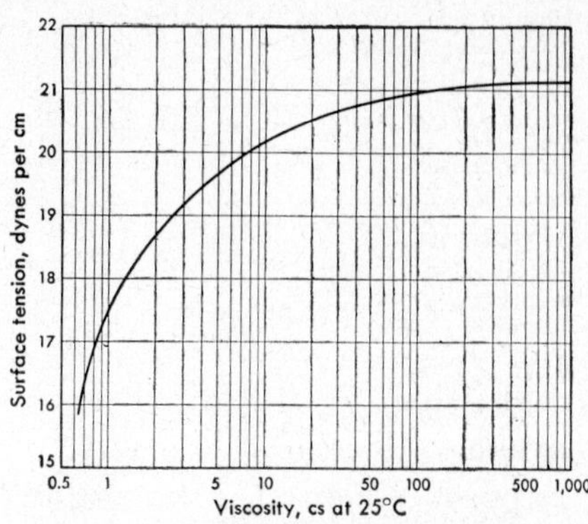

FIGURE 6 Relation between surface tension and viscosity of dimethyl polysiloxane fluids.

also responsible for creep on metal surfaces, and at times special precautions are necessary to retain these fluids.

Compressibility

The compressibility of the dimethyl siloxanes is high compared with that of light mineral oils, petroleum hydraulic fluids, and glycerin. With an homologous carbon series compressibility becomes less as the molecular weight increases. This holds true for dimethyl siloxanes of increasing viscosity, but the rate of decrease is less rapid. Table 7 shows the per cent compressibility at four different pressures for a normal

TABLE 7 Per Cent Compression

	500 kg per sq cm (7,100 psi)	2,500 kg per sq cm (35,500 psi)	20,000 kg per sq cm (284,000 psi)	40,000 kg per sq cm (568,000 psi)
0.65-cs silicone[a]	6.3	16.3	freezes	
1.0-cs silicone	5.4	15.1	31.7	36.6
2.0-cs silicone	4.9	14.3	31.5	36.9
12.8-cs silicone	4.5	12.9	29.1	34.3
100-cs silicone	4.5	12.7	28.6	34.0
350-cs silicone	4.5	12.8	28.9	35.2
1,000-cs silicone	4.6	12.7	28.2	33.5
12,500 cs silicone	4.5	12.5	28.1	33.5
n-Heptane[b] (0.57 cs)	5.0	14.3	freezes	
n-Octane[c] (0.73 cs)	4.4	13.3		
n-Decane[d] (1.18 cs)	4.0	12.3		
n-Dodecane[e] (1.82 cs)	3.5	freezes		
n-Hexadecane[f] (4.01 cs)	freezes			

[a] Freezes at 4,010 kg per sq cm.
[b] Freezes at 11,450 kg per sq cm.
[c] Freezes at 5,510 kg per sq cm.
[d] Freezes at 3,050 kg per sq cm.
[e] Freezes at 1,700 kg per sq cm.
[f] Freezes at 420 kg per sq cm.

straight-chain hydrocarbon series and a series of dimethyl siloxanes of increasing viscosity.[51]

A point of interest is that, although the lowest-viscosity silicone fluid froze at a pressure of 4,010 kg per sq cm, all the other silicone fluids remained liquid throughout the entire range of pressures applied. The hydrocarbons all froze at relatively low pressures.

Specific Heat

The dimethyl silicones in viscosity grades ranging from 0.65 to 50 centistokes have a specific heat of 0.33 to 0.35 cal per g between 0 and 100°C. Specific heat for these fluids having a room temperature viscosity of 100 to 1,000 centistokes is 0.35 to 0.37 cal per g between 0 and 100°C. These values are about one-third of the values given for water and are as low as the lowest members of the hydrocarbon series.

Thermal Conductivity

The thermal conductivity of a liquid is the quantity of heat in calories that is transmitted per second through a thickness of 1 cm across an area of 1 sq cm when the temperature difference is 1°C.

The first member of this silicone series has the lowest thermal conductivity. There is a rapid rise with viscosity up to 100 centistokes. From this point on the conductivity shows little change. Table 8 shows the values for fluids of various viscosities.[54]

TABLE 8

Viscosity (cs)	*K(50°C)*
0.65	0.000236
2	0.000255
10	0.000317
20	0.000338
100	0.000368
350	0.000386
1,000	0.000381
2,000	0.000380
12,500	0.000370

The values for some common liquids are given in Table 9.

TABLE 9

Liquid	*K*
Ethyl alcohol	0.000423
Methyl alcohol	0.000495
Glycerin	0.000637
Water	0.00143

Thus the thermal conductivity of the dimethyl silicones is below that of the alcohols and is only about 25 per cent that of water.

Thermal Expansion

The thermal expansion of the dimethyl silicones is of the same order of magnitude as that of benzene but is much greater than that of water or mercury. The expansion is not constant for all viscosities, but becomes less as the viscosity increases.

The curves for Fig. 7 show the expansion for fluids of different viscosities. The curves for benzene, water, and mercury are included for comparison. All the curves pass through a point at 0°C. and all the values are given in relation to volume at that temperature.

Given the volume of any one of these fluids at a temperature of T_1 its volume at T_2 can be calculated by multiplying the T_1 volume by

$$\frac{T_2 \text{ (ratio of volume)}}{T_1 \text{ (ratio of volume)}}$$

Light Transmission

The light transmission of the dimethyl silicones is substantially 100 per cent in all visible wavelengths. In the ultraviolet region, transmission of light decreases with decreasing wavelengths. At 280 millimicrons, the transmission is about 50 per cent. In the infrared there are strong absorption bands between 8 and 14 microns.

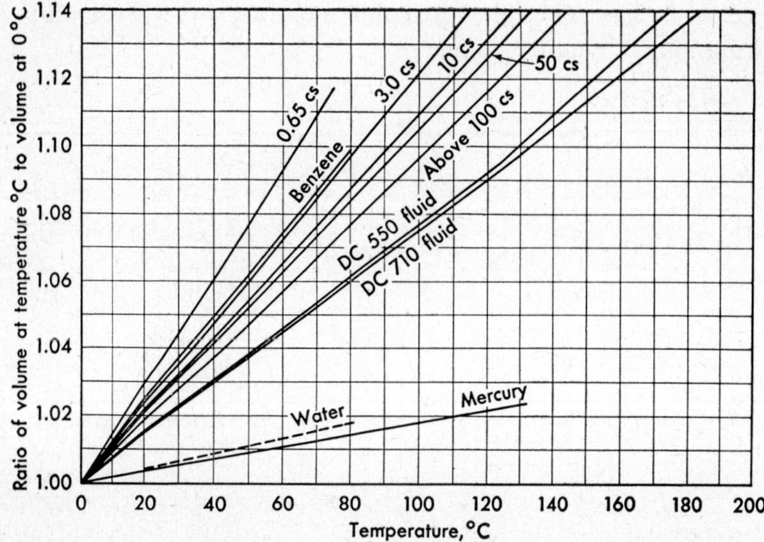

FIGURE 7 Volume expansion of silicone fluids.

As with all carbon-containing compounds, typical absorption bands are to be found across the spectrum. The infrared absorption spectra have been studied in detail by Wright and Hunter.[55] The approximate wavelength of prominent absorption maxima in the ultraviolet have been reported by Burkhard and Winslow.[56]

If these fluids are to be used as coatings on lenses or other optical apparatus, note should be made of the fact that there are absorption characteristics. Needless to say, great confusion could result in some cases if this were not taken into account.

Sound Transmission

In the dimethyl silicones the velocity of sound and its temperature coefficient are comparable to the values given for most organic liquids. Velocities increase with increasing viscosity and approach an asymptotic value of 1 kilometer per sec at 25°C. The data in Table 10 illustrate these sound-transmission characteristics.[57]

TABLE 10

Viscosity Grade, cs at 25°C	Velocity of Sound, in m per sec	
	At 30°C	At 50.7°C
0.65	873.2	795.3
2	931.3	863
5	953.8	892.1
20	975.2	918
100	985.2	929.6
1000	987.3	933.3

Refractive Index

Knowledge of the refractive index is useful in helping to identify these fluids or determine their purity. Table 1 (page 38) shows that the refractive index increases with molecular weight (or viscosity) from 1.375 to 1.4035. If the viscosity and the index of a liquid agree with the figures given there can be reasonable assurance that the fluid is pure. The addition of organic solvents is likely to raise the index and lower the viscosity. The substitution of methyl groups on silicon by other organic groups is likely to raise both index and viscosity, and the presence of the nonmethyl group will be shown by a deviation from the proper relation between these two properties.

2. Applications of Dimethyl Silicone Fluids

The applications of the dimethyl silicone fluids can be described conveniently under three headings:

1. As films
2. As additives to other materials
3. Bulk uses

AS FILMS

ON GLASSWARE

To the man in the street the best known of the silicone applications is that of treated tissue for cleaning spectacles. These are booklets of lens tissue impregnated with dimethyl silicone fluid. The thickness of the film deposited on the spectacles is scarcely measurable, but the surface imparted is brilliant, and dust and grime are much more easily removed from this surface than from the glass itself. The value of the application does not lie so much in the detergent properties as in the ease with which the coated surface can be cleaned later.

A word should be said about the use of these tissues with optical instruments. For microscope eyepieces, lenses, and reflectors for general use they are of value. For coated lenses no cleaner that involves rubbing should be used, for there is a danger of damaging the carefully deposited surface. This holds for silicone-treated tissues as well as for any other type of paper. Nor should these impregnated tissues be used on instruments for the determination of spectral absorption. As noted earlier, the silicone fluids have characteristic absorption bands, as do all organic materials, and a film of the fluid could introduce confusion in the interpretation of results.

The fluids may be used with a solvent, with or without added detergents or mild abrasives, to obtain cleaning action along with the polishing effect.

One simple way to prepare a liquid cleaner for glass is to dissolve the fluid in isopropyl alcohol. The alcohol will take up about 1 per cent of its volume of fluid, which is ordinarily sufficient. The fluid can then be applied from a spray bottle or simply wiped on with a cloth. As the glass is polished the alcohol evaporates, and the silicone remains to provide a polished, slick surface that is easily kept clean.

Usually a 1 per cent solution is found satisfactory, and 4 per cent is generally found to be a maximum beyond which there is no advantage. The application of too much fluid will leave an oily film which will need to be rubbed off. To prepare a solution containing more than 1 per cent silicone, other compatible solvents such as toluol may be added to the alcohol. The list of solvents and partial solvents given on page 42 will serve as a guide for preparing solutions.

Mild abrasives, which can serve a double purpose, may be added. They may be physically helpful in removing dirt and they may adsorb excess silicone which might otherwise coat the surface with an excessively thick and oily film.

Water emulsions can be prepared. Directions for preparing these are given on page 62. These are, in general, less satisfactory for glassware, for the emulsifier may give an undesirable cloudiness.

The life of a film applied in this manner will vary with the conditions to which it is submitted. With normal indoor exposure the ease of cleaning will be evident for many months. With outdoor exposure the film will be evident on glass for a few months to a few weeks, depending on conditions.

Stabilizing Films on Glassware

The methods just described for applying these films are simple, give a reasonable life, and can be repeated with little trouble. But there are occasions when a more durable film is wanted, as it may have to stand up against conditions more severe than normal weathering.

A method developed for the deposition of more durable films has been described by Johannson and Torok.[58] Three important steps are emphasized:

1. The glassware should be scrupulously clean. A solvent-degreasing operation may be carried out, or the glassware may be held at 400°C (752°F) for 1 hr or 450°C (842°F) for 30 min to remove any greasy film. The second method is preferable.

2. A 2 per cent solution of dimethyl silicone (350 centi-

stokes) in carbon tetrachloride or perchlorethylene should be prepared, and as soon as the temperature of the glassware is below the boiling point of the solvent the glass should be dipped. The glass should be drained and the solvent allowed to evaporate. When all the solvent has been eliminated the glass is ready for baking.

3. Baking should then be carried out at some time and temperature chosen from the graph shown in Fig. 8.

Glass coated by this method retains infinite surface electrical resistance at 100 per cent relative humidity after standing in 2 per cent salt solution for over 6 weeks. Failure to observe any one of these three points results in marked loss of resistivity after immersion in salt solution for about 48 hr.

These stable films are useful in a number of applications:

1. For maintenance of surface electrical resistivity in all types of electrical equipment, particularly in radio and precision equipment.

2. For complete drainage from medicinal glassware such as penicillin vials. The use of solvents other than water may be a factor in the life of the film, and determination of that life should be made by immersion in those solvents.

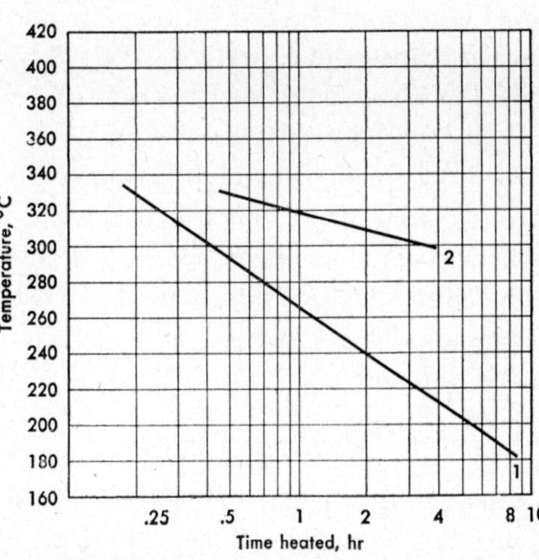

FIGURE 8
Optimum baking conditions for 774 Pyrex-brand glass rods treated with a DC 200 fluid. The times of baking should not be less than those given by curve 1 or greater than those given by curve 2.

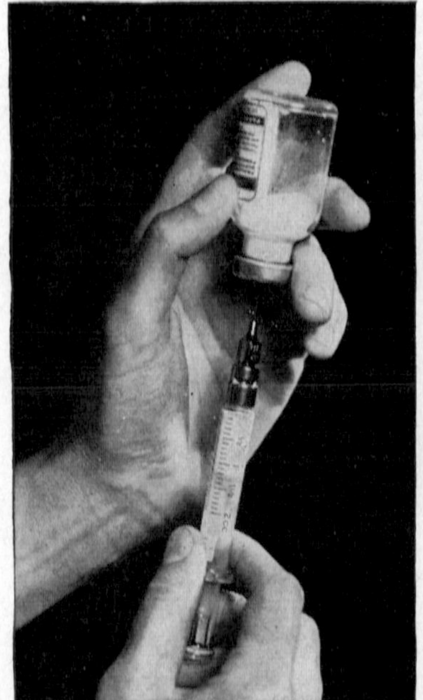
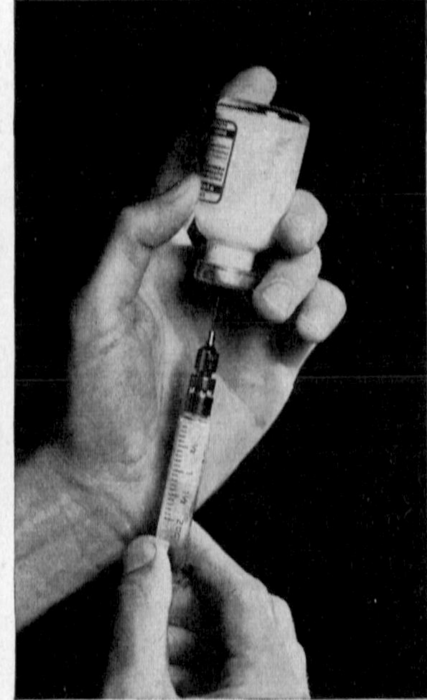

Silicone-treated (left) and untreated (right) penicillin vials.

3. For complete drainage from glassware used in microanalysis. Glassware coated in this way allows more nearly quantitative transfer of liquids.[59]

4. The glass barrels of hypodermic syringes are lubricated and give better transfer.

5. Blood passed through ordinary glass tubing has a shortened clotting time, but when passed through tubing whose interior surface has been coated this effect is much less noticeable. This has proved particularly useful in the operation of "artificial kidneys" where blood is carried through glass tubing to the dialyzer.

Vapor Method of Film Formation

Silicone films may be deposited by the use of volatile chlorosilanes. The articles to be coated are exposed to the fumes of the chlorosilanes in a chamber containing ample water vapor to ensure complete hydrolysis of the chlorine. Polymerization takes place on the surface of the articles to be coated, and a water-repellent surface is developed. Care must be taken to exhaust the hydrochloric acid developed, and a final treatment with ammonia vapor is recommended. If paper or textiles are to be treated there should be quick neutralization of the acid to avoid loss of mechanical strength.[60]

Two forms of these liquids are on the market, one having a boiling point of about 70°C (158°F), and the other a boiling point of about 220°C (428°F) at 10 mm Hg. Dow Corning Corporation distributes these under the designations of DC 1208 and DC 1205 respectively. The General Electric Company refers to them as members of their "Dri-Film" series, SC 77 and SF 99.

POLISHES

The use of a dimethyl silicone as a polish for cars or furniture has gained a well-merited popularity. The silicone may be used alone or in combination with waxes.

Car Polishes

As a polishing agent for cars it is favored because of the ease of application. The time required for polishing a car with the silicone fluid is variously estimated at one-half to one-quarter that required with a good hard wax. The luster is at least equal to that of a hard wax and the protective action against water and dirt is superior because there is no softening with heat. The life of a silicone film is little different from that of a wax coating.

The polish can be prepared as a solution or as a water emulsion with or without the addition of waxes.

If it is to be used as a solution, any appropriate and reasonably volatile solvent may be selected from the list given on page 42. A solution containing 4 per cent of the silicone fluid is generally adequate and good results can be obtained with as little as 2 per cent. The polish may be applied by spraying or by wiping. It should then be rubbed with a lint-free cloth. The usual mild abrasives may be added if a cleaning action is desired. If a wax is to be added the weight used is generally equivalent to that of the silicone.

If a solution containing wax is to be prepared, the formulation in Table 11 is suggested.

TABLE 11

Weight, %	*Material*
3	Dimethyl silicone (350 cs)
2	Wax
95	Naphthol mineral spirits

If it is to be used as an emulsion, the formula in Table 12 may be used as a guide.

TABLE 12

Weight, %	*Material*	*Supplier*
4	Dimethyl silicone (350 cs)	Dow Corning Corp. or General Electric Company
19	Stoddard solvent	
2	Kerosene (deodorized)	
2.5	Oleic acid	
16	Water	
1.5	Morpholine	Carbide and Carbon Chemicals Company or Dow Chemical Co.
14	Snow Floss	Johns Manville Corp.
41	Water	

Mix the first six materials with rapid stirring on an Eppenbach mixer or colloid mill to form a thick phase or water in oil emulsion. Mix the Snow Floss and water in a separate container. Add this mixture to the thick phase with stirring to form the finished emulsion.

For an emulsion containing wax, see the formulation suggested under Furniture Polishes (page 65).

Although the silicone is applied as a fluid and does not set up to a solid, the surface has no soft or sticky feel if properly applied. It presents a shiny surface that feels as hard as the base upon which it is placed. A greasy or oily feel is a sure sign that too much has been applied.

The first time that a silicone polish is applied to a car the life of the polish will be shorter than that obtained with subsequent applications. The reason for this may be that the fluid is partly dissolved or taken in by the lacquer. Later applications remain and the surface gives increasingly longer life.

For car polishes the addition of a wax is not essential, but it is considered by some to be an advantage. The silicone has little solubility in a wax but it makes a hard wax surprisingly easy to rub down. An explanation that has been offered for this curious situation is that the silicone provides a lubricant between the planes of the wax crystals. Thus a thin film of wax is obtained with a minimum of effort.

While each formulator will prefer some particular wax, it has been found that carnauba, beeswax, paraffin, or microcrystalline waxes are applicable.

PAINTING OVER POLISHED CARS. A repaint job on cars that have been polished with a silicone sometimes presents a difficulty. The paint may not wet evenly, or "fish-eyes" or "craters" may appear.

There are two ways to meet this difficulty:

1. Add to the lacquer or enamel that is to be sprayed 0.1 to 1 per cent of dimethyl silicone fluid. The proper amount for a particular application can be determined by adding increasing amounts of the silicone until the effective concentration is reached.

2. The conventional method of preparing the surface by removing the paint may be employed if a few minor changes from standard practice are observed:

a. Wash the area to be repainted with a strong solution of a detergent in hot water. Most of the more commonly used household or car-washing detergents are equally effective.

b. Dry thoroughly and then wipe the surface with clean cloths wet with a solvent such as naphtha or kerosene or one of the many commercial wax-removing solvents and compounds.

c. Apply masking tape; bump out dents; sand broken paint to bare metal; lightly sand other surfaces to remove gloss; rinse with solvent and wipe with a prepared "tack" cloth to pick up dust and grit.

d. Spray prime coat on bare metal and allow coating to dry.

e. Spray with lacquer or paint.

f. If either the prime or finish coat does not wet properly, the paint should be wiped off and the surface should be thoroughly cleaned again with a solvent.

There are only two minor departures from standard practices observed by any good body and fender repair shop. One is the use of disposable cloths soaked in a solvent to avoid picking up and transferring the residual film. The other is a difference in sequence. The surface should be cleaned before bumping and grinding to avoid the possibility of grinding the silicone film into the metal surface. Ordinary precautions must be taken to prevent pinholes caused by dust. Cars should not be repainted near other automobiles that are being polished.

Furniture Polishes

Furniture polish can be formulated in much the same fashion as car polishes. Although a car may be polished satisfactorily with the silicone alone, a wax addition is generally needed in a furniture polish. Hairline cracks in furniture polish appear to be filled in by the wax. The presence of the silicone gives improved luster, reduces water spotting, and makes even a hard wax easier to rub down.

Furniture with a rubbed finish is reported to be improved in appearance by the application of a dilute solution of the silicone. The grain of the wood is brought out more distinctly.

For a silicone-cream type of furniture polish, the formulation in Table 13 is suggested.

TABLE 13

Weight, %	*Material*
4	Dimethyl silicone (350 cs)
2	Alrose O (Alrose Chemical Co.)
2	Wax
1	Oleic acid
10	Naphthol mineral spirits
81	Water (boiling)

Mix the first five ingredients and then heat until the wax is melted. Add the boiling water a little at a time with constant stirring.

Floor Polishes

The addition of silicones to floor polishes for general household use is not recommended. The slick surface that is so desirable in car and furniture polishes constitutes a hazard in a floor finish.

RELEASE AGENT

In the molding of rubber and plastics and in the die casting of metals, there is an ever-present problem of releasing the article from the mold. Some type of dressing on the mold is nearly always needed if sticking is to be avoided. The dressing is commonly referred to as a "mold release" or a "parting material." This may take the form of an oil, a grease, or a solid such as mica, talc, or soap. Different release agents are used for the molding of different materials and even, by different molders, for the same material.

There are certain disadvantages in the use of these agents.

The oils, greases, and soaps carbonize in time as a result of the heat. When rejects become too numerous, the mold must be removed for cleaning. The inorganic materials are dusty and they contaminate the molding. With complicated moldings or in cases where sharp definition is required the "down-time" of the mold must be increased if it is to be kept clean enough.

The ideal release agent should (1) give easy release from the mold, (2) cause no contamination of the molded part, (3) cause no contamination of the mold, (4) have no odor, (5) be nontoxic, and (6) have long life.

The dimethyl silicone fluids have been found to meet these specifications to an unusual degree.

Experience has shown that they give good release for rubber and a wide variety of plastics and even for metal die castings. They are poorly soluble in rubber and plastics and so do not affect appearance other than to give a high surface finish. Proper application calls for the use of extremely small amounts of the silicone, for the fluid wets metal readily and spreads to an even film. The high heat resistance is such that there is no decomposition and there is little or no build-up on the mold. The fluid itself has no odor and as nearly as can be determined is completely nontoxic. The life will vary with conditions. One spraying may give good release for several cycles but most pressmen prefer to use a more dilute emulsion before each heat.

Not all silicone fluids are good mold-release agents. Fluids containing phenyl groups are not recommended. As the phenyl content is increased, the compatibility with organic material increases and the "nonstick" property is lost.

In spite of the relatively high cost of most silicone materials, the cost per gallon of the release agent as applied is not greatly in excess of that for the other usual agents. This, of course, is due to the great dilution allowable. In addition, there is abundant experience to the effect that the drop in number of rejects and the improved appearance of the moldings are substantial factors in realizing an over-all economy.

Fluids are available in forms that allow their economic use as mold-release agents. They may be obtained from the Dow Corning Corporation or the General Electric Company as fluids or as emulsions.

The *fluids* are 100 per cent silicone and may be used directly or by dilution with a volatile solvent. The solvents most commonly used are carbon tetrachloride, methyl ethyl ketone, naphtha, or white gasoline. The usual concentration is 0.5 to 2 per cent.

The *emulsions* contain about 35 to 40 per cent of the fluid and may be diluted with water. They are used at concentrations as low as 0.1 per cent depending on the work and the method of application. At 0.1 per cent concentration, the cost is about 4 cents a gallon.

Rubber Moldings

An emulsion at a concentration of 1 part in 75 to 125 parts of water is used as release agent in molding most of the passenger and heavy-duty tires made in this country. Some rubber companies prefer to use a solution of 1 to 2 per cent of fluid in methyl ethyl ketone or white gasoline. In either case the exact concentration depends on the nature of the tread stock, the complexity of the design, and the curing time.

The silicone film formed on tire molds is so stable at molding temperatures and so adherent to metal surfaces that only a minimum application of the diluted silicone emulsion or solution is required between heats to give easy release and high surface finish. Excessive application is wasteful and may result in puddling or slight surface defects. Any standard spray that delivers a fine mist is satisfactory. Individual spray guns or a central tank from which the dilute silicone release agent is piped may be used.

The fluid in white gasoline or other solvent carrier is used to spray raw tire carcasses. A metered amount of such a solution is applied by a fixed spray to the tread surface of each tire. The virtual elimination of dusting powders greatly improves outside appearance and keeps molds clean for very long periods of time.

The same procedure is applicable to all types of rubber moldings.

Plastic Moldings

Release agents are incorporated in many of the more commonly used plastics, but sticking is still a problem in fabricating various thermosetting and thermoplastic materials. In handling such materials or where release is difficult, as in the deep drawing of plastic sheeting or in molding knurled or threaded parts, the silicone mold-release agents are helpful. A point that should be recognized is that the silicone fluid acts as a lubricant as well as a release agent, reducing the friction between hot plastics and the mold surfaces. This reduces surface strains and striations.

Metal Castings

The high heat stability of the silicone release fluids has made them of great interest in the Croning Metal Casting Process, or, as it is more generally known, the Shell Metal Casting Process.

In this process the die is a shell prepared by pouring a powdered mixture of sand and a thermosetting phenolic resin against a hot metal pattern. The pattern has been previously coated with a silicone release agent. In a few seconds the resinous binder softens from the heat and flows readily to conform with the outlines of the pattern, building up a thickness of between ⅛ and ¼ in. The pattern with this adhering sand-resin coating is then baked for a few minutes at 500 to 600°F to completely cure the resin. The presence of the silicone release agent allows the easy removal of the thin but rigid mold. Two such mold halves are clamped together to receive the molten metal for the casting.

The success of the mold-release agent for the preparation of the sand-resin pattern depends on its ability to remain undecomposed by the heat and to retain its release characteristics.

The silicone release agents, again because of their high heat stability, are also finding a use in the casting of metals such as zinc and aluminum.

MISCELLANEOUS FILM APPLICATIONS

Films of these silicone fluids are applied in a great variety of ways that cannot be described conveniently under the previous headings.

Glass fibers passed through a mist of the silicone fluid and then heated develop two properties. One property, which should not be unexpected, is that the fibers become water-repellent. While glass fibers do not absorb water, water will wick along them, for they are readily wetted. A film of silicone fluid makes them so water-repellent that they present a barrier to water rather than a point of entrance.

The second property developed is that of resiliency. Untreated glass fibers can be crushed into small pieces under a hydraulic press. But silicone-treated fibers maintain their integrity and upon release from pressure resume the original volume.

The explanation for this is that the fibers all carry a thin layer of lubricant. They slip across one another without scratching, and so the most important factor in ease of breaking is removed.

Both these properties were necessary in the development of fillers for life jackets. The treatment stops water absorption and in addition allows the jackets to be stored in deep piles without being crushed into uselessness.

An application that might come under the heading of release agents is that of the treatment of aluminum trays used in the drying and baking of ceramic extrusions. The percentage of rejects due to sticking to the trays is sharply reduced because of the reduced adhesion.

Laundries experience trouble at times from the adhesion of starch to hand irons or metal rolls. Wiping the metal with a silicone-treated cloth has been found an effective solution for the trouble.

An extremely thin coating of this liquid silicone on metal has been found to be a convenient "antispatter" coating to stop the adhesion of droplets of metal to the surrounding metal during a welding operation. It also prevents the metal from becoming tarnished.

The fluid is used to provide a nonstick surface for heating irons used in the heat sealing of plastics. The iron comes away cleanly from the plastic.

As a dressing for skis, particularly metal ones, there is an advantage in using silicone rather than wax in that even at extremely low temperatures the silicone does not become hard or chip off.

A dilute solution in a volatile solvent makes a simple and effective means of waterproofing a fisherman's dry flies. Some prefer to add wax as well to increase the rigidity of the fly as it stands on the water.

The treatment of leather goods such as shoes, jackets, or luggage with a dimethyl silicone gives a water-repellent surface that is scuff-resistant. The addition of a small amount of the silicone to the resin-wax dressing on shoes is said to improve the appearance and feel of the leather.

The list of applications for silicone films could be much extended. The films are nongreasy, glossy, water-repellent, and heat-resistant. They do not allow the adhesion of other materials. Wherever any of these properties are required there is a possible application for silicone films.

AS ADDITIVES TO OTHER MATERIALS

TO PAINTS

One of the outstanding characteristics of the dimethyl silicones is that the addition of very small amounts to some products affects the properties markedly.

This holds for silicone fluids especially formulated for addition to organic paints. The amount used may vary from 1 to 50,000 ppm of the coating material. They are useful as antifloating and antiflooding agents in paints. They also aid gloss retention and eliminate orange peel.

The dimethyl silicone fluids are used for this purpose, although special formulations have been prepared that are reported to be more effective for some paints. The silicone manufacturer should be consulted if special formulations appear to be needed.

The amount of silicone to be added for the best results is somewhat critical, for too much can be as bad as too little. But 0.3 per cent is the order of magnitude normally required and the best amount for each type of paint should be determined by trial.

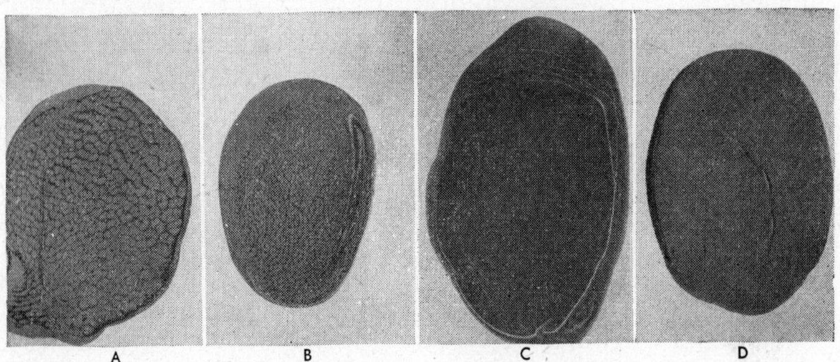

Effect of silicones on pigment floating in paints: (*A*) control; (*B*) phenyl methyl polysiloxane, 3 parts per 10,000 enamel; (*C*) dimethyl polysiloxane, 3 parts per 10,000 enamel; (*D*) methyl silicone resin, 3 parts per 10,000 enamel.

While a great deal of practical experience shows that these materials can be a great help in correcting some faults in paints it must be recognized that there is no one procedure that is applicable to all paints. Paints differ greatly in composition and so present many variables that must be taken into account. Careful experimentation and trial are needed to find the best method for a particular paint formulation.

TO RUBBER

A coating or film of a dimethyl silicone on rubber prevents the rubber from sticking to other surfaces. Because of the slippery nature of the coating, abrasion of the rubber is less. The rubber is less subject to oxidation.

Some attempts have been made to incorporate the silicone into a rubber formulation in the hope of developing a rubber having the properties of nonsticking at elevated temperatures, better abrasive resistance, and improved resistance to oxidation.

The results of one study have been reported. The silicone was added to the black in increasing amounts up to 5.7 parts based on 100 parts of rubber in the base formula. The most marked effect was that on abrasion resistance. The graph in Fig. 9 shows the abrasion resistance plotted against amounts of silicone added. It was found necessary to incorporate the silicone into the black first and then mill it into the formulation. With higher amounts of silicone there was a decrease in surface tack which made milling difficult. There was no bleeding out with the amounts used for test, and the molded surface had a fine luster.

The results were summed up in the following statement:

> Stocks containing silicone oil extrude more rapidly and are smoother in appearance. There is some indication that silicone oil addition imparts improved weather and suncheck resistance. The compounds are self-lubricating, and the vulcanizates have in many respects the water-repellent characteristics of the silicones.[47]

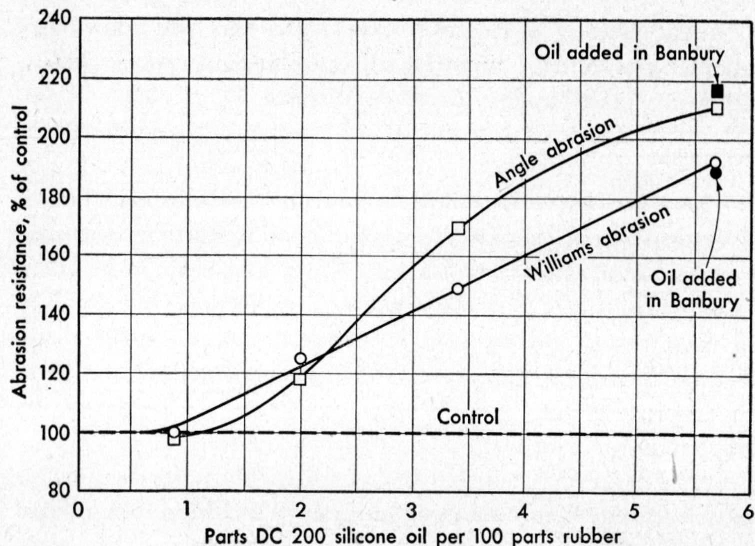

FIGURE 9 Abrasion resistance of rubber containing increasing amounts of dimethyl polysiloxane fluid.

There seems to be no doubt that the cost of the silicones has been a barrier to attempts at commercial application. This should not be a permanent restriction, for there has been a continuous drop in price from about $6 per pound when they were first introduced in 1943, to the present price of about $3.70 per pound in quantity. This price trend seems sure to continue.

TO WAXES

In the statement about polishes it was pointed out that the addition of a dimethyl silicone to a wax makes the rubbing-out process much easier.

The addition of very small amounts of silicone fluid to paraffin wax is claimed to give better oxidation resistance.[61] Color change and rancidity are said to be reduced by the addition of as little as 0.01 to 0.04 per cent of silicone.

In the coating of electrical parts with wax the addition of about 2 per cent of dimethyl silicone improves surface resistance, especially under humid conditions.

TO RESINS

There are few reports of these fluids as plasticizers for resins. The properties of high boiling point, good oxidative resistance, lack of color, and very wide range of viscosity make them appear inviting. But their poor solubility or compatibility in most resins (one reason why they are good mold-release agents) means that they are likely to bleed. Some means of incorporating them usefully into resins may yet be developed but so far their application in this field is limited.

It has been reported that the addition of 0.1 per cent or less in polystyrene before molding eliminates the need for a release agent.

BULK USES

ANTIFOAM

The dimethyl silicone is an effective antifoam agent for petroleum oils, hydraulic fluids, tar, thermoplastic adhesives, and similar materials.[62] Its use has been suggested for increasing the productivity of oil wells.[63] The amount required may be as low as 1 ppm, while 1 part per 100,000 is often considered sufficient to provide a factor of safety.

It should be pointed out that any antifoam agent is poorly soluble in the medium in which it is effective. But if such an agent is mixed with a liquid in which it is readily soluble, foaming will be accentuated. Thus if a dimethyl silicone is added to a poor solvent such as a petroleum oil it will prevent foaming. But if it is added to a good solvent such as benzene the mixture will foam excessively.

The poor solubility of the silicone in the product to be treated makes it necessary to consider the best way of distributing it uniformly.

One method is to prepare a dilute solution (1 to 5 per cent) in a solvent such as perchlorethylene. By adding this slowly, with stirring, good distribution may be obtained.

With a hydraulic oil or lubricating oil it may be preferred to make a concentrated suspension of the silicone in the oil by the use of a colloid mill. The use of this concentrate obviates the addition of solvents.

For use with tars it is sometimes convenient to crush a hard tar and coat the granules with the silicone. A scoopful of the coated tar granules can then be added to the main batch.

While the dimethyl silicones are extremely effective antifoam agents in nonaqueous liquids such as petroleum oils and tars the effect is largely lost if much moisture is present. Silicone antifoams which are effective in the presence of moisture are described under Silicone Compounds, page 87.

DAMPING FLUIDS

The fluttering of instrument pointers before coming to rest or the transmission of vibrations from one part of a mechanism to another often interferes with efficient operation. At times this condition may be serious enough to require redesign of the mechanism. In place of redesign it is often possible to install a magnetic damper or to use a fluid that will absorb the vibrations. In general the use of a fluid is simpler, but if the instrument is to operate under a wide variety of temperature conditions there may be a great change of response as the fluid becomes thick at low temperatures or thin at high temperatures. In addition fluids of different viscosities are needed depending on the damping force required.

The dimethyl silicones have characteristics that make them particularly desirable for damping purposes. As has been mentioned earlier, they are available in almost any desired viscosity. This means, of course, that they can be used to provide a very small or very large damping force. The small change of viscosity with change of temperature means that there is small change of damping effect with change of temperature. In some instruments the damping force must be kept constant within narrow limits. This requires controlling the temperature closely so that the viscosity remains constant. If a silicone damping fluid is used the temperature control is less critical, or with the same temperature control, the viscosity remains more uniform.

Table 14 shows the change of damping force of a silicone with change of temperature compared with a petroleum hydraulic oil under the same conditions.

TABLE 14

Damping Medium	*Pounds of Damping Force*	
	At −*40°C* (−*40°F*)	*At 70°C (160°F)*
Dimethyl silicone 30,000-cs grade	210	70
Petroleum hydraulic oil (very high viscosity)	70	0.028

Note: Over a temperature range of 110°C (200°F) the damping effect of the high-viscosity dimethyl silicone fluid decreases in the ratio of 3 to 1 compared with a decrease in the ratio of 2,500 to 1 for the petroleum fluid.

When considering the use of these fluids as damping agents their behavior under shear and under compression should be taken into consideration. These properties are described on pages 47 and 52.

Some typical applications are cited.

The torsional vibration damper developed by the Houdaille-Hershey Corporation[64] requires the use of a high-viscosity dimethyl silicone as a damping medium. This device consists of an inner flywheel and a hollow-disk casing attached to the end of the crankshaft. The inner flywheel is separated from the outer casing by a very thin film of a high-viscosity dimethyl silicone. Because of the high viscosity of the fluid, the inner flywheel, or inertia mass, rotates uniformly at engine speeds. When critical speeds that cause torsional vibration are reached, however, the flywheel tends to continue to rotate at a constant speed. Hence the torsional vibrations are damped by the drag of the viscous film between the casing and the inner flywheel.

The device damps both major and minor critical orders of vibration and requires no tuning. It is in general use on internal-combustion engines ranging in size from automobile engines to locomotive diesels.

In shock absorbers the silicone fluids offer greater permanence and uniformity of action. They are now being used in a number of small shock absorbers that must give constant performance over a wide range of temperatures and the advantages they offer as damping media have stimulated a good deal of original thinking about the design of automobile shock absorbers.

The pointers of automobile and aircraft instruments and gauges are now damped with silicones to prevent fluttering and to permit more accurate readings. A minute amount of very high-viscosity silicone fluid is applied to the bearings of the pointer spindles in such instruments as gas gauges, ammeters, speedometers, and tachometers. Wide commercial acceptance of this damping method came as a result of extensive laboratory and field testing.

In overload relays, circuit breakers, thermostatic controls, and other devices, the silicones are used as dashpot liquids. Their use gives uniform and reliable damping with minimum maintenance.

Crystal pickups on phonographs are damped with high-viscosity dimethyl silicones for greater permanence and for uniformity of performance in spite of high humidity.

Other miscellaneous applications are (1) in galvanometers; (2) in strain gauges to take out extraneous vibrations which interfere with readings; (3) in scales or balances; (4) in the timing devices of a circuit breaker.

HYDRAULIC FLUIDS

An excellent study of the performance of dimethyl silicones in hydraulic systems has been reported by Zisman *et al.*[65] They point out the obvious advantages of good temperature-viscosity relationship, oxidation stability, and shear resistance. They found at least three difficulties which they were able to solve but which should be considered by anyone planning to use the fluids in a hydraulic system.

One difficulty was that of lubrication, and the solution of it involved the determination of proper bearing-metal combinations. The second difficulty was due to the facility with which the silicone creeps on metal surfaces and is thereby made difficult to retain. The third is that rubber O rings lost plasticizer to the silicone, particularly at elevated temperature, and became brittle. Satisfactory O rings were developed but it had become evident that the usual type of O ring could be bothersome.

A point should be made of the fact that good resistance to shear breakdown with silicone fluids of less than 1,000-centistoke viscosity makes it possible to work at higher pressures than would otherwise be the case.

The difficulties pointed out, even though they were met ingeniously, suggest that the use of silicones as hydraulic fluids should be considered only for special situations. With a constant ambient temperature, one would expect little advantage in their use. Where the fluids must operate over a wide temperature span, as in the hydraulic system in aircraft, they should prove useful. The fact that the silicone fluids can be made to burn should be kept in mind if they are to be used in proximity to extremely high temperatures.

LUBRICANTS

Two points to be observed in the application of these fluids as lubricants are that the proper combination of bearing metals must be used and that only light to moderate loads should be imposed. In spite of these limitations there are many places where these fluids are more satisfactory than petroleum lubricants and are, in the long run, more economical. As an example the use of these fluids in parking meters may be cited. The extremes of summer heat and winter cold have little effect on the viscosity of the silicone; it does not volatilize; it does not oxidize or become gummy. In other words it stays put and maintains its original condition over a very long period of time. This constancy of viscosity and form results in reduced servicing which, with a large number of small units, can be an item of considerable expense.

The same general considerations apply to the use of the silicone with synchronous motors, precision machinery, instruments and speedometers, and for impregnating porous bronze bearings.

As lubricants for plastics the dimethyl silicones have gained wide acceptance. They have no softening effect on plastic materials and they reduce friction and wear to a minimum. This applies not only to plastic bearings but to the tools used in the cutting and machining of plastic parts.

Another application in the handling of plastics is as a lubricant and waterproofing agent in drawing plastic-covered cable into a rubber or metal conduit.

A more exhaustive statement covering silicone lubricants will be found in Sec. 3, page 95.

LIQUID DIELECTRIC

An examination of the dielectric properties of the dimethyl silicones given on page 49 will show that they are at least the equal of other liquid dielectrics. They have the advantages of high resistance to heat and oxidation, relatively slight change in viscosity or dielectric properties with temperature changes, and a high degree of water repellency. They are of particular value where the operating temperatures are high.

Examples of their uses are in capacitors and small transformers. The heat and moisture resistance results in good performance and long life.

A study pointing to their possible usefulness in transformers has been reported by Morris.[66] The problem was that of developing a thoroughly reliable transformer having the smallest possible size for a given rating. A conventional oil-filled transformer with a rating of 200 VA (40°C rise) required the same volume as a 500 VA (100°C rise) filled with silicone oil.

FLUID SPRINGS

The relative compressibilities of the dimethyl silicones is shown on page 52. With compressibilities of this order, it should not be surprising that they have been considered for use as "fluid springs." Like so many of the silicone applications this use depends not on one property only but on a combination of properties; for not only are they compressible but the compressibility is not greatly affected by temperature. They will not distil away with heat nor will they freeze except at abnormally low temperatures and at extremely high pressures.

B. Fluids Other than Dimethyl

Fluids are prepared in which the substituents on silicon are both methyl and phenyl, $—C_6H_5$. The use of phenyl groups brings about better oxidation stability, improves the lubricating properties, and in some cases lowers the freezing point spectacularly.

Certain types can be held at 250°C (482°F) for 750 to 1,500 hr before gelation, with a loss of only 10 to 15 per cent by volatilization. Lower temperatures will, of course, extend the time before gelation and decrease the rate of volatilization. Something has to be given up to obtain these improvements. We find that they show a greater change of viscosity with change of temperature than the pure dimethyl fluids do; they are not as useful in polishes or as release agents.

The use of these fluids in lubricants is of great interest. Lubricants (in both fluid and grease form) in which these fluids are used will be dealt with in a separate section (see Sec. 3, page 95).

Another type of fluid is that in which the substituents on silicon are methyl and hydrogen. Applications for developing desirable properties in textiles and paper by the use of these materials are described in subsections (4) and (5) below.

1. Low-temperature Uses

Silicone fluids of the methyl-phenyl type can be used to answer a need for a material that will remain liquid at very low temperatures and yet have low volatility at ordinary temperature. Silicone fluids are available with freezing points below −70°C (−94°F) and a flash point of about 290°C (550°F). They are used to provide damping action at extremely low temperatures, and as a low-temperature medium that can be circulated.

2. High-temperature Uses

The oxidation stability and low vapor pressure of fluids of this type make them particularly useful in many types of high-temperature baths. As the sterilizing medium in baths for dental instruments they have several advantages. They do not smoke at sterilizing temperature and so are superior to organic oils. They lubricate and prevent rusting and so are superior to water. They are economical to use because of their long life; and the life can be increased greatly by the use of a suitable oxidation inhibitor.

The properties that make them useful as a sterilizing medium also recommend them for high-temperature baths

[250°C (482°F)] of many kinds. They are used in laboratory temperature baths, calibration baths, and as heat-transfer fluids.

3. Diffusion-pump Fluids

For the development of high vacuum for electron microscopes, vacuum tube evacuators, metal evaporator systems, etc., a mechanical forepump is used to back up a diffusion pump. The latter pump operates as a result of vaporizing a high-boiling liquid. The vapors sweep out the already attenuated air and produce a lower pressure than the forepump itself is capable of. The specification for the diffusion-pump liquid calls for:

1. High boiling point
2. Stability to operating temperature at atmospheric pressure

Many of the organic fluids for this purpose are esters. Because they can be both oxidized by the air and hydrolyzed by moisture it is necessary to cool them considerably below the operating temperature before exposing them to the atmosphere.

Silicone fluids that are useful in diffusion pumps are available. The fact that they are very resistant to oxidation and cannot be hydrolyzed means that they can be exposed to the atmosphere even at operating temperature. This combination of properties also conspires to give them long life of operation without their gumming or developing decomposition products. Freedom from decomposition eliminates the fouling of boiler surfaces and also protects the forepump because neither tars nor corrosive vapors are present to gum up or corrode metal surfaces. It should be pointed out that ionization gauges should be protected by the use of cold traps because constant exposure of hot filaments to the silicone vapors tends to decrease the sensitivity of this type of gauge. Other types of gauge are not affected.

Pressures in the order of 5×10^{-7} mm are obtainable by the use of these fluids.

4. Water Repellency on Textiles

The outstanding water-repellent properties of the silicones have prompted the use of them in a great many different fields. For some time all attempts to apply them to textiles met with defeat. The fluids would not give permanence on fabrics and were removed by dry cleaning. The resins were too harsh, and they required such a high temperature for cure that the fabric would be destroyed. Continued work on this problem brought the development of materials that might be described as hybrids between the fluids and the resins.[67]

Actually two such products are available. The first is a fluid polymer which is similar to the dimethyl fluid polymers but in which each silicon has attached to it one methyl group and one hydrogen

$$\left[\begin{array}{c} CH_3 \\ | \\ -Si-O- \\ | \\ H \end{array}\right]_x$$

instead of two methyl groups

$$\left[\begin{array}{c} CH_3 \\ | \\ -Si-O- \\ | \\ CH_3 \end{array}\right]_x$$

The second product is similar but contains fewer hydrogens. The products have the water-repellent properties of the fluids but can be set up quickly at an acceptable temperature [150°C (302°F)] to a semirubbery material that is insoluble in water or in dry-cleaning solvents. They can be applied to most fabrics and have some fortunate characteristics. They impart what the textile people call a soft, full "hand." They are relatively free from "mark-off" or the tendency of some finishes to streak when a fingernail is scratched across them. On some fabrics they have a stabilizing effect, making them somewhat more shrink-, crease-, and shine-resistant. They have no odor and are nontoxic.

While this treatment is applicable to nearly all types of fabric (including wool and cotton), it is particularly useful with the newer synthetic fibers such as acetate, viscose, nylon, Orlon, and the acrylics. These newer fabrics have presented processing difficulties with the conventional water repellents, but the silicone water repellents are both effective and durable.[68] Treated fabrics show initial spray ratings of 100. After three dry cleanings, of 1-hr duration each, with Stoddard solvent and dry-cleaning soap test samples showed spray ratings of 90 to 100. After three standard launderings of 45 min each the spray ratings were from 50 to 80.

The reduced spray rating after laundering, as compared with dry cleaning, has been observed frequently. The original spray rating can often be restored by a dry cleaning. Investigation of this phenomenon brought the answer that some soap or other wetting material had not been completely removed by rinsing after washing. Continued rinsing finally restored the spray rating as effectively as dry cleaning.[69]

The application of this material is simple. It can be applied from a solvent, but it is generally more desirable to apply it as a water emulsion. It is applied by padding at room temperature, using an emulsion designed to give 2 or 3 per cent pickup of the silicone. The fabric is dried and is then heated for 5 min at 150°C (302°F) or for less than 30 sec at

Ink droplet on acetate rayon sharkskin: left, untreated; right, treated with silicone textile water repellent.

200°C (392°F) to 240°C (464°F). This completes the treatment. No final wash is required.

These silicones are low-viscosity liquids having a light straw color. As the presence of water causes a slow chemical reaction which evolves a small quantity of hydrogen gas, the emulsion should not be stored for extended lengths of time. A 50 per cent master emulsion can be prepared which is stable for a month or more, but it should be stored in a vented container. This emulsion should be diluted with water in order to give thedesired concentration as required by the work in progress.

To make a 50 per cent master emulsion of one of the products, *e.g.*, Dow Corning 1107, the following ingredients are combined at room temperature in a high-speed mixer or an Eppenbach mixer or colloid mill:

50.0 per cent by weight of Dow Corning 1107
43.1 per cent by weight of water
6.9 per cent by weight of Pluramine S-100

The master emulsion can be diluted with water to the desired concentration. It can then be applied as directed above.

The very high water repellency imparted to a textile can be demonstrated spectacularly by treating an open-weave fabric such as marquisette. A small bag formed from this transparent material will hold appreciable amounts of water, for a definite head of water must be present before any drops will break through.

No description of the application to textiles would be complete if it failed to point out the nonsoiling characteristics of water-borne stains. A properly treated fabric is not stained by such liquids as milk or soft drinks, or even by ink. Even if these materials are allowed to evaporate to dryness the solids can be washed away quite readily.

5. Treatment of Paper

Paper properly treated with the textile water repellent develops two valuable properties: (1) it becomes extremely water-repellent; (2) it becomes nonadhesive to partially cured rubber, asphalt, pressure-sensitive tapes, and to most adhesive materials.[70] The paper shows no apparent change in texture or color nor are the physical properties altered.

The high order of water repellency prevents initial wetting and greatly retards the subsequent rate of wetting. This property suggests the use of such treated paper for paper rain wear and for special purpose bags and wrapping papers.

The nonadhesive characteristics suggest its use as interleaving sheets for uncured rubber stocks, camelback, tire-tube repair patches, and pressure-sensitive rubber tape. It is also used as interleaving strips for adhesive and friction tapes and as shipping bags for materials such as asphalt.

Section 2:

Silicone Compounds

The dimethyl silicones previously described are formulated, by the addition of a few per cent of a very finely divided silica, into products described as "compounds."[71] The products so formulated may vary in consistency from relatively free-flowing liquids to heavy salvelike materials. They retain substantially all the properties of the dimethyl silicones, such as high heat resistance, low freezing point, low volatility, and good electrical properties. But the processing brings about added properties. In some cases the product is found to be unusually effective as an antifoaming agent in systems containing water. In other cases the soft salvelike material has lost any capacity to flow, even at elevated temperatures. These added properties provide materials of such different form and usefulness that they should be discussed separately.

Applications of Silicone Compounds

ANTIFOAM

The development of foam is a disadvantage in many industrial processes. It may result in the loss of product, or it may require the use of oversize vats or reactors. It may expose the product to undesirable oxidation or may even constitute a fire hazard. There are situations where foaming is beneficial, but in general it is unwanted, often to the point of being unallowable. For such an unpopular side product the demand is "off with its head." It is impossible to predict on the basis of theory whether a given mixture will foam, but practical experience supplies the answer to the processor. If foaming occurs, for whatever reason, he generally wants to get rid of it.

Each foaming difficulty presents its own problems and needs its own method of solution. No one method of treatment is effective for every foaming condition, and the best one can do is to try out additives or mechanical methods until the best and most economical answer is obtained.

The mechanical methods for breaking foams include centrifuges, change of pressure, rotating disks, and a multitude of devices that aim at physical destruction. The additives include alcohols such as octyl alcohol, polyamides, castor oil, and many proprietary compounds, most of which aim at prevention of foaming rather than at destruction of the foam already formed.

The silicone antifoams fall into the second category. They are not effective in all cases any more than the other antifoams are, but in the large number of cases where they are effective they have some auxiliary advantages.

One of these advantages is that extremely small amounts are generally required. Typical applications use 2 to 5 parts per 100,000, and there are numerous instances where 1 ppm is sufficient. When it is realized that this latter figure means roughly one drop in 25 gal, the amount required seems fantastically small. This is most important where contamination of the product must be kept to a minimum.

A second advantage is that the silicone is substantially nonvolatile. Because of this it remains effective at high temperature and can be used in distillations run at low pressure.

The chemical inertness and resistance to oxidation result in long life under what would normally be considered severe conditions.

The lack of toxicity, coupled with the very small amounts needed, permits its use in food products.[72]

The use of the silicone is economical. This statement may seem surprising when it is added that the price of the silicone is about $6 per pound as compared with a few cents for many other defoamers. Yet if the calculations are made on the basis of the cost to defoam a gallon of the product the silicone is frequently shown to be the cheapest, the reason being, of course, that so little is needed.

These general-purpose silicone antifoams are useful in a wide variety of products in which the pure dimethyl silicone is ineffective. They are available as liquids of a honeylike consistency or as water emulsions. They may be applied as received or from a dilute solution in organic solvents; they may be dispersed in the product as a concentrate; or the emulsion may be further diluted with water. In some cases a certain height of foam can be tolerated or may even be desired. Under these circumstances a thin line of the silicone may be painted or smeared around the inside of the vat at the desired height. The foam will not rise above this. Or a wire netting treated with antifoam may be suspended at the proper height. These treatments often remain effective for long periods of time.

A listing of all the various products to which these antifoams are economically applicable is not practicable. But a statement of typical groups is given below, followed by a description of several somewhat unusual applications, which may, in turn, suggest others.

The antifoam may be incorporated in: adhesives such as casein; phenolic, melamine, and urea resins; rubber; edible materials such as chewing-gum bases, cooking oils, gelatin, skim milk, yeasts; paints, lacquers, rosins, shellacs; detergents, cleaners, water softeners; dyes and insecticides.

The antifoam has been used to control foaming in the following operations:

The bottling of fruit juices, molasses, soft drinks, wetting agents, soaps, etc.
The concentration of sugar, whiskey, caustic
The beating of paper
The cooking of varnishes, linseed oil

The dehydration of alkyd, melamine, phenolic, urea resins
The loading of tank cars with rubber or latex or tar
Laboratory distillation
Wire drawing

In looking over this abbreviated catalogue of uses one sees that special properties of the silicone antifoams are required in nearly every case. For edible products the amount of additive must be small, tasteless, and nontoxic. For the heat treatment of varnishes and resins it must have reasonably long life and be nonvolatile. For laboratory distillation it must be nonvolatile and stable.

It takes little imagination to see that it could be used by the housewife in jelly making, in preserving, and in the making of candies.

It has been used by the veterinarian to combat "bloat" in cattle. A suspension of the silicone is injected hypodermically into the rumen of the affected animal. The foam that is the cause of the trouble is broken, and relief is almost immediate.[73]

STOPCOCK GREASE

When the compounds are formulated into heavier or salve-like materials they show the peculiar properties of maintaining a constant viscosity over a very wide temperature span and of being more slowly taken up by solvents. They are resistant to decomposition and have low vapor pressure. These properties have given them wide acceptance as stopcock greases for the lubrication and sealing of stopcocks, for use on distillation flasks, take-offs, and desiccator lids, and for similar applications.

For this type of application two types of grease are on the market. The softer of the two is in perhaps more general use for it is more easily applied. The stiffer grease, although requiring somewhat more care in application, presents a sturdier film and is designed for sealing and lubrication in vacuum systems operating in the range of 10^{-6} mm. Both are adapted as lubricants for glass and ceramic stopcocks and joints over a temperature range of −40° to 250°C (482°F). The point might be made that neither these stopcock greases nor any other can be expected to atone for poorly ground cocks or joints. All such greases should be applied sparingly and should be considered as lubricants and seals rather than as fillers.

Although both these greases can be dissolved in a solvent such as benzene they give good service in the presence of benzene and similar solvents if properly prepared joints or cocks are used. There are two reasons for this. In the first place, the very physical state of the compound makes solution difficult, and the fact that the solvent does not have full access to it but must leach it out adds to the resistance to solvents. Secondly, it is well nigh impossible to free glass from the last trace of a silicone fluid by the use of organic solvents, even under the best of conditions. A residual film always remains.

The question has been frequently asked as to the vapor pressure of these greases. About all that is known is that it is extremely low. No results of such a determination are known to have been published.

Removal of Stopcock Grease from Glass

The stopcock greases, like other silicone materials, are very water-repellent. This is in many cases a useful property, but it can be a great bother if the coating is spotty. It is particularly annoying if the inside of a burette shows signs of being partially coated with a film of the grease. Water does not wet the wall consistently and the burette becomes useless for accurate work. None of the organic solvents removes the last traces of silicone, and the use of strong alkalies on carefully graduated glassware is not advisable.

The most satisfactory method of removing a silicone film

from glass is by the use of concentrated sulfuric acid. The burette should be filled with the acid and allowed to stand for a few hours. The acid should be drained off and the burette washed at least once (preferably twice) with clean concentrated sulfuric acid. Following this the burette may be washed with water and will be found free of silicone.

The reason for the use of sulfuric acid is that it depolymerizes the silicone into small molecules with sulfonated ends. These are soluble in sulfuric acid. The reaction may be shown in condensed form:

$$(R_2SiO)_x + (2H_2SO_4)_x \rightarrow x[R_2Si(HSO_4)_2] + xH_2O$$

The sulfonated molecules should be completely washed away with strong acid. If any remain they will be hydrolyzed by water and the silicone will be reprecipitated.

Other types of glassware may be treated similarly.

MOLD RELEASE

The ability of the dimethyl silicone fluids to act as release agents in the molding of plastics and rubber has been described previously (page 65). But for the release of heavy or particularly intricate moldings one of the compounds is even more effective because a heavier coating can be applied. It may be wiped on or sprayed on from an emulsion.

In the tire industry it is used as a tire-bag lubricant. It prevents the soap solution from sticking to the air bag. It prevents glue and resin from sticking to press platens and loading equipment in the manufacture of plywood and to the heat-sealing iron in the handling of plastic film.

The emulsion of this heavy release agent has been used very effectively in the shell-casting process for metals. In this process two metal patterns are prepared which conform to two halves of the casting desired. The patterns are sprayed with the emulsion to give complete coverage. They are then heated, and a heavy layer of a mixture of sand and Bakelite resin is applied. The heat of the pattern is sufficient to melt and finally set up the resin to a thickness of about ⅛ in. The silicone release agent is so heat stable that it does not decompose at the pattern temperature. The result is that the shell of resin-sand mixture can be removed cleanly. The two shells are then fitted together securely and the casting metal is poured in. Because of the effectiveness of the release agent the shell has sharp definition, and the castings obtained require a minimum of machining.

ELECTRICAL APPLICATIONS

The silicone compounds have found wide application in the electrical industry. The electrical properties are similar to those of the dimethyl fluids. The resistance to heat and to attack by chemicals is also similar. The physical form of a soft, water-repellent, nonflowing, and heat-resistant material which has good dielectric properties is an advantage in many applications. Almost any specified penetrometer range is available.

The range of properties of compounds is shown in Table 15.

TABLE 15

Flash point: 290°C (554°F)
Dielectric constant (1,000 cycles): 0.07
Dielectric strength at 10 mils: 500 volts per mil
Penetrometer (unworked ASTM D-217-38T): 190–300
Penetrometer (worked – max): 250–350
Per cent volatility (max at 200°C): 2.0–5.0
Per cent bleed (24 hr at 200°C): 8.0–10.0
Solidification point °C: −40° to −54°C (−40° to −65°F)
Melting point: None

The compounds are particularly useful as moisture-and-water-repellent high-dielectric-strength sealing compounds for aviation-type spark plugs, as well as for moisture seals for electrical connectors. Also, as moisture-proof seals or corrosion inhibitors they are used on aircraft radio antennas, X-ray equipment, switches, terminals of various electrical devices, ignition systems of marine engines, battery cases, outdoor switches, and cables.

GENERAL APPLICATIONS

There are many general applications of the compounds which are made possible by their resistance to many ordinarily corrosive chemicals. They are affected slightly or not at all by chemicals such as chromate solutions, liquid ammonia, acetic and stearic acids, phenols and chlorinated phenols, concentrated phosphoric acid, solutions of ferric or aluminum chloride, sodium chlorate, 30 per cent hydrogen peroxide, molten sulfur, sulfur dichloride, or aqueous solutions of mineral acids. They are decomposed by concentrated sulfuric acid, nitric acid, and dry hydrochloric acid.

Because of their ability to withstand this chemical attack the compounds are often used as impregnants for pump packing where there are conditions of high temperature or corrosive atmosphere. Data are at hand concerning a pump which handled a mixture of ammonium sulfate and sulfuric acid. Use of a silicone compound to impregnate the packing increased the life of the pump by a factor of 10.

The heavier compounds have been used for the sealing of pressure and vacuum equipment and also as vibration dampers in phonograph pickups.

The compounds as a class are put to a variety of uses other than those cited. For instance they are used for the waterproofing and preservation of leather. Their application to rubber goods, such as diaphragms, results in longer life. They have been used to lubricate rubber tubing inserted in the nose of hospital patients, to prevent the growth of algae on the side of fish bowls, and to treat the cork-covered joints in wood-wind instruments. It is impossible to outline in detail all the possible applications for materials with the properties described.

Imagination and experimentation will show many fields of usefulness.

Under some conditions the compounds may act as lubricants. This property is discussed in the section on Silicone Lubricants. The compounds are referred to there as "grease E."

Section 3:

Silicone Lubricants

The value of lubrication has been recognized since early times. The first materials used to reduce the friction between moving parts appear to have been vegetable and animal oils. Indeed, castor oil, lard oil, and tallow were still in common use as lubricants even after the middle of the nineteenth century. It seems difficult to believe that less than 100 years ago tallow was used to lubricate commercial steam engines and that lard oil was the accepted lubricant for machine-shop engine bearings.

The instability of these lubricants to heat and their rapid gum formation made it difficult to operate complicated machinery. Machine design had to be simple. When petroleum lubricants became widely available, after about 1860, many of the restrictions of design were removed. These oils were able to provide lubrication for higher loads, for longer periods, and under more severe conditions.

While these better petroleum lubricants permit great improvement in machine design they still have limitations that fail to permit operation under all conditions. Efficient operation in extreme heat or extreme cold is still beyond their capacity.

The silicone lubricants offer solutions to many of the difficulties still unsolved by petroleum lubricants. In so doing they contribute to the possibilities of still further improvement in machine design or in better operation of present design. Lubricants of this type are available for use, under appropriate conditions, throughout a temperature range of −75°C (−103°F) to +250°C (482°F).

The widest variety of silicone lubricants on the market is that supplied by the Dow Corning Corporation. As a description of them will give a sharper picture of the field of silicone lubrication these products are referred to and described specifically. The General Electric Company also offers silicone lubricants for sale but not, at the moment, in as wide a range.

The lubricants being discussed are obtainable as either liquids or greases, the greases being formed from the liquids by the addition of appropriate fillers or additives. Although each of these lubricants has properties of its own that make it preferable to the others for specific applications, there are certain properties common in more or less degree to all.

A. Fluid Lubricants

The basic chemical structure of the fluid lubricants is that of a linear siloxane chain in which two organic groups are attached to each silicon. In one type all the organic groups are methyl. In succeeding types increasing amounts of phenyl groups are substituted for methyl groups. These changes in chemical constitution bring about the changes in physical properties that differentiate one fluid from another.

The change of viscosity with temperature was described on page 45 for those liquids where the organic groups are all methyl. As phenyl groups are exchanged for methyl groups the slopes become poorer, although the poorest of them is still superior to that of petroleum oils. Figure 10 shows the effect of temperature on the viscosity of various silicone oils and on SAE 30 oil. The line *A* refers to an all-methyl oil, *B* to one

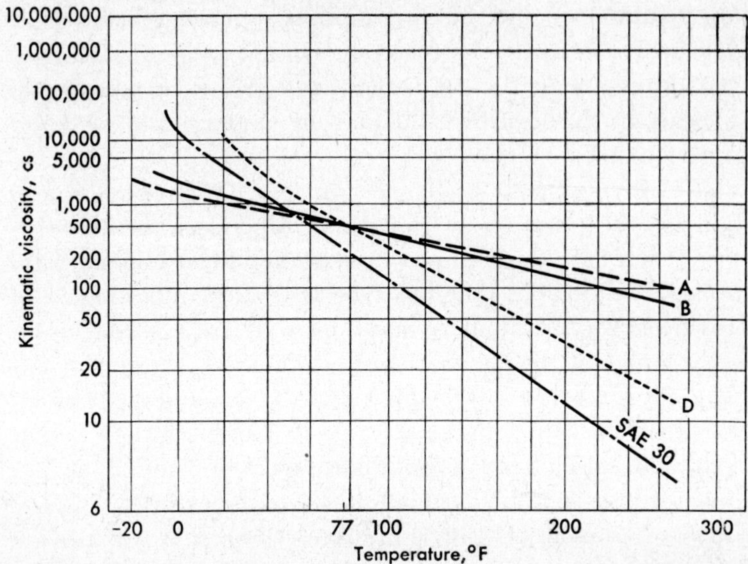

FIGURE 10 Temperature-viscosity slopes of silicone lubricants.

containing a small percentage of phenyl groups, and *D* to one containing a large percentage of phenyl groups.[74]

As shown in Table 16 the useful temperature span changes as the amount of phenyl groups is increased.

The type A fluid, it will be noted, is the dimethyl silicone described previously. As a lubricant its claim to distinction lies in its very small change of viscosity with temperature and in the wide range of viscosities obtainable. Particular atten-

TABLE 16

	Dow Corning Number	Amount of Phenyl Groups	Useful Temperature Span
A	200	All methyl	−45 to 150°C (−49 to 302°F)
B	510	Low phenyl	−75 to 200°C (−103 to 392°F)
C	550	Medium phenyl	−50 to 250°C (−58 to 482°F)
D	710	High phenyl	−23 to 250°C (−9 to 482°F)

tion should be paid to the combination of bearing metals used. It is a poor lubricant for steel on steel unless proper breaking-in procedures are used. Its wide applicability to other types of bearings is described further on under Uses of Fluid Lubricants.

The very low pour point (−75°C, −103°F) of the type B fluid and the grease made from it recommends its use in operations where low torque must be maintained at low temperatures. It is obvious that this type will allow movement and provide lubrication under conditions that are completely out of the range of the conventional lubricants. We should not lose sight of the fact that the high-temperature stability is good, too: this lubricant is servicable up to 200°C (392°F). It is even more stable to oxidation than type A, in spite of the fact that it is also operable at much lower temperatures.

Type C is more heat-resistant than type B. It will provide lubrication at temperatures as low as −50°C (−58°F) and as high as 250°C (482°F). It may thus be said to be the "work horse" of the series, for it can be used over the widest temperature range.

Type D is the most heat stable of the silicone lubricants. While it has a comparatively high pour point [−23°C (−9°F)], its high temperature stability is such that it may be held at 250°C (482°F) for over 1,000 hr without gelation.

The upper limits of temperature have been described as 250°C (482°F). This refers to the point at which good life may be expected with a minimum of attention. If the temperature exceeds these limits there is no immediate breakdown but simply a shortening of life. If bearings are relubricated the operating temperature may be increased to as much as 370°C (698°F).

A very great increase in the life of these lubricants may be obtained by the addition of oxidation inhibitors. Many of these have been described,[45] a representative member of this list being para-aminophenol. The high temperature at which these lubricants often operate results in destruction of the inhibitor in time. Periodic additions, nevertheless, help to protect the silicone oils over extended periods.

The remarkable low-temperature and high-temperature operability of these fluids and greases is a most important reason for the unique position they hold in the field of lubricants. Certain specific applications of each one are described under Uses of Fluid Lubricants.

All lubricants vary in their ability to lubricate all combinations of bearing metals, and the silicones are no exception to this rule. An important point to note is that where sliding friction of steel on steel bearings is involved, these fluids and greases are not satisfactory under heavy loads or where boundary lubrication is required. In some cases they have been used satisfactorily with steel against steel when the sliding friction involved light loads. In the lubrication of ball bearings the greases have given satisfactory performance and long life.

Grant and Currie[74] make the following statement with regard to various bearing-metal combinations and load-carrying capacity:

> Many functional or simulated functional tests have been conducted to determine the relative effectiveness of silicone lubricants between various metal combinations in journal bearings. The Falex lubricant machine has been used for this purpose. The results of these tests reported in Table 17 indicated that such bearing pairs as steel against zinc, bronze, nylon, chrome or cadmium will be effectively lubricated by silicone fluids. Babbitt and silver have also been found to be satisfactory bearing materials with silicones.
>
> Zisman and his associates[75,76] found that a silicone lubricant performed well on a chrome plated shaft rotating in a bronze bearing. Even at temperatures as high as 220°C. performance was good. They found that the type A fluids (all methyl) were better lubricants for the bearing pairs studied than silicone fluids

of type D (high phenyl). In addition to journal bearings studies, some exploratory work was reported with Pesco-type gear pumps in hydraulic systems.[65]

TABLE 17 Effect of Various Bearing Surfaces and Loads on Wear-preventive Properties of Silicone Fuids

(Falex Lubricant Machine)

Bearing Surfaces		Load, psi	Fluid A		Fluid D	
V block	Shaft		Wear, in. per min × 10[5]	Rating	Wear, in. per min × 10[5]	Rating
Steel	Zinc-plated	800	0.7	Good	0	Good
Steel	Zinc-plated	1,600	0.8	Good	0	Good
Steel	Zinc-plated	2,400	0.8	Good	0.6	Good
Steel	Zinc-plated	3,200	1.1	Good	1	Good
Steel	Zinc-plated	4,000	0.8	Good	0	Good
Steel	Cadmium-plated	800	0.7	Good	0.2	Good
Steel	Cadmium-plated	1,600	1.3	Good	0	Good
Steel	Cadmium-plated	2,400	15.7	Poor[a]	0.8	Good
Steel	Cadmium-plated	3,200			8.5	Poor[a]
Steel	Chrome-plated	800	4.1	Good	4	Good
Steel	Chrome-plated	1,600	0.7	Good	0	Good
Steel	Chrome-plated	2,400	0.8	Good	0	Good
Steel	Chrome-plated	3,200	0.8	Good	0	Good
Steel	Chrome-plated	4,000	1.1	Good	0.2	Good
Steel	Bronze	800	5.4	Good	0.9	Fair
Steel	Bronze	1,600	0.8	Good	1.5	Fair
Steel	Bronze	2,400	0.4	Good	2	Fair
Steel	Bronze	3,200	0.4	Good	3.5	Fair
Steel	Bronze	4,000	0.8	Good	5.9	Poor
Graphitar	Steel	800	5.7	Poor	6.5	Poor
Graphitar	Steel	1,600			9.8	Poor
Nylon[b]	Steel	800	3	Good		
Nylon[b]	Steel	1,600	4.1	Good		
Nylon[b]	Steel	2,400	4.4	Good		
Nylon[b]	Steel	3,200	6.5	Good		
Nylon[b]	Steel	4,000	8.9	Good		

[a] Excessive wear caused by removal of cadmium plating.

[b] It is probable that most of the wear reported here was due to deformation of the vee block.

In general where heavy loads were involved, independent researchers[65,77] found that the deposition of a polymerized silicone film was beneficial. This oxidized silicone film was deposited by heating the bearing in the presence of a type A fluid. A combination of silicone fluid and its decomposition film produced desirable effects on both friction and load capacity at sliding velocities as high as 7600 fpm with an initial Hertz surface stress as high as 126,000 psi.

It appears that the load-carrying capacity of the silicone lubricants in antifriction bearings of standard design is adequate for most applications. Where the applied load is greater than ⅓ of the rated load silicone lubricants, in general, and type G in particular, may not give as satisfactory service as petroleum greases. Antifriction bearings are most commonly operated, however, under loads considerably below ⅓ of the rated load where silicone greases give superior performance because of their high resistance to oxidation and thermal degradation.

The value of using one combination of bearing metals rather than another is emphasized in the case described by Zizman.[65] Because of the small change of viscosity with temperature it was desired to use a silicone fluid in a hydraulic pump. Two trials of 65 and 80-hr duration with fluid A resulted in pump failures. "The pump failures in these tests had in each instance been caused by the rapid wearing of the steel universal link and steel knuckle." Bronze knuckles were then substituted for the steel knuckles. The pump was then tested for a period of 650 hr. "The universal link pins and knuckles were not unduly worn and the general condition of the pump was considered excellent."

The concluding paragraph in the discusssion of this test states:

> Hence the use of steel pins and bronze knuckles improved the lubrication characteristics so much as to permit the silicone fluid to be a practicable hydraulic fluid in this type of pump. However, it has not been established here that steel pins and bronze knuckles

are the best possible choice of materials. Other combinations of metals deserve consideration by those interested in the necessary changes in design required in pumps to be used with these new fluids.

Uses of Fluid Lubricants

The type A fluids show the smallest change in viscosity with temperature of any of the fluid lubricants. Consequently they are used where this characteristic is important. They are used in damping devices such as viscous torsional-vibration dampers, shock absorbers, and dashpots. They are useful as hydraulic fluids. Their lubricating properties are employed in porous-bronze bushings, centrifugal oxygen compressors, and in oxygen valves operating at temperatures below 200°C (392°F). They are among the best lubricants for natural and synthetic rubber and for polystyrene, phenolics, and most other plastics. They are effective lubricants for fiber gears and plastic or rubber bearings, and for rubber- or plastic-insulated cable that must be drawn through metal harnesses or conduits. They are used in synchronous clock motors and in demand meters.

The type B fluids show somewhat more change in viscosity with temperature than the A fluids, but they have a much lower pour point and are considerably more stable to heat. The type B fluids are to be preferred where a very wide range of temperature is to be encountered. The mechanisms of parking meters and automobile speedometers that must operate throughout the cold of winter and the heat of summer are illustrations of appropriate places for these lubricants.

The type C fluids have higher pour point [−50°C (−58°F)] than type B but they are more heat stable. They are used as lubricants for journal bearings, ball bearings, and porous-bronze bushings where long life, serviceability over a wide temperature span, or heat stability is required. Typical application includes the permanent lubrication of clocks, instruments, parking meters, and electric razors.

The type D fluids are the most-heat-stable silicone fluids known. The relatively high pour point [−23°C (−9°F)] means that their major use is for high-temperature lubrication. They are used for the lubrication of oven doors and for valves handling corrosive materials at high temperatures; to prevent the seizure of hold-down bolts and guide pins on presses and of the nozzles on injection molding machines. They are also used as lubricants for oven conveyors at temperatures above the limits of type C fluids.

B. Lubricating Greases

Greases are prepared from the four types of fluids previously described. Table 18 shows the fillers used and some of the properties resulting.

TABLE 18

Fluid Used	Filler	Grease Type	Dow Corning No.	Dropping Point, °C	Bleed,[a] %	Evaporation,[a] %	Useful Temperature Range °C	Useful Temperature Range °F
A	Silica	E	4	None	1	1.5	−50 to 200	−58 to 392
B	Lithium soap	F	33	200	3	3	−75 to 150	−103 to 302
C	Lithium soap	G	44	200	2	1.5	−40 to 200	−40 to 392
D	Carbon black	H	41	None	4	1	−30 to 260	−22 to 500

[a]Bleed and evaporation determined after 24 hr at 150°C in a wire mesh cone.

Type E grease is the material described under Silicone Compounds, page 87. As a lubricant its uses are largely limited to parts which move intermittently, such as valves, or for bearing members, such as rubber against steel.

It will be noted that the useful temperature range of the greases is similar to that of the fluids. Grease G shows a lower upper limit than its parent, fluid C. This results from the presence of the soap, the thermal stability of which is not equivalent to that of the silicone fluid. There is no such limiting factor in grease H.

The shear stability of the silicone greases has been investigated by Grant and Currie,[74] who report as follows:

> The behavior of the silicone greases under shear is similar to that of most organic greases. At low rates of shear the amount and type of soap is most important. At high rates of shear, consistency is determined largely by the oil. Surprisingly enough the rheological properties of type H grease compounded with carbon black are similar to those of the type F and G greases, which are thickened with an organic soap.
>
> The stability of the silicone greases classified as types F and G under prolonged shearing in a motorized grease worker is indicated by the values given in Table 19. The ASTM penetration of the type F grease was increased by less than 30 points and the penetration of the type G grease was increased by less than 25 points after 100,000 strokes.

TABLE 19

No. of Strokes	*ASTM Penetration*	
	Grease F	*Grease G*
60	294	314
1,000	307	324
10,000	316	340
100,000	323	336

In general the lubricating properties of the greases parallel those of the liquids from which they are compounded. The load-carrying capacity may be limited or excellent depending upon the bearing-metal combination. As with the liquids the operating temperature may be as high as 370°C (689°F) if the bearings are relubricated. They are particularly recommended for use at temperatures that are too high or too low to permit petroleum greases to function, or where the life of petroleum greases is so limited that very frequent lubrication is required.

Uses of Grease Lubricants

The different types of grease are all obtainable in a range of consistencies varying from liquid to thin, medium, and thick.

The type E greases are not used, in general, for the lubrication of continuously moving parts, either ball bearings or journal bearings, but rather for plug and control valves, where movement is intermittent. They have proved to be of the greatest use in lines carrying solvents and corrosive chemicals. Valves controlling the flow of steam and gas, nitrite solutions, phosphoric acid, chlorine, carbon disulfide, hot caustic brine, and many other chemicals, are kept free. Valves which must function at elevated temperatures show much less tendency to seize when this type of lubricant is used. They make excellent lubricants for places where rubber must move against steel.

> Evidence of the exceptional stability of silicone grease, type E, is given by its performance in a bank of stellite-treated valves handling hydrocarbon gases at temperatures ranging from 200°C (392°F) to 500°C (932°F) for about 21 hours each day, with temperatures in the range of 500°C (932°F) to 700°C (1292°F) during the other 3 hours. Three years of experience with silicone grease, type E, has proved that these valves no longer have to be reground; valve life has been tripled; and the cleaning schedule has been changed from once every 4 to 6 weeks, to once every 6 to 8 months.[74]

Type F greases have as their outstanding characteristic the ability to lubricate at extremely low temperatures. They are designed primarily for use in ball bearings operating under light to moderate loads. For example they are used in small motors that must be started after exposure to very low temperatures and on the free ball bearings in transits which may

In one foundry 7,200 of these trolley bearings are exposed several times a day to temperatures ranging from 550 to 700°F. Silicone lubricants have given good service for years.

have to operate under arctic conditions. They have been used in circulating pumps handling alcohol and acetone at temperatures as low as −75°C (−103°F).

The fact that the type F greases are useful at high temperatures as well as low greatly increases their usefulness. Bearings on motors and fans are cases in point. Certain very low-torque motion picture equipment which is required to operate in the range between −30°C (−22°F) and 150°C (302°F) is successfully lubricated with grease of this type. Other applications that may be mentioned are in geophysical instruments, electric-demand meters, time clocks, radar tuning devices, microphone switches, and in the gears of X-ray machines. In general this type of grease is used where uniform performance is required over a very wide temperature span.

The type G greases are of more general application than the others. One very important use is in the ball bearings of motors operating at high speed and high temperature. Bearings running at 150°C (302°F) can be lubricated with petroleum greases, but this approaches the upper limit of their usefulness and the life is short. A type G silicone grease was compared with a good high-temperature petroleum grease using two identical motors operating at 150°C (302°F) and 1,800 rpm. The life of the silicone grease was 5,733 hr while that of the petroleum grease was 553 hr. This corresponds to the usual findings. As still higher temperatures of operation are used the ratio of life becomes even greater.

A case that illustrates another type of use is the lubrication of the transverse screws on the tenter frames employed in textile mills. The ovens operate at temperatures of 150°C (302°F) to 250°C (482°F) and the screws need to be adjusted from time to time. Petroleum greases coke up quickly and soon make adjustments impossible. The much longer life of a silicone grease at this temperature has reduced the shutdown time and, at the same time, has called for less frequent lubrication.

The chemical inertness of the silicone grease is responsible for better operation at times. An example of this is the use of type G grease in the motors operating the ventilating equipment in the smoke house of a meat packing company. Although the temperature was not unduly high, the atmosphere caused very rapid deterioration of petroleum greases. The silicone grease did not appear to be affected.

The temperature of use may exceed 200°C (392°F) but the

life becomes proportionately shorter. When the grease begins to lose its effectiveness it may be rejuvenated by the addition of a few drops of the type C or D fluid.

The type H grease is the most heat resistant of all the greases, for it contains no organic soap. It will not operate at high speeds as well as type G and so is not preferred for use in ball bearings. It is intended for use in low-speed, high-temperature applications, such as the wheel bearings of carts that go in and out of ovens, high-temperature conveyors, oven doors, trolleys carrying articles through ovens for heat treatment, etc. Reports have been received of short time lubrication at temperatures of 540°C (1,004°F) and higher. The addition of a few drops of type D fluid acts as a rejuvenator.

Section 4:

Silicone Resins

Prior to 1920 there were few resinous compounds sold commercially that were not of natural origin. These were such materials as shellac, linseed oil, tars, rosins. In the following 30 years a large number of synthetic resins were developed whose properties varied widely. It became possible to select a resin with the appropriate properties for almost any application, whether it was for coatings, moldings, or the preparation of synthetic fibers.

Even with this array of products available there were many industrial applications which could not be provided with a material that completely met all the requirements. Some coatings did not resist abrasion well enough, all moldings did not have the necessary physical or electrical properties, and some fibers decomposed below the temperature of contemplated operation.

But new resins are constantly being developed. Some show

long-looked-for properties which bring about improvements in old applications or the development of new ones.

The silicone resins fit into the category of new resins that contribute improved properties for some applications. Not all resinous properties are improved, and there are many applications for which they are not fitted. But certain properties, such as water repellency and resistance to heat, are so marked that the use of silicone resins brings about notable advances in electrical insulation, protective coatings, and other applications where these and other special properties are of value.

Many silicone resins are commercially available. The properties differ somewhat, depending on the use for which they are designed. The following properties are particularly noteworthy: heat stability, water repellency, good dielectric properties, resistance to many chemicals, weather resistance, non-yellowing. Adhesion varies from good to poor depending on the base to which they are applied. Although some of the resins will air-dry, they all require a baking or heat treatment if they are to show their best properties.

The heat treatment required is a limiting factor in the use of most of the silicone coatings. So far there is little to be gained by applying them to wood or to organic surfaces that cannot accept a temperature of at least 150°C (302°F). This is the situation at the moment, although it seems likely that certain organic-silicone formulations will be developed that will require little or no heat for setting up to useful films. Because of the present requirements for curing at high temperature the use of the available coatings is largely confined to application to metals, such as iron or aluminum. They serve to protect the metals against chemical attack, oxidation, or weathering. Catalysts are often used to assist curing.

Although the resistance to petroleum and vegetable oils is good, the resistance to solvents is generally poor. Some of the resins may be baked to a hard finish, but in the process they become brittle. They do not, in general, have high abrasion resistance. The hardness and abrasion resistance can be improved by the incorporation of certain organic resins, but at a cost of some reduction in heat resistance.

The resins are practically all provided in solvent at a strength varying from 50 to 70 per cent solids. Higher solids content generally shortens shelf life. The solvent is usually toluene or xylene. Most applications call for lower solids content, so that other solvents may be added for proper solvent balance.

The types of resin can be divided into six categories, although there is overlapping because some can be applied in more than one way:

A. Coating resins
B. Laminating resins
C. Release resins
D. Water-repellent resins (for use on concrete and masonry)
E. Molding resins
F. Electrical resins

These resins are described in the following pages in the order listed.

A. Coating Resins

Protective and decorative coatings have been used for centuries to stop the ravages of sun and rain and to present a more pleasing surface to the eye. The labor of application emphasized the need for coatings with longer life. The drying oils were developed, and when appropriate fillers and pigments had been added to them, it became possible to apply coatings that had both good life and attractive appearance. Natural resins were incorporated to give hardness and gloss. With the advent of synthetic lacquers great strides were made in developing coatings for specialized uses. Some are particularly useful when applied to wood, others to structural steel, and still others to the lining of food containers.

The progress of modern industry has placed ever-increasing demands on the manufacturer of protective coatings. Longer life is wanted because of the increasing cost of application; better color retention is needed if the life is to be longer; in many a factory, corrosive atmospheres must be combatted; many manufacturing operations must be carried out at temperatures that reduce the life of coatings necessary to protect the equipment.

The combination of corrosive atmospheres and high temperatures makes it difficult to provide good protection. Most organic films lose adhesion and coherence under the attack of corrosive gases and moisture, and all show increasing breakdown with increasing temperatures. Where these severe conditions are present the silicone coatings often provide a satisfactory answer. They, too, of course, have their limits of durability, but these limits are often far enough beyond those of the organic coatings to provide a protection otherwise impossible to attain.

The properties of silicone coatings that are distinctive are (1) heat resistance; (2) water repellency; (3) resistance to most aqueous chemicals, reagents, and corrosive gases. For certain applications the full measure of these properties may not be required. Under these circumstances organic film formers may be added to the silicone, either by cold blending or by cooking. By this means quicker drying and better handling properties may be obtained. Of course, a compromise of properties between those of the organic material and the silicone must be accepted.

As far as temperature resistance is concerned, the listing in Table 20 may provide a useful comparison.

These temperatures are intended to be comparative rather than specific, for the conditions of exposure will have a great

TABLE 20

Type of Coating	*Maximum Temperature of Usefulness*
Organic	150°C (302°F)
Silicone and organic (cold-blend)	200°C (392°F)
Silicone and organic ("cooked")	200°C (392°F)
Silicone	250°C (482°F)
Silicone + organic and aluminum	500°C (932°F)

deal to do with the life of the coating. However, other conditions being the same, these various types will give about the same length of service at about the temperatures indicated. Naturally, lower temperatures will result in longer life.

1. Silicone and Organic (Cold-blend) Resins

The compatibility of the usual silicone coating resins with many organic resins is somewhat limited, but for cold-blending compositions special silicone resins are obtainable whose compatibility is fairly wide. They are compatible with both reactive and nonreactive phenolics, acrylic esters, urea formaldehyde, melamine formaldehyde, cumarone resins, ethyl cellulose, chlorinated diphenyl, ester gum, tung oil, linseed oil, and styrene alkyds. They are partially compatible with oxidizing and nonoxidizing alkyds, nitrocellulose, and vinyl chloride-acetate.

Cold blending of an organic resin with a silicone film former results in a product with intermediate properties. These properties, naturally, depend not only on the relative amounts but on the types of resins used in the blending. The organic component generally contributes handleability, quicker drying characteristics, hardness, abrasion resistance, solvent resistance, and adhesion. The silicone resin generally improves heat resistance and water repellency, and it contributes nonyellowing characteristics.

The properties of the silicone addition are seldom in evidence if less than 25 per cent of this material is present, although there are cases where quite low percentages (5 to 10 per cent) give improved weathering properties. With the higher percentages heat-stable modified silicone paints can be formulated.

2. Silicone and Organic ("Cooked") Resins

A silicone and organic or "cooked" resin is one to which heat has been applied to bring about reaction between the components. The product differs from the previous type in that an actual silicone-organic polymer is formed rather than simply a solution of one resin in another. The superiority of one over the other is still a moot question. A great deal of work is being done to answer this question and it seems that much depends on the choice of organic base that is preferred. With some types the solubility of the silicone is immediate and effective. With others mutual solubility is improved if the silicone is chemically reacted with the organic resin. The final answer will probably be that both methods are useful and that one or the other will be used for certain applications or to meet certain specifications.

In spite of the fact that many silicone-organic copolymers are theoretical possibilities, no great amount of development has been done with any of the organic film formers except the alkyds.

The organic alkyd resins are reaction products of glycerol, fatty acids, and phthalic anhydride.

The first step in forming an alkyd is the reaction of the fatty acid and part of the glycerol:

$$CH_2OH—CHOH—CH_2OH + RCOOH \rightarrow$$
$$CH_2OH—CHOH—CH_2—OOCR + H_2O$$

The remaining hydroxyls on the glycerol are free to react with phthalic anhydride and so form a polymer.

Now, the properties of the alkyd polymer may be altered in many ways, and the nature of the fatty acid is of great importance in this alteration. For instance, the use of nondrying acids, such as stearic, palmitic, and oleic, increases flexibility, but the resin is relatively soft. If drying oils are used the hardness is improved, but the film tends to yellow with age.

The silicones enter the picture by virtue of the fact that they can replace some or all of the fatty acids. For this purpose silicone esters are commonly used:

$$CH_2OH—CHOH—CH_2OH + R_3SiOC_2H_5 \rightarrow$$
$$CH_2OH—CHOH—CH_2OSiR_3 + C_2H_5OH$$

R may be any desired radical.

A modification of this procedure makes use of a silicone diester. In this case the silicone replaces not only some or all of the fatty acid, but also some of the phthalic anhydride, and so takes an active part in the polymerization by tying two glycerols together:

$$CH_2OH—CHOH—CH_2OH + C_2H_5[OSi(R_2)]_xOC_2H_5$$
$$+ HOCH_2—OHCH—OHCH_2 \rightarrow CH_2OH—CHOH—$$
$$CH_2O—[Si(R_2)O]_xCH_2—OHCH—OHCH_2$$

The molecular size of the silicone diester may be large or small, and the R groups may be varied to alter the properties of the finished polymer.

This reaction goes readily with heat, forming "silicone-modified" alkyd resins. This is a simplified statement of the reaction. The manufacturer may add to it the techniques and many variations now practiced in the preparation of alkyd resins.[78]

The advantages of the incorporation of a silicone in this manner are that it gives finishes with greater flexibility and hardness plus stability at elevated temperatures. Further than that, color retention is improved, for there is much less yellowing at elevated temperatures or during weathering.

Resins of this general type are available, as completely formulated resins ready for application, from silicone manufacturers or from the Plaskon Division of the Libbey-Owens-Ford Glass Company. Also available are the partly reacted intermediates, which may be further modified by addition of the usual alkyd components. Finally the silicone esters, from which the paint manufacturer may form his own intermediates or finished products, may be obtained.

PREPARATION OF RESIN INTERMEDIATES

For the preparation of an intermediate one should be guided by some knowledge and experience of silicone chemistry. The type of R groups on silicon should be known, and the desirability of the various types should be recognized. In some cases it will be an advantage to add the silicone as a monomer and in other cases as a small polymer. The type of reactive end groups, whether hydroxyl, ester, or halogen, should be known and appraised.

USE OF RESIN INTERMEDIATES

For those who wish to formulate in a more direct manner, intermediates are available from silicone manufacturers. These have been developed expressly for use in the manufacture of silicone-modified alkyd resins.

Heat resistance and non-yellowing characteristics are functions of the amount of silicone present, provided proper attention has been paid to the amount of unsaturated fatty acids in the formulation.

Properly prepared films of this type will provide protection at about 50°C (90°F) higher than similar films containing no silicone and will, at the same time, maintain good appearance.

Most of the work that has been done in the field of cooked

silicone-organic coatings has been limited to alkyd types. There are wide and unexplored avenues for research in similar products, and it seems reasonable to expect that the unique characteristics of the silicones will, before long, be more generally applied.

3. Silicone Coatings

The presence of organic film formers in combination with silicone resins is useful in improving the ease of application and in shortening curing times. But these advantages must be paid for in poorer heat resistance. The pure silicone films will withstand about 50°C (90°F) higher than any of the organic-modified films. Or stated in another way, the silicone films will give much longer life than the organic-containing films if both are at the same temperature. The peak temperature of usefulness is about 250°C (482°F).

Films of this type provide the ultimate in heat-resisting, pigmented coatings. They are surpassed only by the inorganic enamels and by metals in one form or another. They protect not only against heat but against corrosive and humid atmospheres. They are particularly useful on stacks, exhausts, outdoor signs, heaters, electric motors and turbines, stoves, furnace and oven parts, incinerators, boilers, steam pipes, and the great variety of places where conditions are too severe for the usual type of protective coating. The coating itself is completely non-yellowing, and there is good color retention provided heat-stable pigments are used. This makes them particularly desirable for application to hospital equipment where non-yellowing whites are called for.

Different applications demand different properties in the coatings. Silicone resins that are mutually soluble are available, and properties may be adjusted by blending. Table 21 shows the results that may be obtained by blending two different silicone resins.

TABLE 21 Physical Properties and Drying Characteristics of Aluminum Paints Made with Blends of Two Silicone Resins, A and B

Resins in Paint	Grams Paint per sq in.	Film Condition after 16-hr Air Dry	Baked 1 hr, 70°C		Baked 1 hr, 140°C		Baked 4 hr, 140°C			Baked 16 hr, 200°C			Baked 16 hr, 250°C		
			Pencil Hardness	Film Condition	Pencil Hardness	Print Test, 1 lb per sq in.	Pencil Hardness	Print Test, 1 lb per sq in.	Flexibility, 180° Bend over ½-in. Mandrel	Pencil Hardness	Flexibility, 180° Bend over ½-in. Mandrel	Adhesion after 1-hr Immersion in V.M. and P. Naphtha	Pencil Hardness	Flexibility, 180° Bend over ½-in. Mandrel	Adhesion after 1-hr Immersion in V.M. and P. Naphtha
100%A	0.063	Tacky	...	Tacky		(Very slightly tacky)	3B	No Print	OK (no cracking)	5H	OK	Poor	7H	OK	Poor
80%A, 20%B	0.058	Tacky	...	Slightly tacky	3B	Slight Print	F	No Print	OK (no cracking)	4H	OK	Fair	7H+	Few fine cracks	Poor
60%A, 40%B	0.058	Tack-free but soft	6B	Tack-free but soft	B	Trace of print	F	No Print	OK	4H	Few fine cracks	Fair	7H+	Fine cracks	Fair
40%A, 60%B	0.057	Tack-free	3B	Tack-free	B	Trace of print	F	No Print	NG	4H	Fine cracks	Fair	7H+	Fine cracks	Good
20%A, 80%B	0.053	Tack-free	3B	Tack-free	F	Trace of print	H	No Print	NG	6H	Fine cracks	Good	7H+	Fine cracks	Good
100%B	0.050	Tack-free	3B	Tack-free	F	No Print	3H	No Print	NG	7H	NG	Good	7H+	NG	Good

PIGMENTS

Having formulated the type of resin needed, one must consider the proper type of pigment to be used. As the resins are so commonly used at high temperature, heat-stable pigments must be used. The following list shows some of the pigments that have been found satisfactory:

PIGMENT	SUPPLIER
Aluminum paste	Aluminum Company of America
Monastral green	E. I. du Pont de Nemours & Company
Monastral blue	E. I. du Pont de Nemours & Company
Cadmolith golden	Chemical and Pigment Co.
Deep cadmium red	Chemical and Pigment Co.
Light cadmium red	Chemical and Pigment Co.
Orange cadmolith	Chemical and Pigment Co.
Lemon cadmolith	Chemical and Pigment Co.
Titanox ALO	Titanium Pigment Corp.
Titanox RA10	Titanium Pigment Corp.
Neo Spectra beads	Binney and Smith Co.
Superba beads	Binney and Smith Co.
Peerless beads	Binney and Smith Co.
Mapico No. 297	Binney and Smith Co.
Zinc oxide AZO-ZZZ-22	American Zinc Sales Co.
Lithopone	Eagle Picher Lead Co.
Zinc yellow Y-539-D	E. I. du Pont de Nemours & Company

DRIERS

While the silicone resins can be cured by heat alone, the process can be speeded up by the use of driers of the type commonly used with drying oils. Zinc, cobalt, and manganese, as the naphthenates, have been found effective, but the most generally satisfactory drier is zinc octoate. Quantities of any of these metals up to 0.3 per cent based on the resin-solids content will decrease the drying time materially.

Lead, calcium, and iron compounds also accelerate the drying of silicone resins, but they result in poor storage stability and are likely to bring about embrittlement in use.

PREPARATION OF SURFACES

All surfaces to which any coating is to be applied must be properly prepared if the best results are to be obtained. All grease and rust must be removed by solvents, pickling, or shot blasting. This is particularly true where silicone coatings are to be applied to combat severe conditions.

Attention to the metal surface is especially desirable in the case of steel. Many steel surfaces that appear to be entirely free of scale will develop a nonadhering film under the enamel when the coating is aged at temperatures over 200°C (392°F). To eliminate this film completely it is necessary to resort either to chemical cleaning or to sandblasting. Of the chemical treatments either Bonderizing or Parkerizing appears to be most effective, but even a simple acid etch followed by a dichromate treatment can give completely satisfactory results.

In some cases it has been necessary to develop primers for iron and steel surfaces. One very satisfactory formulation consists of 1 part silicone resin solids to 1 part of the following pigment mix: 35 per cent red iron oxide; 35 per cent zinc chromate; and 30 per cent asbestine. When used at elevated temperatures the zinc chromate will darken considerably, but this does not seem to impair its corrosion inhibiting properties.

Adhesion to aluminum can be improved greatly by using one of the standard priming treatments, such as dipping in a solution containing alcohol, phosphoric acid, and zinc chromate. On magnesium the Dow No. 7 treatment is very effective as a base for silicone enamels. This consists of a 5-min immersion in 20 per cent HF followed by 45 min in 15 per cent sodium dichromate.

APPLICATION

The methods used to apply ordinary baking enamels are generally applicable to silicone coatings. Silicone enamels are best applied by spraying. They have also been applied successfully by roller coating. Brushing is difficult, however, because of poor leveling characteristics. This difficulty can be overcome to some extent by thinning with high-boiling solvents.

CURE

Some of the silicone resins will air-dry to a tack-free film. But in no case are the best protective properties present until the film has been heat cured. Formulations will differ somewhat in their requirements, but as a general proposition, curing is not complete until the film has been held at 250°C (482°F) for at least 1 hr, or at 200°C (392°F) for at least 4 hr. The particular resin used and the properties required of it will dictate the best time and temperature of cure.

These temperatures refer to those coatings that contain no organic modifiers. The latter type can be cured at substantially lower temperatures.

ADHESION

As measured by a knife-scratch test, the adhesion of these silicone resins to aluminum surfaces is excellent. Adhesion to magnesium metal is also excellent. Adhesion to tin is good. The normal adhesion of these silicone resins to steel is only fair, but chemical cleaning, sandblasting, or the use of a primer coating considerably improves their adhesion to steel.

HEAT RESISTANCE

Probably the most useful property of the silicone resins is their heat stability. Because this is so well recognized there have been attempts at times to use the resins far beyond their capacity. It is true that certain special types of silicone coatings may be applied that will give protection at 500°C (932°F). These are described in the next section. But the usual type, as described here, have a maximum temperature of usefulness of about 250°C (482°F). The length of life, as in the case of other coatings, is dependent on the severity of exposure to such conditions as humidity and corrosive gases as well as to temperature. Lower temperatures and less corrosive conditions naturally give longer life. The whole matter may be summed up by saying that under severe conditions of exposure a properly cured silicone coating will give many times the life of an organic or organic-containing coating. The saving in application cost becomes a factor of considerable importance.

MOISTURE AND WATER RESISTANCE

These silicone resins, in common with the other silicone products, are unusually water-repellent. Moisture absorption is in the order of 0.2 per cent after 168 hr of immersion in water. This combination of water repellency and low moisture absorption contributes to the weatherproofness of silicone finishes and enables them to give added protection against rusting. Experience confirms the expectation that silicone finishes give good protection against the rusting of metal surfaces in humid atmosphere even after long exposure to high temperatures.

CHEMICAL RESISTANCE

Table 22 shows the resistance of a representative silicone film to some different chemicals and solvents. In general, films of this type have unusually good resistance to most aqueous chemical reagents. Their resistance is poor to many organic solvents. Increasing the temperature of the reagents reduces the resistance of the resin.

Unpigmented resins resist attack better than those which are pigmented. Chemically resistant pigments should therefore be used when resistance to chemical attack is important. A silicone primer coat on metals improves adhesion and increases resistance to chemical action. Longer baking periods also increase the chemical resistance of silicone coatings.[79]

TABLE 22 Chemical Resistance of a Silicone Coating Pigmented with TiO_2, Baked 1 Hr, 250°C

Chemical Reagent	Rating after Immersion at 70°F for			Rating after Immersion at 100°F for		
	3 hr	20 hr	100 hr	3 hr	20 hr	100 hr
Acetic acid, 2%	E	E	E	E	E	E
Acetic acid, 100%	G	O	O	O	O	O
Hydrochloric acid, 2%	E	E	E	E	G	G
Hydrochloric acid, 10%	E	E	E	E	G	F
Nitric acid, 2%	E	E	E	E	G	O
Nitric acid, 10%	E	E	E	E	G	O
Phosphoric acid, 2%	E	E	E	E	E	E
Phosphoric acid, 10%	E	E	E	E	E	E
Sulfuric acid, 2%	E	E	E	E	G	G
Sulfuric acid, 10%	E	E	E	E	E	O
Sodium hydroxide, 2%	E	E	G	E	E	O
Sodium hydroxide, 10%	E	E-x	E-x	E-x	E-x	O
Butyl alcohol	E	E	E	E	E	E
Kerosene	E	E	E	E	E-x	E-x
Methyl ethyl ketone	O	O	O	Not tested		
Turpentine	P	O	O	Not tested		
Sodium chloride, 2%	E	E	E	E	E	E
Sodium chloride, 10%	E	E	E	E	E	E
Sodium polysulfide, 2%	E	E	G	E	G	P
Sodium polysulfide, 10%	E	O	O	Not tested		
Linseed oil	E	E	E	E	E	E
Oil SAE 30	E	E	E	E	E	E
Petroleum grease	E	E	E	E	E	E
Clorox	E	E	E	E	E	P
Distilled water	E	E	E	E	E	E
Hydrogen peroxide	E	E	E	E	E	E

Note: E = Excellent; G = Good; F = Fair; P = Poor; O = Failure; E-x = Panel attacked at edge but film intact.

4. High-temperature Coatings

Coatings are available that will provide protection at temperatures in the order of 500°C (1,000°F). These products contain both organic and silicone resins as vehicles, and alu-

The two stacks at the left were painted with silicone-base aluminum paint. The stack at the right was painted with conventional aluminum paint at the same time as the others.

minum flake as the pigment. Very high curing temperatures [400°C (750°F)] are essential if the best properties are to be realized.

These coatings are designed for application to metal surfaces that are to be exposed to extreme heat. Typical applications are those for hot stacks, furnaces, manifolds, ovens, and high-temperature processing equipment.

A useful application is in painting identification marks on materials, such as steel pipe, that require repeated heat treatments during fabrication. The markings remain bright and readily recognizable after holding at 800°C (1,500°F).

As is the case in the application of all coatings, the surface of the metal must be free from grease and rust. The coating may be applied by brushing or spraying. Curing may be carried out by baking or by operating the equipment at the high temperature for which it was designed.

As the temperature of cure is being attained, the first effect is that of setting the organic resin. Higher temperature results in decomposition of the organic and, at the same time, a setting or curing of the silicone so that the aluminum is still held securely in place. As the temperature comes into the range of 350 to 400°C (650 to 750°F) there is a decomposition of the silicone, and, at the same time, a lattice work of the aluminum appears to be formed along with a welding to the base metal. The final result is a firmly adhering coating of aluminum which will withstand repeated cooling and heating. It gives excellent resistance to weathering and to corrosive gases. These coatings are reported to give protection for extended periods at temperatures of 550°C (1,000°F) and above.[80]

B. Laminating Resins

One of the major contributions of the resin industry to technological advance has been the development of resins useful in the preparation of laminates. The resins act in a double capacity. In the first place they act as a glue, holding in one compact piece the multilayers of paper, cotton, asbestos, Fiberglas, or whatever material is required for a proposed use. Secondly the resin contributes to the laminate such properties as hardness, flexural strength, waterproofness, and electrical resistance. By proper selection of the sheet material and the resins it is possible to form strong and durable products suitable for molding into table tops, wall paneling, tanks, electrical panel boards, cabinets, and a multitude of useful articles. In many applications they are superior to glass, metal, or wood. They lack the brittleness of glass; they have a lower specific gravity than metal; they are less easily marred than wood; they present a decorative finish.

As is the case with all useful products, demands are continually being made for properties that are somewhat beyond the capacity of the materials being used at the moment. This is a spur to further development. The manufacturer is forced to look further to find materials that will help in meeting the new specifications. Had there been no use for laminates beyond table tops, cabinets, and the conventional electrical applications, it is doubtful if any silicone-containing laminates would ever have been made. But industrial machinery is operating at increasing speeds, higher voltages are used, new devices develop more heat and are working under more severe conditions. Improved properties and longer life are demanded. To meet these extra requirements silicone resins have entered the laminating field and have shown an ability to meet some of the more exacting specifications.

The interest in laminates containing silicone resins is due to the high-temperature stability and good electrical properties of these materials. Slot wedges in motors operating at high temperature must remain intact; electrical panel boards should not present a conducting path following an arc-over, nor should noxious gases be evolved in case of fire; the high-temperature properties are useful in aircraft applications, such as on radomes.

While marked improvements have been made in the physical properties of the silicone laminates in the last year or two, they do not yet equal, at room temperature, those of the organic laminates, such as the phenolics and melamines. But as the temperature is increased the physical properties of the silicone laminates remain relatively constant while those of the organics fall off markedly. These characteristics show the possibilities and the limitations of the silicone laminates. For use at ordinary temperatures and for ordinary applications they offer no competition to the organic laminates. But as the temperature of operation is increased they become of greater interest because of smaller changes in properties and greater stability. Within the temperature range of 200 to 300°C (400 to 575°F) they have become almost essential to good operation, for in this temperature range the organics show rapid breakdown.

High-pressure molding has been the general practice, but recently low-pressure techniques have been developed that have given very satisfactory laminates.

Regardless of which method is used, the laminating sheet must be of inorganic material, for silicone laminates are generally intended for high temperature use. The most satisfactory materials are the Fiberglas cloths ECC112, ECC126, ECC128, ECC181, and ECC261. Of these ECC181 shows the greatest ease of handling and molding when laminates of the order of ⅛-in. thickness are desired. For extremely thin electrical laminates ECC112 is superior, although it is more difficult to impregnate and mold because of its more open weave and thinness.

All glass cloth for silicone laminations should be cleaned by heat or an appropriate washing technique before use.

In the cleaning of glass fabric by heat care should be taken to see that the time and temperature are enough to destroy organic sizing material but not enough to injure the glass unduly. A temperature of 300°C (572°F) to 325°C (617°F) is recommended for this type of cleaning. The fabric may be passed through the oven in sheet form, or the roll of fabric may be placed in the oven for 24 to 48 hr. The fabric should be tested for completeness of cleaning by drying a piece at 150°C (302°F) for 1 hr, weighing, and then igniting for 30 min at about 680°C (1,256°F). If the loss in weight upon ignition is less than 0.2 per cent the fabric may be considered to be properly cleaned.

Heat cleaning, even when properly done, generally brings about a loss of about 50 per cent in tensile strength. If the loss is greater than this, it is a sign that too much heat has been applied. A temperature of 370°C (700°F) will soften the glass sufficiently to set the weave.

The cloth is impregnated with resin by being passed through the resin bath at a rate that will give a pickup of about 45 per cent resin solids. It is then air-dried for 30 min in filtered circulating air, after which it is given a precure of 5 min at 110°C in circulating air. Following this the stock is soft and tacky when hot, but it is flexible with practically no tack when cool. It may now be shaped and straightened.

If the high-pressure technique is to be used, a pressure of about 900 psi should be applied at a temperature of 175°C (347°F) for 75 min. It should then be cooled under pressure for 30 min. The aftercure should be carried out in a mechanical convection oven according to the schedule in Table 23.

TABLE 23

°C	*°F*	*Time, hr*
90	194	15
130	266	4
160	320	4
190	374	16
250	482	4

If the low-pressure technique is to be used, the stock should be brought to 175°C (347°F) under contact pressure. The time of cure in the press will vary from 15 min for ⅛-in. laminates to 60 min for 2-in. pieces. An aftercure according to the schedule in Table 24 is advised.

TABLE 24

°C	*°F*	*Time, hr*
90	194	16
125	257	1
150	302	1
175	347	1
215	419	1
250	482	80–150

At no time during the aftercure should the laminates be allowed to cool off.

Main advantage of silicone laminates, made by either high or low pressure, is the maintenance of strength after long aging at high temperatures. To the present time, tests indicate that no additional deterioration of silicone laminates occurs up to 250°C (482°F) for 200 hours of aging. Tests also indicate that there is a possible usage of silicone laminates for short time exposure up to 480°C (900°F).[81]

Table 25[82] shows the change of flexural strength for three different types of laminates after they were held at elevated temperatures.

TABLE 25 Flexural Strength, psi

Temperature of Test		Time of Heating	Temperature		Silicone Laminates Fiberglas 181-A-12	Phenolic Laminates Fiberglas 181-38 Finish 114	Melamine Laminates Fiberglas ECC128
°C	°F		°C	°F			
25	77	.....	...	...	29,200	46,500	51,600
25	77	200 hr	250	482	26,400	200	17,600
150	302	200 hr	150	302	14,300	39,100	30,300
250	482	200 hr	250	482	13,400	550	15,600
325	617	200 hr	325	617	9,800	......	1,500

The properties of four different types of laminates are shown in Table 26.[81]

Although the information given refers more particularly to sheets, laminated tubing may also be formed. Tubes may be used in places such as class H sealed-network transformers. They act as coil supports and as a dielectric barrier between the high- and low-voltage coils in class H transformers designed to operate up to 250°C (482°F) with a 250 V/M dielectric breakdown barrier. For assurance of good dielectric strength it is advisable to dip the tube in an electrically insulating silicone resin just prior to the 250°C (482°F) cure. The tubes are also used for the distribution of hot air in aircraft. Their low heat conductivity makes them self-insulating.

TABLE 26 Comparison of Various Types of Laminations

	Fabric and Resin			
	Cotton, Phenolic	Glass Cloth, Melamine	Fiberglas ECC261, Silicone DC2103	Fiberglas 181-112, Silicone DC2104
Flexural strength, psi, ⅛-in. panel, flatwise	18,000	48,500	22,000	25,000–35,000
Tensile strength, psi	9,000	30,000	15,000	35,000–45,000
Bonding strength, lb, ½-in. panel	1,600	1,900	1,250	1,000
Water absorption, 24 hr, %, ⅛-in. panel	1.25	1.45	0.21	0.5–1.0
Dielectric strength, ⅛-in. panel, volts per mil	200	260	250	Up to 400
Power factor (D-24/25), %, 100 mc	......	....	0.97	0.32
ASTM arc resistance, sec	10	190	300	>350

Tube and disk electrical insulators on switches of a 45,000-amp graphitizing transformer: left, cotton-phenolic after one month; right, silicone-glass after one year.

Fiberglas laminates are somewhat more difficult to machine than those composed of paper or cotton cloth, but most machine shops have the necessary equipment, and this plus a little experience is sufficient. Techniques helpful in machining these materials have been described in the literature.[83]

The silicone laminates are among the newest materials of this type. Development work has brought about great improvement in properties. Further work should make them still more competent to operate in those fields where their unique properties are demanded.

C. Release Resins

The release characteristics of the silicone fluids and compounds, described previously, carry over into the resins. It was noted that certain of the fluids and compounds were much more effective than others. Similarly certain of the resins show better release characteristics than others.

Where some "nonstick" surface is required to facilitate the release of molded or formed materials (rubber, plastics, metals, bread, glue, etc.), one may use either a silicone fluid, a compound, or a resin. Generally one type will be found to be about as effective as another. The choice will usually be dictated by economy, length of life desired, or ease of application. In the molding of rubber or plastics, for instance, it is generally simpler to apply a light spray of release fluid every few moldings; in the baking of bread the release agent on the pan should have long life, and for this reason a resin is generally used.

The most common use for the release resins is in the preparation of baked goods, notably bread. The resin is applied to the pan by spraying or dipping, after which the pan is baked to set the resin. With this amount of preparation the pan can be used for 100 to 500 bakes without the need for any greasing.

When the bread fails to release easily from the pan the treatment is repeated.

A number of advantages resulting from this method of treating the pans have been responsible for its acceptance by many bakeries, both large and small. The most evident, of course, is that the cost of the grease and the labor for applying it are eliminated. An important by-product is increased cleanliness in the bakery. Much of the light haze of smoke often found in bakeries results from breakdown and distillation of the grease. With the elimination of the grease there is a reduction in costs for cleaning and painting. When using grease, even under the best of conditions, it is impossible to avoid the accumulation of some rancid grease in the corners of the pan. The use of release resins prevents the off-flavor of bread that can often be traced to this source. Further, there is much less damage to the pan or the tinning when cleaning and reglazing are necessary if grease has not been allowed to accumulate and oxidize.

The cost of coating a pan with a silicone resin is about equal to that of the grease and labor to process 100 pans by the conventional method. Thus if the resin-coated pan gives 100 bakes the cost of the two methods is about equal if one neglects the incidental advantages noted above. Anything beyond 100 bakes represents an economy.

Test runs should be made before this method is introduced as general practice in any bakery. The conditions in the proof box, sugar content of the loaf, moisture conditions in the oven, etc., are matters that affect the release characteristics of the resin. Different types of resin are available, and the one best suited to particular conditions should be determined.

The schedule for cleaning and reglazing of the pans should also be decided on. One type of resin allows overcoating when the original coating begins to break down. Another type is harder and gives more bakes per application but must be removed before another coat can be applied. Thus if the conditions in the baking and ovens and the general method are known, an appropriate resin can be chosen.

The baking of the coating can be done in the baker's oven, but as this removes the oven from production for that length of time, it is becoming common practice to have the cleaning and coating done by specially equipped "pan laundries." This service is available over a large part of the country. The names of "laundries" serving specific locations may be obtained from silicone manufacturers.

Pan manufacturers are marketing pans that are coated with resin and ready for immediate use.

There are almost innumerable applications for the release resins. Waffle irons that are coated by the manufacturer or that may easily be coated by the user are now on the market. A small amount of the resin can be applied with an absorbent cotton applicator; it is allowed to air-dry and can then be cured by the heat of the iron. A nonstick waffle iron is considered in some quarters to be one of the major blessings brought by modern technology.

The resin may be used on pans for the baking of rolls, cookies, cup cakes, fruit cakes, etc. It is not, in general, as satisfactory with foods of high sugar or high water content. In spite of this, it has been used successfully as a coating on caramel candy cooling pans.

The meat processing industry supplies some examples of the value of this material. It improves the release from meat loaf pans. It can be used on "smoke sticks" made from aluminum tubing which are used to hold sausage during the smoking process. The coating keeps the smoke sticks clean and prevents the formation of an undesirable greenish deposit.

An application that might not be suspected is found in frozen food processing. If vegetables are placed in a resin-coated pan and are then frozen they will release readily without being warmed.

The applications cited do not by any means exhaust the list. They do suggest that there is a wide variety of materials to which the resins present a nonstick surface and that they operate under many different conditions.

D. Water-repellent Resins for Masonry and Concrete

A problem that commonly besets the building construction engineer is that of waterproofing masonry and concrete. Even when the materials of construction and the workmanship are of the best, there is the possibility of leakage with time. The slight porosity of brick or concrete can result in extraction of salts and so produce efflorescence. An unsightly appearance develops, and at times moisture may be transmitted all the way through the wall.

Materials to meet these troubles should

1. Be water-repellent
2. Prevent efflorescence
3. Allow "breathing"
4. Have long life
5. Not affect appearance
6. Be easy to apply

Many types of water-repellent cements, or solutions, or emulsions have been developed. Some act by sealing off the surface and require careful working in to fill or coat over the pores. Solutions such as those of linseed oil fill the pores more readily, but they generally present a shiny surface and can be saponified by the alkali of the mortar. Synthetic resins are sometimes applied in emulsion form. Some are inclined to "blush" when damp, and their resistance to efflorescence is only fair. None of these materials is completely satisfactory for all types of application.

The latest arrivals in the field of water repellents for masonry and concrete are the silicones. There are actually three types, differing in the method of obtaining the same end result.

The earliest, which may be considered as a forerunner of the other two, is ethyl silicate.

> A silicic acid ester diluted with a suitable volatile solvent is applied to stone, which is then exposed to the atmosphere so that the volatile solvent is evaporated and the silicic ester hydrolyzed so as to form hydrated silica which cements together the particles of the stone, holding them together and preventing the stone from further decay and at the same time partially waterproofing the stone.[84]

The second type is a partially condensed silicone and is similar to the type described above in that some hydrolyzable groups remain. On reaction with the moisture in the wall and with the hydroxyls in the masonry, it forms a condensed silicone, rather than silica.

The third type is a fully condensed silicone resin which requires no reaction with water or hydroxyl groups but sets up on loss of solvent.

In both the latter types the solvent helps to carry the material into the masonry instead of laying it down as a continuous film on the outside. As the solvent evaporates the thin film is deposited on the sides of the capillaries in the masonry, and there is no discoloration or shiny appearance to indicate that anything has been applied. Setting up of the resin is completed as previously described. Penetration is in the order of $\frac{1}{16}$ in. or more, depending on the porosity of the masonry. Surface weathering, therefore, does not destroy the effectiveness of this kind of treatment.

In the case of the partially condensed material polymerization is not instantaneous, and the full water-repellent properties are not evident until about 24 hr have elapsed after application. Once developed, the water-repellent effect has long life. Following a study of these materials, Anderegg states that "where (conditions are) not too severe, an effective life of 8 to 10 years may be reasonably predicted."[85]

Laboratory tests and practical experience have shown these materials to be helpful in the control of efflorescence.[86]

Both the silicone types are applied similarly. They are marketed in water-free solvents. For use they are diluted with a solvent such as xylene to about 5 per cent solids. They can then be applied by brushing or spraying. If a brush is used the painter should flood the masonry surface with a liberal application. The coating should not be brushed out.

Spraying is the cheaper and more effective way to apply the coating. The painter should apply a liberal coating with air pressure reduced to about 5 to 10 psi and with the nozzle held close to the masonry surface.

The cost of application of a silicone coating has been estimated at 8 to 12 cents psf, which compares favorably with other methods of treatment.[86]

When checked against the six requirements stated earlier, it will be seen that the silicones measure up well:

1. Water repellency. It is impossible to measure the water repellency on a masonry surface with high accuracy, but, as measured on a glass surface, silicones are among the most hydrophobic materials available.

2. Prevention of efflorescence. Both laboratory tests and practical experience show that this type of coating is highly effective in preventing efflorescence.

3. Allowance for breathing. As the silicone treatment merely coats the walls of the capillaries there is no obstruction to the passage of vapors.

4. Long life. Life of a treatment will vary with type of exposure. Anderegg suggests a life of 8 to 10 years under normal conditions.

5. Lack of effect on appearance. By visual observation it is practically impossible to distinguish a treated piece from an untreated.

6. Ease of application. Spray application is quick and effective.

One would expect these silicone products, judged by these standards, to find a place for themselves among the more useful of the water repellents for masonry and concrete.

E. Molding Resins

Molded articles may be considered as differing from laminates in that the filler is randomly distributed in the former and regularly distributed (in sheet form) in the latter. This difference is responsible for differences in properties and in methods of forming.

The laminates have higher tensile and flexural strengths because of the presence of the laminating sheets. The molding resins may be formed into more intricate shapes because movement is not restrained. Thus each material has its advantages. The choice of material will depend on the properties required and the ease with which the required piece can be formed.

As in the case of laminating resins, the molding resins find little application under conventional conditions. But where high heat and moisture resistance are required a silicone molding resin will often provide an answer to a difficult problem. Typical uses for silicone molded products are in induction heating apparatus, switch parts, brush ring holders, coil forms, etc. In general they will be found useful in places where plastic moldings would be an advantage but where the temperature is too high to permit the application of conventional materials.

The resin used in the preparation of moldings is similar to that used with laminates. It is mixed with an appropriate filler, such as glass fiber, asbestos, or diatomaceous earth. The solvent is removed by an air pump and then the resin-filler mix is held at 110°C (230°F) for 10 min. When cool it is tack-free and can be broken up or powdered. It is then ready for compression or transfer molding.

TABLE 27

Physical Properties

Specific gravity: 1.6–1.7
Tensile strength: 4,000–6,000 psi
Flexural strength at 20°C (77°F): 8,000–10,000 psi
at 150°C (302°F): 5,000–6,000 psi
Impact strength (Izod-notched), (½ in. × ½ in. compression-molded bar)
at 25°C (77°F): 7 ft-lb per in.
at 150°C (302°F): 5 ft-lb per in.
Water absorption, gain, 24 hr, ⅛-in. thickness: 0.2%
Shrinkage during molding: 0.1%
after bake: 0.1%
Heat resistance: Continuous, 250°C (482°F)
Distortion under heat: >300°C (572°F)
Machinability: Good (carboloy tools or grinding recommended)
Thermal expansion: $\alpha 1.131 \times 10^{-4}$
$\beta 3.78 \times 10^{-6}$

Electrical Properties

Dielectric strength at 60 cycles, ⅛-in. thickness, short time: 150–300 volts per mil
Dielectric constant at 100 cps: 3.91
at 1,000 cps: 3.89
at 1 mc per sec: 3.79
at 100 mc per sec: 3.74
Power factor, at 100 cps: 0.0046
at 1,000 cps: 0.0041
at 1 mc per sec: 0.0042
at 100 mc per sec: 0.0037
Volume resistivity, ohm-cm: 1×10^{11}
Surface resistivity, ohms: 1×10^{10}
Insulation resistance, ohms: 1×10^{12}
Arc resistance: 200–300 sec

Chemical Properties

Effect of sunlight: None
Effect of weak acids: None
Effect of strong acids: Slight attack
Effect of weak alkalies: None
Effect of strong alkalies: None
Effect of organic solvents: Attacked by some
Effect on metals: None

Molding is carried out at 175°C (347°F) and 4,000 to 10,000 psi. Approximately 15- to 30-min mold cure is required. The molding may be removed while hot. It is transferred to a curing oven held at 90°C (194°F), the temperature is raised slowly to 250°C (482°F), and the final cure is effected over a period of 72 hr.

The properties of the finished piece vary according to the amount and type of filler. Table 27 shows representative properties.

F. Electrical Resins

The growth of the electrical industry has been regulated to a large extent by the development of insulating materials. The electrical engineer has always known how to develop more electrical power than he can economically turn into work at any specified spot. The reason for this is tied up with the fact that the passage of an electric current develops heat in the conductor. This heat must be dissipated through the insulating medium that keeps the current in its proper course. The current, or potential power, must, therefore, be restricted so that the amount of heat generated is not enough to decompose the insulation. Insulation that will withstand more heat will allow the transmission of more power in a given mechanism.

This state of affairs was recognized when electrical insulating tape was first woven from glass fibers. The inorganic glass tape would withstand more heat than the cotton tape commonly used. Therefore, it should have been possible to transmit more power. But the voids in the glass tape had to be filled with an organic varnish, and the ability of the varnish to accept heat became the measure of power transmission. The development of silicone varnishes brought about an increase in the ability to transmit power because these varnishes could withstand more heat than the organic varnishes.

Of course, there are limits beyond which the heat-resisting characteristics of the insulating varnish have no practical significance. There are temperature limits beyond which the efficiency of the metals used falls off to amounts that are uneconomical. The silicone varnishes will accept those temperatures. So it happens that the limiting factor in motor design now becomes a problem in metallurgy rather than in insulation.

Before the silicone insulating varnish came into use two classes of insulating material were recognized.

Class A: Cotton, paper, and similar organic materials impregnated or bonded with organic resins or varnishes.

Class B: Asbestos, Fiberglas, mica, and similar inorganic materials impregnated or bonded with organic resins or varnishes.

The recognition of the great difference in the heat stability between the organic varnishes and the silicone varnishes resulted in the establishment of a third class:

Class H: Asbestos, Fiberglas, mica, and similar inorganic materials impregnated or bonded with silicone compounds or materials with similar properties.

The AIEE has recommended that the maximum operating temperatures for these classes be as follows:

Class A: 105°C (221°F)

Class B: 130°C (266°F)

Class H: 180°C (356°F)

The Navy and other agencies use 200°C (392°F) as top operating temperatures for class H.

An excellent presentation of the place of class H insulation in electrical equipment will be found in the book "Electrical Insulation" by G. L. Moses, McGraw-Hill Book Company, Inc., 1951.

The question might properly be asked at this time as to what happens when class H insulation finally succumbs to thermal degradation. For one thing, it does not catch fire. Even the application of a blowtorch does nothing more than decompose that section of the resin to which the flame is applied. The residue is finely divided silica. The gases formed by the decomposition are largely carbon dioxide plus some small amount of aldehydes and organic acids. Animals and men exposed to these decomposition products were apparently unaffected.

Of course, other properties than heat resistance are required in a good insulating material. It should not be affected by water, ozone, or corrosive atmospheres. The silicone varnishes are unusually resistant to attack by these agents.

The mechanical strength, though adequate if reasonable care is used, is less than that of the organic varnishes commonly employed. Certain "modified silicone varnishes" are available where better physical properties are demanded. These contain organic additives which improve strength and toughness. The heat resistance is less than that of a pure silicone, but in some applications this can be accepted for the sake of improvement in handling. Some of these modified varnishes will meet the full class H specifications.

In most cases the original cost of silicone insulation is higher than that of organic insulation. The varnish itself is more expensive, and the baking schedule is generally longer and at higher temperature. A silicone-insulated motor, for example, costs about 50 to 75 per cent more than one with organic insulation.

If satisfactory life is being obtained in a motor with organic insulation there would seem to be no economy in applying silicone insulation. But if a motor in a given location fails to last more than 1 or 2 years without a rewind it is likely that silicone insulation will be cheaper in the long run. When all factors are considered it becomes apparent that silicone electrical insulation is an economy where high temperature due to overload or high ambients are encountered, or where the machine must operate under conditions of high humidity or corrosive atmospheres.

Use in Motors

A typical application for the silicone insulating resins is that in a motor. For best results all insulating components should conform to class H specifications. All tying cords and sleeving should be glass that has been impregnated with silicone. All slot wedges, mechanical supports, spacers, etc., should consist of laminated or molded silicone-glass or silicone-asbestos materials, or silicone-bonded mica. The impregnating varnish should be a silicone varnish.

A cooperative study over a period of several years of motors so insulated was made by the Dow Corning Corporation and the Westinghouse Electric Corporation. The results have been published.[87,88]

The objective of this work was to determine the thermal endurance of silicone-insulated motors and to obtain a comparison between the behavior of class B insulation and class H insulation under the same test conditions.

The test procedure has been described as follows:[88]

> Nine motors were subjected to accelerated life tests—six 10 hp. induction motors with class H insulation treated with silicone (DC 993) varnish, two class B insulated induction motors of similar design, and one DC motor with class H insulation treated with DC 993 silicone varnish. The test cycle began with a period of operation at elevated temperature, followed by cooling to room temperature and exposure of the windings to 100 per cent relative humidity for a 24-hour period. Subsequently, each motor was operated at load to produce high operating temperatures for an accelerated life test. The temperature of the various motors under test (as observed by the resistance method) ranged from 200°C (392°F) to 310°C (590°F). The motors were also subjected to high humidity periodically during their operation to observe their reactions under high-moisture conditions.

Some of the conclusions reached as a result of this investigation are:

1. Failure of class H insulated motor windings occurred

before the bonding of the silicone resin was seriously weakened; in other words, the copper conductors failed before the insulation. Conductor failure was due to oxidation of the copper and reduction in the cross section to the point where localized heating occurred with destructive effect.

2. Silicone insulation presents less fire hazard than other classes of insulation. Ultimate failure of class B insulated motors was followed by fire, whereas failure of class H insulated motors was not.

3. The results of these tests indicate about a 100°C (180°F) temperature advantage for class H insulation compared with class B insulation. If current concepts of thermal aging are correct, the class H insulation could be expected to operate as much as several hundred times as long as class B equipment, where thermal aging is the primary factor in establishing insulation life.

4. Several years of continuous operation at hottest spot temperature of 220°C (428°F) will be required to reach the minimum thermal life of class H insulated equipment. [Subsequent work indicates that motors operating at 240°C (464°F) will last 5 to 10 years.]

5. The maximum life of class H insulation was not determined by these tests, since the ultimate end points were the results of copper-conductor failure rather than mechanical disintegration of the resin.

These conclusions signalized the development of the most stable flexible insulating medium to which industry has access. The stability is due to more than thermal resistance, for resistance to the action of water, oil, corrosive atmosphere, and many chemicals is quite outstanding.

Thermal Life

Information obtained concerning thermal life of class H insulation is plotted in the graph below, along with similar information for class A and class B (Fig. 11).

The use of silicone resins in the manufacture of electrical motors has brought about economies that are startling. These economies may be described in several ways. For instance, under the same operating conditions, a silicone-insulating motor will last many times as long as another with conventional insulation. In many cases the increased dependability is as important as the increased life. The limiting factor in the life of such a silicone-insulated motor becomes the speed of oxidation of the copper or the rusting of the iron, rather than degradation of the insulation.

Another way of stating the difference is that, because of the ability of the silicone to withstand heat, it is possible to get about 80 per cent more power out of a given frame size. This high percentage does not hold for small motors under 1 or 2 hp. In larger sizes a specific example can be given in that a 5-hp conventional motor will deliver 9 hp if insulated with class H components.

Improvement in the power per pound ratio saves copper and iron. This weight saving is an aid in reducing the weight of portable equipment. Where there are space limitations the value of silicone insulation is obvious.

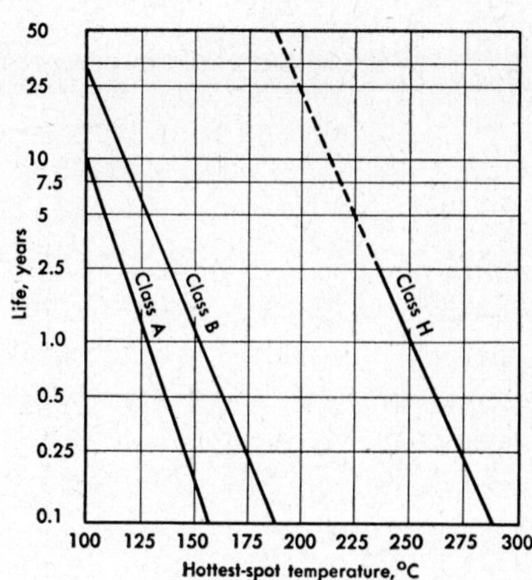

FIGURE 11
Life at various temperatures for class A, class B, and class H electrical insulation.

Traction motors, from small to large, were one of the first fields to find silicone insulation almost essential. Obviously this is because of the high starting loads and the general rough treatment that such types of equipment are required to withstand.

Resistance to Moisture and Chemicals

With the exception of heat, water causes the greatest destructive effect on electrical insulation. The excellent water repellency of silicone insulation makes its use particularly desirable for operation under conditions of high humidity. The tests described previously are evidence of the fact that humidity affects this type of insulation only very slowly. A spectacular demonstration of moisture resistance has been given by alternately submerging under water and raising a running class H insulated motor. This severe treatment was continued for upwards of 10,000 hr before any fault in the insulation became apparent.

The ability to function satisfactorily after having been flooded with water has been observed in practice many times. In cases where they have been submerged in muddy water the class H motors have required only hosing off, while under similar conditions many of the class B motors require drying out before being put back in service.

The resistance of this type of insulation to many corrosive chemicals is good. There are many cases on record of motors giving steady satisfactory service, even when subject to high humidity, caustic drip, or acid fumes. Chemical resistance is improved by baking at 250°C (482°F). This temperature is generally specified for curing but 200°C (392°F) is often considered sufficient for certain applications. If chemical resistance is a factor in the life of the insulation, the high-temperature bake should be carried out.

Table 28 shows the resistance of the silicone varnish to various chemicals.

TABLE 28

Chemical	*Resistance of Silicone Varnish*	*Chemical*	*Resistance of Silicone Varnish*
Acetic acid, 5%	Good	Sodium hydroxide, 50%	Good
Acetic acid, conc	Poor	Sulfur dioxide, liquid	Poor
Acetone	Poor	Sulfur dioxide, gaseous	Good
Ammonia, liquid	Poor	Sulfuric acid, 30%	Good
Ammonium hydroxide, conc	Good	Citric acid, 5%	Good
Carbon tetrachloride	Poor	Sulfur	Good
Chlorine (gaseous)	Good	Copper sulfate, 50%	Good
Freon	Fair	Stearic acid	Good
Gasoline	Poor	Hydrocarbons	Poor
Hydrogen peroxide, 3%	Good	Phosphoric acid, conc	Good
Hydrochloric acid, conc	Fair	Ferric chloride	Good
Methyl chloride	Poor	Alcohol	Good
Mineral oil	Good	Sulfuric acid, conc	Poor
Nitric acid, 10%	Good	Toluene	Poor
Nitric acid, conc	Poor	Stoddard solvent	Poor
Sodium carbonate, 2%	Good	Water	Good
Sodium chloride, 26%	Good	Phenol	Good
Sodium hydroxide, 10%	Good		

An inspection of this table shows that class H insulated motors can continue to give service under conditions that are severe to the point of being abusive. The use of silicone lubricants in the bearings permits mechanical operation, and the use of a silicone coating protects the housing against oxidation and corrosion.

Brush Wear

Brush wear is more marked in totally enclosed motors which are silicone insulated than in similar ventilated motors. Field test results show that the wear is not as severe as laboratory results originally indicated. Ventilation eliminates undue wear, and even in so-called "sealed" motors there is sufficient passage of air to keep brush wear within reasonable bounds. In open motors this trouble is not noted.

Typical Application for Silicone-insulated Motors

Those who are now using silicone-insulated motors have, in general, arrived at the position by a series of cautious steps. In a typical case the motor that has been required to take the most abuse (high ambient, frequent overload, damp location, etc.) has been rewound with silicone insulation. It has then been possible to compare the value of class B and class H under identical conditions. Cost and performance are easily appraised and the economy of using class B or class H has been determined with little or no fear of disrupting production. It may be of interest to know that there are some hundreds of rewind shops throughout the country which are prepared to supply this type of insulation.

Although, as pointed out previously, there is no reason to believe that all motors would benefit from silicone insulation, there are certain conditions where considerable economies can be realized by its use. Some of these are listed for purposes of illustration:

1. Critical motors, *e.g.*, those on which the production of a whole plant might depend. The ability of this insulation to stand up under shock or overload makes these motors more dependable and gives better insurance against shutdown. Motors in this class are those operating conveyor belts, as in an automobile plant, or loading motors in iron-melting furnaces. Many others will come to mind.

2. High ambients, *e.g.*, powerhouse auxiliaries, such as forced-draft fans, or any motor that must operate in close proximity to the boiler; motors on top of ovens; stoker motors; agitator motors on cooking kettles.

Motors of swing grinders are subject to high overloads. Silicone insulation increases their life manyfold.

3. High starting load, *e.g.*, where there is high temporary overload, as with centrifuges, washers in laundries, punch presses.

4. Reversing motors, *e.g.*, tappers and threaders, or tire-molding equipment, in which the motor stops and starts frequently as the molder lays pieces of fabric and raw rubber in place.

5. Intermittent loads, *e.g.*, in cranes and hoists. One case that may be cited is that of a class B crane motor that required rewinding every 30 days. It was finally rewound with silicone insulation and has been operating steadily for over 5 years.

6. Torque motors, *e.g.*, for valves in large pipe lines.

These may operate infrequently and may be seldom inspected. Reliability is a prime requisite.

7. Damp locations, *e.g.*, centrifugal pump motors; motors for strip coilers in steel mills where cooling water spray is constantly present.

8. Corrosive atmosphere, *e.g.*, in packing houses, dye houses, chemical plants, rubber plants; installations near the seacoast where "salt air" or even salt spray is present.

9. Frequent overload, *e.g.*, in motors driving grinders in which each piece is held by hand. In attempts to increase output the workman frequently overloads the motor. In lift trucks there is always the danger of overload.

10. Where space and weight must be minimized, *e.g.*, in motors on ships and aircraft, and in portable motors for many uses. In this case it must be recognized that the heat generated is proportional to the power supplied. Thus a small motor supplying such power will become very hot, and its location should be chosen with care. In addition design must take into account the magnetic saturation characteristic of the iron at that temperature.

General Electrical Applications

The application of silicone insulation to motors has been described in some detail because this is perhaps its most severe test. Rotation in motors and generators introduces a difficulty not present with transformers, solenoids, resistors, etc. The properties noted in the discussion on motors are, of course, equally applicable to the latter class of products. For example, air-cooled transformers have been constructed, up to 3,000 kva in size, in which silicone insulation has made possible better reliability and longer life combined with savings in both space and weight.

In addition to silicone resins, the silicone rubbers are widely useful in developing class H electrical insulation. These materials are discussed in the next section.

Section 5: Silicone Rubber

One of the most widely used materials today in technology and manufacture is rubber. We are so accustomed to its use that we often fail to recognize the debt we owe to this unique product. It is strong, extensible, water-repellent, and it can be calendered into sheets, extruded into tubing, or molded into intricate forms. Rubber in some form is needed in nearly every industry, in the design of a great many mechanisms and instruments, and in the operation of automobiles and aircraft. Without this versatile and unique material design would be cumbersome; machines and instruments would be noisy and of lower efficiency.

But in spite of its industrial value there are conditions in which the use of rubber is denied to the designer and manufacturer. Ozone brings about rapid deterioration, and very few rubbers can resist the attack of hot mineral oils. Temperatures above 100°C (212°F) bring about a rapid softening of most organic rubbers, although some special formulations will withstand 150°C (302°F) for a limited time. Temperatures below −35°C (−30°F) bring about the loss of rubbery properties in most cases, although a few rubbers are operable at somewhat lower temperatures; and those that are operable at the lowest temperature are not resistant to the high temperature. So it happens that rubber is limited to use over a temperature span of about 200°C (360°F) and even within this range may be rendered inoperable by the presence of external agents.

Within recent years industry has demanded faster operation and the development of more power. This has resulted at times in temperatures too high for the economical use of rubber. Activities in the Arctic regions and the development of planes that fly in the stratosphere have called for operation of machinery at temperatures well below those at which rubber will retain its useful characteristics. The presence of ozone, resulting from high-voltage applications, quickly deteriorates organic rubber. It may seem almost providential that just at this time there has arrived on the scene a material with rubbery characteristics which is operable over at least part of the temperature span that is denied to conventional rubber and which retains its properties for long periods in the presence of ozone.

Silicone rubber is difficult to distinguish upon casual inspection from organic rubber. It can be stretched and bounced. It sheds water. It can be calendered into sheets, extruded into tubing, or molded into intricate forms. The simplest way to distinguish conventional rubber from silicone rubber is by burning it. Organic rubber burns with a black smoky flame and leaves an ash of about 5 per cent. Silicone rubber burns with difficulty with a white smoky flame and leaves an ash of about 90 per cent.

As with organic rubbers, many stocks are available. They vary in hardness, tensile strength, dielectric properties, etc. Each application may be considered as a problem in itself. The proper stock must be selected after consultation with the manufacturer. Table 29 shows the range obtainable for many properties.

The properties shown in Table 29 are those for materials that are fully cured, *i.e.*, that have been held for at least 4 hr at 250°C (482°F). Much higher tensile and elongation values are found if the determinations are made on pieces which have had no cure beyond that obtained in the initial molding at 150°C (302°F). Tensiles of 1,500 with elongation of 700 are regularly obtainable with certain commercial stocks under these conditions. But the compression set is then very poor, and exposure to elevated temperature for extended periods of time results in a drop in both tensile and elongation to the values shown in the table. After all, these latter values are the

TABLE 29

	High	Low
Williams plasticity before curing	220	10
Hardness, Shore A scale	95	35
Specific gravity	2.6	1.2
Tensile strength, psi	900	260
Elongation, %	700	40
Brittle point	−56°C (−69°F)	−90°C (−130°F)
Compression set, %, 150°C (302°F)	90	10
Dielectric strength, volts per mil	800	200
Dielectric constant, at 10^2 cps	9.2	3.2
at 10^6 cps	8.4	3.0
Power factor, at 10^2 cps	0.067	0.002
at 10^6 cps	0.045	0.002

ones that will obtain in actual practice, and emphasis on the "as molded" values could be very misleading.

Silicone rubbers are available from the Dow Corning Corporation under the trade name "Silastic" and from the General Electric Company as "Silicone Rubber."

A. Chemical and Physical Properties

1. High-temperature Resistance

The outstanding characteristic of all silicone rubbers is their stability at elevated temperatures. At 150°C (302°F) the life is, for all practical purposes, unlimited; at 200°C (392°F) and 250°C (482°F) there is a change in properties illustrated in the graphs shown in Figs. 12 and 13. At 200°C (392°F) the change is roughly 60 per cent in 60 days, although the greatest effect is noted in the first 20 days; at 250°C (482°F) the change is somewhat more pronounced in 30 days, with the greatest

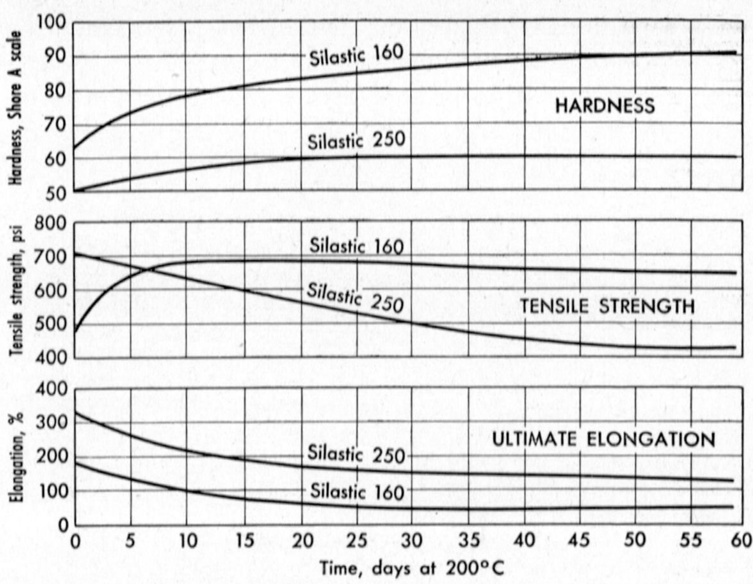

FIGURE 12 Effect of aging at 200°C on the properties of Silastic.

effect being seen in about 5 days. The fact that these curves level off is to be noted. The rubbers illustrated still have a long period of useful life.

The gross appearance of the silicone rubbers on breakdown from severe heating is quite different from that of organic rubbers. Instead of becoming soft and sticky they become harder and drier. On complete breakdown they are dry and friable.

The very high content of noncombustible inorganic matter is responsible for the ability of silicone rubber to pass tests requiring integrity after 200 hr at 400°C (752°F) and 90 hr at 540°C (1,004°F)[89] or impingement of a gas flame for 15 min.

2. Low-temperature Flexibility

Flexibility at low temperature is an inherent property of all silicone rubbers. All of them retain flexibility down to

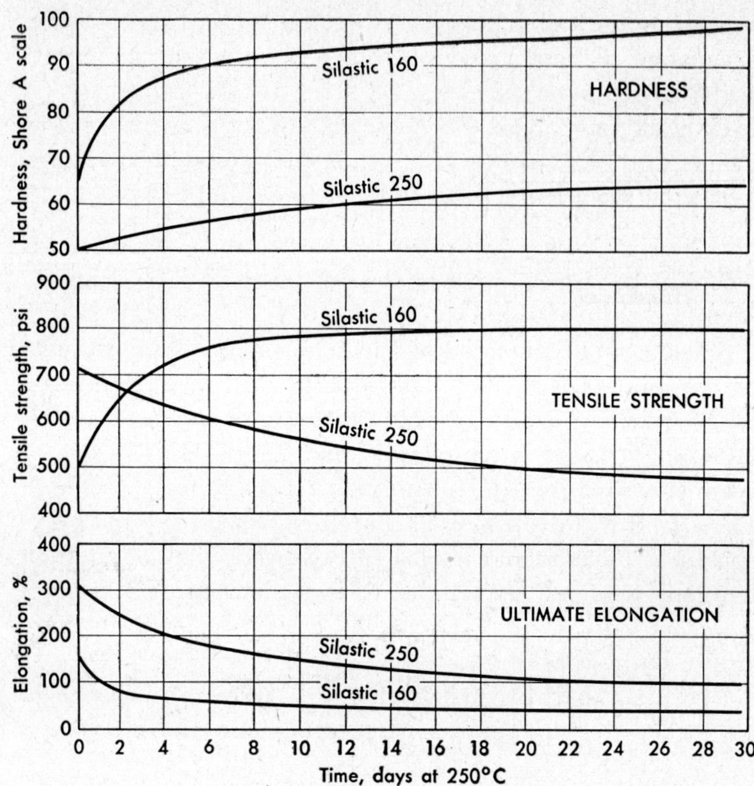

FIGURE 13 Effect of aging at 250°C on the properties of Silastic.

−56°C (−69°F), and special formulations are available that are useful below −90°C (−130°F). The very low-temperature properties are due not to the addition of plasticizers but to a slight change in the base polymer. Because of this there is no sacrifice of high-temperature resistance in the very low-temperature rubbers.

Although the silicone rubbers give service at these extremely low temperatures, the magnitude of the properties changes as the temperature goes down. In general it may be said that changes begin to become apparent at about −30°C (−22°F). Hardness begins to rise, and compression set is greater.

Tensile strength becomes greater and elongation becomes less. The extent of these changes is shown later as these properties are discussed in detail.

It should be realized that these changes of properties at low temperature are temporary. When the temperature returns to normal the original properties are found to be present.

3. Hardness

Silicone rubbers are obtainable in hardness ranging from 35 to 95 (Shore A scale). The change with temperature is relatively small except at the extremely low temperatures. Here the change is temporary and the original value is resumed upon return to normal temperatures. At high temperatures the degree of hardness remains remarkably constant. This should not be surprising in view of the high inorganic content. As temperatures are increased to the point of decomposition, the hardness will finally rise as the organic nature of the rubber is lost.

The accompanying graph (Fig. 14) shows the change of hardness with temperature for typical silicone rubber stocks.

4. Tensile Strength

The tensile strength of silicone rubbers is generally considered as lying within the range of 250 to 900 psi. This may be compared with 1,500 to 3,000 for organic rubbers. While the strength is low, by comparison, it is quite sufficient for many purposes.

Figure 15 shows the marked increase in tensile strength as low temperatures are reached, even though elongation is still maintained. If elongation is not needed the silicone rubber can be reinforced with glass fabric to give greatly improved tensile. It will still be flexible and compressible.

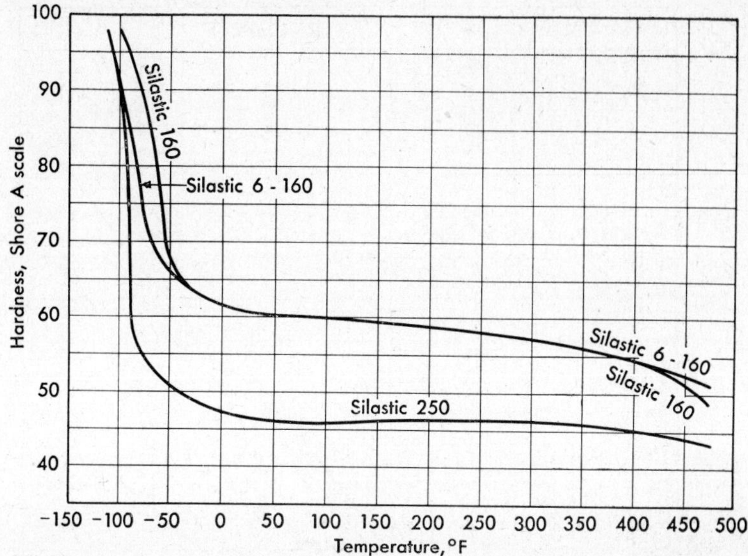

FIGURE 14 Variation of hardness of Silastic with temperature.

5. Elongation

There are few industrial applications where high elongation is needed, and the values for silicone rubber are generally adequate. The values for oven-cured moldings of 300 to 500 per cent will fall off with continued exposure to high temperature to values in the neighborhood of 100 to 250 per cent, the exact value varying with the stock. Very low temperatures will also decrease the elongation but, as with other properties, this is restored on return to normal conditions.

6. Compression Set

The set that rubber retains after being held under compression may be of great importance in some applications. This is expressed as "per cent set," and for organic rubbers it is

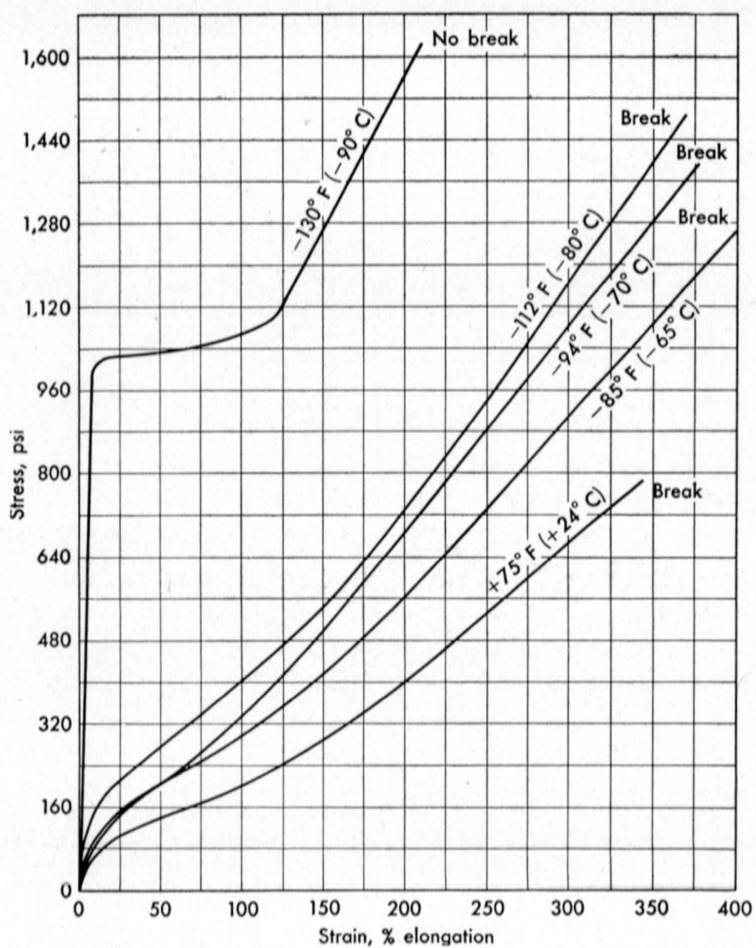

FIGURE 15 Effect of low temperatures on stress-strain relations of Silastic 250.

normally determined by holding the sample under compression for 22 hr at 70°C (158°F). But silicone rubbers are generally required to operate at temperatures far above or below this. To give a better picture as to how they will act under operating conditions their set is usually determined at 150°C (302°F).

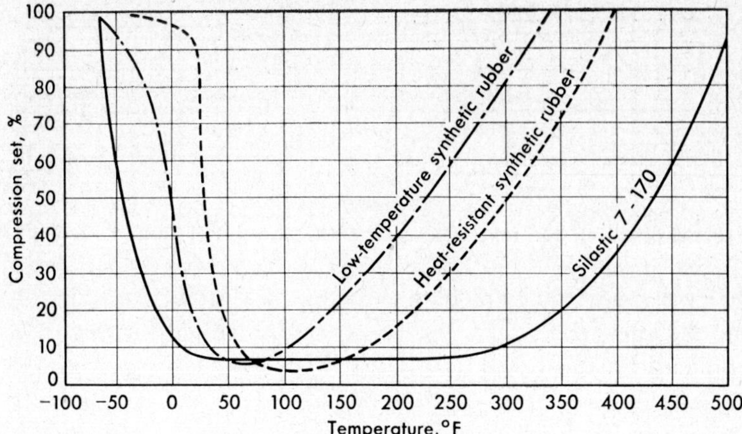

FIGURE 16 Compression set at various temperatures of Silastic and synthetic organic rubber.

Although most of the silicone rubbers show a set of about 50 per cent at this temperature, a figure that is comparable to that obtained with heat-resistant synthetic rubber, special silicone stocks are available that show as low as 10 per cent set. This very low compression set is obtained by the addition of 1 to 2 per cent of mercurous or mercuric oxide to the formulation. More recent formulations have eliminated the need for mercury. The accompanying graph (Fig. 16) shows the value for such a silicone rubber compared with organic rubbers especially compounded for high- and low-temperature use. It should be noted that this particular silicone formulation has substantially the same compression set as the organic rubbers between 10°C (50°F) and 65°C (149°F) and is considerably superior at both higher and lower temperatures.

7. Dielectric Strength

In view of the fact that silicone rubbers are seldom used as very thin films, high dielectric strength is not commonly required. Stocks are available, however, with strengths up to

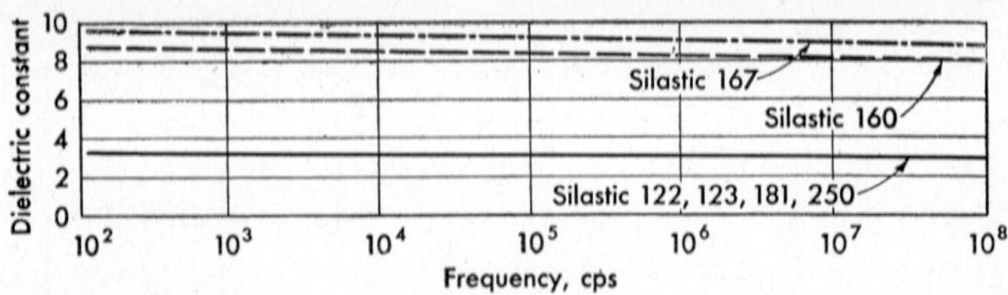

FIGURE 17 Dielectric constants of Silastics at various frequencies.

800 volts per mil, which is generally adequate, considering the thickness used. In the stocks recommended for electrical applications the dielectric strength remains relatively constant at temperatures up to 250°C (482°F).

8. Dielectric Constant

The dielectric constant of the silicone rubbers varies from 3.0 to 10.0 depending on the formulation. The value remains practically constant over a wide range of temperature or frequency (see Fig. 17).

9. Power Factor

The power factor varies for different types of silicone rubber. The graph below shows the variation of power factor with frequency for some representative products of this type (Fig. 18).

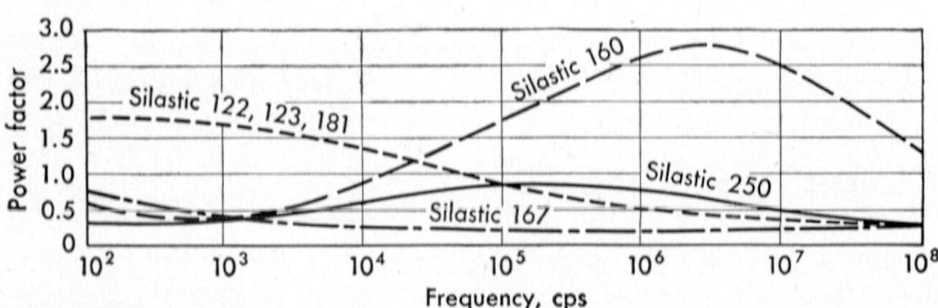

FIGURE 18 Per cent power factors of Silastics at various frequencies.

10. Arc Resistance

The arc resistance of silicone rubbers is high compared with that of organic dielectrics, being in the order of 200 to 250 sec for the rubbers used in electrical applications. One reason for the good resistance is the low carbon content of the rubber. Arcing leaves a track of nonconducting inorganic matter, rather than a carbon track.

11. Corona and Ozone Resistance

The resistance to corona is quite exceptional. The generation of ozone, due to corona, causes speedy hardening of organic rubber. There is little deterioration of silicone rubber from this cause. Tests have shown no deterioration after 2,200 hr under conditions that caused organic rubber to fail in 3 to 30 min.

12. Effect of Water and Steam

Like the other silicone materials, silicone rubber is highly water-repellent and retains high surface resistivity under moisture-condensing conditions. Water absorption for most stocks is about 1 per cent, although certain types may absorb up to 6 per cent. Strangely enough, the absorption of water does not materially affect power factor, dielectric constant, dielectric strength, or surface resistivity.

Although silicone rubber is highly water-repellent it is not recommended for use with steam under pressure. The rubber softens, probably because of depolymerization, and the deterioration is permanent.

13. Abrasion and Tear Resistance

The earliest silicone rubbers to be made were poor from the standpoint of abrasion and tear resistance. Considerable improvement has been made but these properties are still definitely inferior to those of organic rubbers. Still, the value is sufficient for most applications where the other properties of silicone rubber are required. Reinforcement with fabrics of woven glass or metal has proved helpful in raising these values but at the expense of elongation.

14. Thermal Conductivity

The thermal conductivity of silicone rubbers varies with different stocks. It is high in all cases, being about twice as great as that of either organic rubber or resinous insulating materials. This greater ability to dissipate heat brings about an additional increase in the power per pound ratio of electrical machines where a silicone rubber is used as an insulating medium.

15. Shrinkage on Curing

Silicone rubbers shrink somewhat more during fabrication than organic rubbers. Shrinkage of about 3 per cent may be expected during the period of initial vulcanization. An additional shrinkage of 2 to 3 per cent takes place during the final cure. Where close tolerances must be held allowance should be made in designing molds and dies for a total shrinkage in the range of 5 to 8 per cent, depending on the size and shape of the part, the kind of silicone rubber used, and the length of time allowed for final curing at 250°C (482°F).

16. Chemical Resistance

Silicone rubbers are resistant to most bases and weak acids, salt solutions, and oils. The relative resistance of samples molded of various Silastic (Dow Corning silicone rubber) stocks and pastes is indicated by the evaluations given in

Table 30. These evaluations are based on the measurement and observation of samples immersed in various reagents for 7 days at room temperature, as specified in ASTM D-543-43.

TABLE 30 Chemical Resistance of Silastic, ASTM D-543-43[a]

(Test samples molded 5 min at 125°C and cured 4 hr at 250°C)

Reagent	Silastic 121 124 6-124	Silastic 122 123 7-170 181 6-181 7-181	Silastic 125 6-125 126 167 6-167	Silastic 150 6-150	Silastic 151 160 6-160 162	Silastic 161 6-161 7-163 7-171	Silastic 180 6-180 7-180	Silastic 250
Acids								
Acetic, 5%	Good	Good	Good	Poor	Fair	Poor	Good	Good
Acetic, conc	Good	Good	Good	Poor	Poor	Poor	Good	Good
Hydrochloric, 10%	Good	Good	Fair	Good	Fair	Good	Good	Good
Hydrochloric, conc	Poor	Good	Poor	Poor	Poor	Poor	Fair	Poor
Nitric, 10%	Good	Good	Fair	Good	Good	Good	Good	Fair
Nitric, conc	Poor	Good	Poor	Poor	Poor	Poor	Fair	Poor
Sulfuric, 10%	Good	Good	Poor	Poor	Poor	Good	Good	Good
Sulfuric, conc	Poor	Poor	Poor	Poor	Poor	Poor	Poor	Poor
Bases								
Ammonium hydroxide, 10%	Good	Good	Good	Good	Good	Fair	Good	Good
Ammonium hydroxide, conc	Good	Good	Fair	Good	Good	Fair	Good	Good
Sodium hydroxide, 10%	Fair	Good	Poor	Fair	Poor	Poor	Good	Good
Sodium hydroxide, 50%	Good	Good	Good	Good	Good	Poor	Good	Good
Refrigerants								
Ammonia (liquid)	Good	Good	Good	Good	Good	Good	Good	Good
Freon 12	Poor	Poor	Poor	Poor	Poor	Poor	Poor	Poor
Freon 114	Good	Good	Good	Good	Good	Good	Good	Good
Methyl chloride	Poor	Poor	Poor	Poor	Poor	Poor	Poor	Poor
Salts								
Sodium carbonate, 2%	Good	Good	Good	Good	Good	Good	Good	Good
Sodium chloride, 10%	Good	Good	Good	Good	Good	Good	Good	Good
Solvents								
Acetone	Good	Good	Fair	Good	Fair	Good	Good	Fair
Carbon tetrachloride	Poor	Poor	Poor	Poor	Poor	Poor	Poor	Poor
Gasoline	Poor	Poor	Poor	Poor	Poor	Poor	Poor	Poor
Stoddard solvent	Poor	Poor	Poor	Poor	Poor	Poor	Poor	Poor
Toluene	Poor	Poor	Poor	Poor	Poor	Poor	Poor	Poor
Others								
Hydrogen peroxide, 3%	Good	Good	Good	Good	Good	Good	Good	Good
Mineral oil	Good	Good	Good	Good	Good	Good	Good	Good
Water	Good	Good	Good	Good	Good	Good	Good	Good

[a] From *Dow Corning Silastic Facts*, No. 10, p. 13, September, 1950.

All types of silicone rubber are subject to excessive swelling in contact with aromatic solvents, gasoline, and carbon tetrachloride. This does not indicate permanent deterioration, however, because most of the original properties are regained after the solvent has been evaporated.

These rubbers are remarkably stable in contact with ozone, tricresyl phosphate, and most of the chlorinated hydrocarbon fluids used in liquid-filled transformers.

Laboratory testing indicates that there is good resistance at room temperature to such refrigerants as liquid ammonia and Freon 114; poor resistance to methylchloride and Freon 12. Long-term testing in refrigerator units under actual service conditions should precede any specification for such applications.

17. Oil Resistance

It is generally true of all types of natural and synthetic organic rubbers that swelling and deterioration increase with the temperature and the aromatic content of the oil. At temperatures above 125°C (257°F) most organic rubber gaskets and seals deteriorate very rapidly in contact with oil. Silicone rubbers, however, show good resistance to various oils even at temperatures in the range of 125°C (257°F) to 250°C (482°F). They do swell to a certain extent, but the swelling generally does not indicate serious deterioration. On the contrary, silicone rubber seals are frequently improved by contact with hot oil. They are widely used, therefore, as gasketing material in internal-combustion engines.

The relative usefulness of various types of Silastic and an oil-resistant synthetic organic rubber in contact with hot oil is indicated by the data given in Table 31. The values given in this table were measured after 70 hr of immersion in an ASTM No. 1 (low-swell) oil held at 350°F (180°C). The oil-resistant organic rubber retained 67 per cent of its original tensile

TABLE 31 Comparative Oil Resistance of Silastic and an Oil-resistant Synthetic Organic Rubber[a]

(After 70 hr in an ASTM No. 1 low-swell oil held at 350°F)

Type of Rubber	Change in Hardness, Shore A Scale	Tensile Strength Retained, %	Elongation Retained, %	Swell, %
Silastic 151	−3	97	105	+5
Silastic 160	−8	117	108	+5
Silastic 161	−8	104	117	+6
Silastic 162	−9	102	107	+5
Silastic 180	−7	92	118	+6
Silastic 181	−6	96	105	+5
Silastic 6-160	−12	111	113	+7
Silastic 6-181	−8	101	110	+6
Silastic 7-163	−5	95	115	+7
Silastic 7-170	−7	92	105	+6
Silastic 7-180	−7	97	107	+6
Silastic 7-181	−6	100	105	+6
Silastic 250	−3	83	93	+8
Organic rubber (meets AMS 3227B)	−3	67	63	+8

[a] From *Dow Corning Silastic Facts*, No. 10, p. 14, September, 1950.

strength and 63 per cent of its elongation. Swell was 8 per cent. Silastic samples retained 83 to 117 per cent of their original tensile strength and 93 to 118 per cent of their original elongation. Swelling in the range of 5 to 8 per cent is well within acceptable limits for oil-resistant rubbers.

The silicone rubbers, like the organic rubbers, are more seriously affected by oils with a high aromatic content. After heating in an ASTM No. 3 (high-swell) oil for 70 hr at 350°F (180°C), for example, Silastic samples retained from 60 to 70 per cent of their original tensile strength. Elongation increased from 1½ to 2 times the initial values. Swelling was in the range of 50 to 55 per cent. Under the same test conditions, samples of an oil-resistant synthetic organic rubber retained less than 36 per cent of their original tensile strength; elongation was reduced to only about half of the initial values; and the samples showed an increase in volume of about 50 per cent.

The foregoing statement of general properties should make it apparent that silicone materials having rubbery properties can be used at both high and low temperature, and also at normal temperatures under some conditions that have been too severe for conventional organic rubbers.

B. Preparation of Silicone Rubber

The silicone rubbers are prepared by milling together a dimethyl silicone polymer, an inorganic filler, and a vulcanizer.[90]

The polymer is of high molecular weight, and in terms of viscosity may be from 3,000 to 1,000,000 centistokes or more. By altering the polymers somewhat, such as by replacing some of the methyl groups by phenyl or similar bulky groups, one may lower the freezing point materially.

Many different inorganic fillers may be used: titania, zinc oxide, iron oxide, silica, and other materials of this nature. They act as reinforcing or modifying agents. Varying the type and amount of these agents alters the chemical, physical, and electrical properties. Thus it is possible to provide stocks to fit a variety of specifications. It may be noted that carbon black, which is almost universally used with organic rubbers, is not included among the fillers for silicone rubbers. The presence of carbon black in the silicone rubbers interferes with the usual type of vulcanization, and products containing this filler have poor physical properties.

The vulcanizing agent is generally some type of peroxide, such as benzoyl peroxide. The most satisfying explanation of its reaction is that free radicals are formed on heating and that these intermediate products extract hydrogen from methyl groups of the polymer. These latter groups are then free radicals, which react with one another, bringing about a cross-linking bonding.

(1)
$$C_6H_5\overset{\overset{\displaystyle O}{\|}}{C}{-}O{-}O{-}\overset{\overset{\displaystyle O}{\|}}{C}{-}C_6H_5 \rightarrow C_6H_5^{\bullet} + CO_2 + {}^{\bullet}O{-}\overset{\overset{\displaystyle O}{\|}}{C}{-}C_6H_5$$

(2a)
$$C_6H_5^{\bullet} + {-}O{-}\underset{\underset{\displaystyle CH_3}{|}}{\overset{\overset{\displaystyle CH_3}{|}}{Si}}{-}O{-} \rightarrow C_6H_6 + {-}O{-}\underset{\underset{\displaystyle {}^{\bullet}CH_2}{|}}{\overset{\overset{\displaystyle CH_3}{|}}{Si}}{-}O{-}$$

(2b)
$$C_6H_5\overset{\overset{\displaystyle O}{\|}}{C}{-}O^{\bullet} + {-}O{-}\underset{\underset{\displaystyle CH_3}{|}}{\overset{\overset{\displaystyle CH_3}{|}}{Si}}{-}O{-}$$
$$\rightarrow C_6H_5\overset{\overset{\displaystyle O}{\|}}{C}OH + {-}O{-}\underset{\underset{\displaystyle {}^{\bullet}CH_2}{|}}{\overset{\overset{\displaystyle CH_3}{|}}{Si}}{-}O{-}$$

(3)
$$\begin{array}{c} CH_3 \\ | \\ {-}O{-}Si{-}O \\ | \\ {}^{\bullet}CH_2 \\ + \\ {}^{\bullet}CH_2 \\ | \\ {-}O{-}Si{-}O{-} \\ | \\ CH_3 \end{array} \rightarrow \begin{array}{c} CH_3 \\ | \\ {-}O{-}Si{-}O{-} \\ | \\ CH_2 \\ | \\ CH_2 \\ | \\ {-}O{-}Si{-}O{-} \\ | \\ CH_3 \end{array}$$

The presence of reducing agents, such as carbon black, destroys the free radicals at room temperature. They cannot, therefore, be used successfully as fillers.

Curing

The useful peroxide vulcanizing agents are stable at ordinary temperatures, but at elevated temperature they decompose and react as described above. This provides an explanation for the necessity of molding at temperatures above 115°C (239°F), preferably 150°C (302°F). At lower temperatures the reaction is too slow for practical purposes and may even take place without sufficient energy to give the desired result.

The equation given above shows that carbon dioxide is formed in the reaction. When thin pieces are molded the gas normally diffuses out readily. But as the thickness of the piece is increased there is danger of bloating if it is not held under compression during cooling.

The nature of the vulcanizing agent requires that the reaction be carried out in the absence of oxygen. Reaction with oxygen destroys the free radicals and gives an unvulcanized and sticky surface. With compression moldings there is, of course, no difficulty, but with extrusions or coated sheets special precautions must be taken. The simplest way to provide an inert atmosphere for the curing of extrusions and other cold-formed products is to use an autoclave from which the air has been purged by the steam. The pieces should be exposed to steam only long enough to bring them to 125°C (257°F) and to hold them at that temperature for 5 min.

Coated sheets may be cured in towers or horizontal ovens. Towers should be designed to allow a curing time of 3 to 5 min at 200 to 300°C (392 to 572°F). The carbon dioxide produced can diffuse out of these thin sheets and it provides its own nonoxidizing atmosphere for the initial part of the cure.

Following the initial cure in the press, autoclave, or tower, the pieces should be given a final cure of some hours between 200 and 250°C (392 and 482°F) in an air-circulating oven to develop the best properties. In the final cure oxygen should be present. Any residual vulcanizing agent is destroyed. Properties such as compression set and hardness are improved and any residual carbon dioxide is expelled. To obtain the minimum compression set and the maximum hardness pieces should be given a final cure of 24 hr at 250°C (482°F).

The rate at which the peak temperature of 250°C (482°F) should be attained depends on the thickness of the piece. Carbon dioxide must be allowed to diffuse out. If the piece is thick and the heating is fast bloating may result. As a general rule it can be stated that pieces up to 1/16 in. in thickness require no intermediate heating but can be placed at 250°C (482°F) immediately. Pieces between 1/16 to 1/8 in. in thickness should be heated in an air-circulating oven for 30 min at 150°C (302°F) before final curing at 250°C (482°F). Pieces 1/8 to 1/2 in. in thickness should be given an intermediate cure at 150°C (302°F) and 200°C (392°F), or they should be exposed in an oven at temperatures gradually increased from 150°C (302°F) to 200°C (392°F). The precise times and temperatures will vary with the dimensions of the piece and even with the type of stock. Advice covering exact procedures for particular stocks can be obtained from the manufacturers.

A special point should be made of the fact that good air circulation with adequate ventilation is required during this final cure. Pieces should be heated uniformly. It is very important that parts be placed separately, rather than stacked, on shelves of metal screen to permit free access of hot air to all surfaces.

The properties required in the finished product determine the time and temperature necessary for final curing. If maximum elongation is most important in the finished product, only a short time at 150°C (302°F) to 200°C (392°F) in an air-circulating oven is required for final curing. If maximum tensile strength and minimum compression set are required, final curing at 250°C (482°F) for 24 hr will be necessary.

C. *Types of Silicone Rubber*

One of the most intriguing factors to one considering the use of silicone rubber is that it is available in an almost infinite variety of forms from thin slips to heavy moldable stocks. The rubbers are prepared as pastes that may be of a smooth, buttery consistency, or thick and heavy enough to require a stout putty knife for application. They are also prepared as stocks which can be handled very much like organic rubber crepes. The hardness of the finished product may vary from 35 to 95 on the Shore A scale. Either the pastes or the stocks may be dispersed in organic solvents to give free-flowing dispersions, which can be applied by brushing or spraying or dipping. In spite of the high temperature of cure required it is possible to coat cotton or other fabrics. Special stocks are formulated to give quick cure, which allows the rubber to set before the fabric is injured by the heat.

Such a variety of pastes and stocks is available that it is beyond the scope of this chapter to describe each in detail. Certain formulations are available for the best in dielectric properties, chemical resistance, compression set, speed of cure, or other needed properties. The manufacturer should be consulted as to the best material for a specific application.

1. Dispersions

Dispersions in solvent may be prepared which are useful for dip coating, spraying, or brushing of organic or inorganic mats or fabrics. The materials to be coated or impregnated may be cotton, nylon, asbestos, Fiberglas, etc. The thickness of the dispersion can be adjusted from very thin to very thick. One may want particular solids contents, depending on the amount of pickup desired or the type of machinery being used.

The solvents used in the preparation of dispersions are usually toluene, gasoline, or xylene. If a paste is used to prepare a dispersion the solvent should be added slowly, while stirring rapidly with a mechanical mixer, until the desired solids content is reached.

If a stock is to be dispersed it should be divided into small pieces so that a maximum surface area will be exposed. Enough solvent to cover the stock should be added, and the material should be allowed to stand for a few hours or overnight. After being soaked it should be stirred rapidly with a mechanical mixer until the solution becomes smooth. Stirring should be continued while enough solvent is added to give the solution the desired consistency. A typical dispersion contains from 20 to 30 per cent of stock or paste by weight.

A dispersion as usually prepared has a consistency similar to a paint. It may be applied by a brush to metal surfaces or can be brushed into a fabric. A similar effect can be obtained by spraying. Panels may be dipped into the dispersion; fabric may be immersed in it and then impregnated more completely by being passed through squeeze rolls.

After the coating is applied it is important that all the solvent be driven off at as low a temperature as is practicable. The temperature should be definitely below 50°C (122°F), and in most cases the lower the temperature the better the final result. After removal of solvent the coating may be brought to its initial vulcanizing temperature of about 150°C (302°F). If the solvent is not driven off blowing or incomplete vulcanization may result. The time and temperature for setting up the rubbery coating vary, depending on the number of coats to be applied, the nature of the fabric, and the temperature available. If only one coating is to be applied the temperature of cure may be as high as the fabric can stand. The higher the temperature the quicker the cure. It should be recognized that the coating protects the fabric from oxidation and even from the full heat of the oven. If more than one coat is to be applied each coat need be cured only to the point where it is tack free. When all coats have been applied the full vulcanization can be completed.

The number of coatings required to build up a given thickness depends on the concentration of the solution. Coatings up to 20 mils in thickness can be cured in an air-circulating oven at 250°C (482°F). They can also be cured in 3 to 5 min in a coating tower held at 200 to 300°C (392 to 572°F).

USES OF DISPERSIONS

Dispersions are normally used where a good impregnation or light-weight coating is required. Thin gasketing material can be prepared in this way using asbestos mat or glass fabric. Multiple layers of these impregnated materials give laminates suitable for the manufacture of reinforced tubing or hose. The glass or asbestos fabric may be impregnated and then wound on a mandrel. The same principle may be applied in the preparation of fabric-reinforced ducts for aircraft, as in deicers, flexible couplings, etc.

Belting coated with silicone rubber has found use in conveyor systems for the handling of frozen foods. It remains flexible at the low temperature used and can be sterilized by heat if necessary.

The cured silicone rubber has the release characteristic of the silicone fluid and resinous release agents. Belts carrying candy or similar sticky materials give easy release.

A dispersion can be used for the coating of steel molds to give release of coating resins. This type of coating must necessarily be thicker than that of the fluids or resins and will, therefore, not give the same sharpness of definition with moldings, even though it does give good release.

2. Pastes

The pastes are obtainable in consistencies ranging from 10 to 90 as measured by a Williams plastometer. The former are thin and salvelike but have slow flow in the uncured state. The latter are rather stiff and need to be applied with a calking gun or putty knife.

The thin pastes are not suitable for dipping, brushing, or spraying but must be applied by spreading with a doctor blade or by some similar technique. All the pastes are of thin enough consistency to be used as a potting compound or for the filling of voids. The fact that they contain no solvent makes them simpler to handle than the dispersions, for curing can be commenced as soon as the application is completed. They may be applied to fabrics, or to ceramic, glass, or metal surfaces.

The pastes that are available differ not only in consistency. They may be slow or fast cure, and the final product may be particularly formulated for electrical uses, for chemical resistance, for hardness, or for any of the various applications to which they may be directed. So the selection of the paste that is best suited to a given application will depend on the way it is to be handled and on the properties required in the finished product.

If a coating is to be applied to inorganic fabrics or to woven metal screen by doctoring, spreading, or roller coating a paste having a Williams plasticity value of 10 to 40 should be considered. Such coatings may be applied and cured, or they may be applied as an intermediate step in the production of laminations or parts made by mandrel wrapping.

When some pastes are cured the products have good mechanical strength but inferior electrical properties. Others have combinations of both properties. One type is formulated to give quick cure so that it can be used as a coating for organic fabrics or for the application of very thin films to inorganic fabrics, ceramics, glass, or metal surfaces.

For most sealing, calking, or potting applications a paste having a Williams plasticity value of 40 to 90 is generally preferred. Within this range application is usually made by calking gun or putty knife.

It should be made clear that these variations in consistency are obtained by the proper selection of the base silicone polymer. No organic thinner or softener is used. Therefore no attempt should be made to alter the consistency by such additions. If a thinner consistency is required the best method is to mix in a lower-viscosity silicone-rubber paste. Or if one of the very thick pastes is to be used it can be made more workable by milling on a rubber or paint mill for a short time.

METHODS FOR COATING

Inorganic Fabrics

For the coating of inorganic fabrics, such as glass, asbestos, or metal, any silicone paste having a Williams plasticity value of 10 to 40 may be used. It may be applied by doctoring or spreading.

The fabric must be clean and free from organic sizing. Heat-treated or heat-cleaned glass cloth may be bought from the manufacturer. Sizing and other volatile materials can also be removed by heating the glass fabric at 300°C (572°F). Asbestos fabrics should be prepared by exposing them to temperatures of 225°C (437°F) to 250°C (482°F) for a few hours.

Single coatings up to 20 mils in thickness may be applied by doctoring or spreading. They may be cured by heating for 3 to 5 min in an air-circulating oven at 200°C (392°F) to 300°C (572°F).

These coatings may be applied most economically to inorganic cloth and tape by continuous coating and curing. The paste is applied continuously by doctor rolls or blades at the entrance to an electrically heated tower, where the coating is cured at temperatures of 200°C (392°F) to 300°C (572°F). Either towers or horizontal ovens may be used. Coating and curing speeds will depend on the length of the tower, operating temperatures, and the thickness of the coating.

Organic Fabrics

The coating of organic fabrics differs from that of inorganic fabrics in three respects:

1. No preparation of the fabric is required beyond removal of any excessive amount of sizing.

2. The only paste to be used is one formulated for rapid cure.

3. The curing conditions should be 4 to 6 min in a tower at 130°C (266°F) to 150°C (302°F). The time of cure may be shortened by using higher temperature if the fabric will stand it without deterioration.

With the observation of these points the coating of organic fabrics is similar to that of the inorganic fabrics.

Ceramic, glass, or metal surface

The silicone pastes may be applied to ceramic, glass, and metal surfaces in a manner similar to that described for inorganic fabrics. It is essential that the surface should be clean and free of grease. Metal surfaces should be solvent cleaned, then sandblasted or grit blasted, and cleaned again before coating.

Rounded or irregular shapes can best be coated by the use of a dispersion, as described earlier.

The curing procedure for coatings up to 10 mils in thickness requires 3 to 5 min in an air-circulating oven at 200°C (392°F) to 300°C (572°F). The coating must reach the temperature of cure quickly and then be held at that temperature for the necessary length of time. One should recognize that if the ceramic or metal piece is large, some amount of time may be required to bring the piece to oven temperature. For this reason large pieces may require a longer time in the oven even if the coating is of the same thickness as that applied to smaller pieces.

Obtaining good adhesion to copper is usually troublesome,

and attention should be given to proper priming of the surface with a silicone primer. Advice on primers for particular applications may be obtained from the manufacturer.

Adhesion to the surfaces described is generally good if proper precautions are taken to clean them thoroughly. If, however, good adhesion is not obtained, auxiliary techniques are available. These are described on pages 182–183.

METHODS FOR LAMINATING

Laminates may be formed by using successive layers of coated fabric or by interleaving the layers with silicone-rubber paste or sheeted silicone-rubber stock. To obtain good adhesion and guard against delamination one must bear in mind one simple principle: cured silicone rubber will not adhere to cured silicone rubber and therefore at least one of the two adjacent surfaces must be uncured. Thus a laminate can be made of successive layers of uncured coated fabric; the coated fabric may be cured and interleaved with silicone paste or sheeted uncured stock; sheeted cured stock may be interleaved with uncured coated fabric. All surfaces should be clean and should be completely free of talc or similar release agents.

For molding the laminates any steam-heated or electrically heated molding press that operates at temperatures of 125°C (257°F) to 150°C (302°F) can be used. Conventional press plates should be sprayed with a 5 per cent solution of a synthetic detergent, such as Dreft, Vel, or Orvus, in water to prevent sticking. Care should be taken to see that all the water has evaporated before the plates are used. Thickness of the lamination is controlled by a chase, a frame, or by shims. Normal molding pressures are in the range of 100 to 500 psi. If a chase or shim is not used molding pressures should be reduced to keep the fabric from breaking or to prevent excessive squeezing out of the rubber paste.

Laminations up to ¼ in. in thickness should be molded under pressure for 3 to 8 min at a temperature of 125°C

(257°F) ±10°. Laminations between ¼ and ½ in. in thickness should be held under pressure at 125°C (257°F) ±10° for 10 min or more. Before pressure is released the lamination should be cooled to about 65°C (149°F) to prevent porosity and poor adhesion.

It will be recalled that the vulcanizing agent liberates carbon dioxide during the cure. The procedure described provides the proper temperature for reaction and allows time for diffusion of the gas from the laminate.

Following the molding the final curing should be carried out in an air-circulating oven. Laminations up to ⅛ in. in thickness can be placed directly in the oven at 250°C (482°F) and cured for 4 to 24 hr, depending on the properties required in the finished piece. Compression set in particular is improved by longer curing. Laminations between ⅛ and ¼ in. in thickness should be given an intermediate cure at 150°C (302°F) for 2 hr and at 200°C (392°F) for 3 hr before final curing for 4 to 24 hr at 250°C (482°F).

The intermediate cure for the thicker pieces is for the purpose of removing any last traces of carbon dioxide that might cause blowing at the highest temperature.

It will be recognized, of course, that if the sheeting material is organic all temperatures and times must be held below those at which breakdown would occur.

MANDREL WRAPPING

Fabrics coated as previously described can be mandrel wrapped to form hose or tubing for various purposes.

To obtain good release from the metal the mandrel should be treated with talc or with a 5 per cent solution of a synthetic detergent, such as Dreft, Vel, or Orvus, in water. When the water has evaporated the wrapping can proceed.

The completed assembly should be tightly wrapped with a damp cotton cloth or tape and given an initial cure of 3 to 5 min in a steam vulcanizer under a pressure of 50 psi before it is removed from the mandrel. After this initial cure the cotton cloth and the mandrel should be removed. The piece should then be given the final cure in the air-circulating oven. The same time-temperature schedule as described for other types of laminates should be observed.

It may be of interest to know that coated tapes ready for wrapping and subsequent vulcanization are available from the manufacturers of silicone rubbers.

SEALING, CALKING, AND POTTING

For sealing, calking, and potting, the silicone-rubber pastes having Williams plastometer values of 40 to 90 should be used.

The surfaces to which the paste is to be applied should be clean. As these materials are used for the sealing of voids and for mechanical seals in high-temperature machinery, they are generally applied and allowed to cure at operating temperature. One to three hours at 100°C (212°F) is sufficient to complete the cure.

It should be noted that these pastes expand slightly when they are heated and form a tight seal. If heated too rapidly when unconfined they are likely to foam.

USES OF PASTES

The pastes may be used to coat organic fabrics for applications at low temperatures and at temperatures not above the decomposition point of the fabric. Such uses include application to diaphragms, belting, gasketing, and sheeting. Sheeting coated with rubber for hospital use has the advantage that it can be sterilized repeatedly without becoming hard.

Tents to be used in cold weather need an aperture in the top to accommodate a stove pipe. The heat of the pipe against the fabric constitutes a fire hazard. The hazard may be greatly diminished if a few square feet of the tenting in this location is made of asbestos or Fiberglas which is coated with silicone rubber.

Glass fabrics through which heating wires are woven can be coated to form flexible heating pads. The high rate of heat transfer of the silicone rubber is a factor that adds to the effectiveness of the pad.

Tapes are available which have been coated with the paste and semivulcanized. They are used as electrically insulating wrapping tapes. Following the wrapping the assembly is heated to complete the curing and form a continuous void-free silicone-rubber jacket. The high heat conductivity of the silicone rubber results in rapid heat dissipation, so that the unit actually operates at a lower temperature than one insulated with varnish. This method has been used with singularly good results for the insulation of diesel-electric locomotive field coils. Cost is comparable to that of conventional wrapping.

Laminates made from coated fabric are used for the preparation of heat-stable, flexible, and compressible pads. They may be used for gasketing, instrument mounting for vibration damping, and in pressure pads to be used at high or low temperature. Where extensibility is not required it is often preferable to use a laminate rather than solid silicone rubber, for the tear resistance is improved.

Hose or tubing formed by mandrel wrapping finds many applications, such as on flexible couplings, hot-air ducts in planes, hose for carrying hot gases or liquids, and radiator hose.

The pastes may be applied directly to ceramic ware, glass, or metal to provide an adhesive electrically insulating coating. Resistors have been prepared by winding wire around a ceramic or glass tube and coating the assembly with a silicone paste. The resiliency of the coating allows expansion and contraction of the wire without damage to the assembly. It repels water and is not affected by sudden temperature changes.

The pastes may be applied as dielectric materials to any surfaces that are free from oil, rubber, soldering flux, or other organic materials. They are used as space fillers around electrical equipment, as in the voids around the lead wires of coils and motors. They are also applied to transformer coils or solenoids.

For calking purposes the pastes may be applied with a calking gun or putty knife. If they are unconfined they expand slightly when they are heated and form tight seals.

3. Stocks

A large variety of silicone-rubber stocks is available. Table 29 on page 151 shows the range of physical properties obtainable. The manufacturer should be consulted as to the proper stock to be used for specific applications.

The stocks are much stiffer than the pastes and are comparable in methods of handling to organic rubber crepes. They may be compression molded, extruded, calendered, or mandrel wrapped. The temperature of molding is higher than that required for organic rubber but the time in the press is generally shorter. Compression moldings require from 3 to 10 min in the press at about 115°C (239°F) to 150°C (302°F), the time varying with the stock used and the nature of the piece being molded. For the development of the best properties an aftercure of a few hours at 250°C (482°F) is needed.

For the fabrication of silicone-rubber parts conventional rubber-handling equipment is used. Necessary equipment includes a two-roll mill equipped with a scraper blade, a calender, a rubber or plastic extruder, a steam-heated or electrically heated molding press that operates at temperatures up to 150°C (302°F) and an air-circulating oven. A steam vulcanizer operating at 25 to 100 psi is desirable, and a variable-speed conveyor belt is useful in taking the formed material from the extruding head.

The importance of good air circulation and ventilation in

the after-curing oven should be stressed. Volatile materials given off during the aftercure may be toxic or irritating, or they could reach the explosive state if combined with certain concentrations of air. High concentration of volatiles can cause discoloration of the rubber and bring about abnormally low durometer hardness and tensile strength. All these difficulties can be met by the use of good ventilation.

For the vulcanizing or curing of stocks two steps are always required:

1. The precure in which the peroxide vulcanizer reacts to give the initial set. This must be carried out in the absence of air. In compression molding this is no problem for the piece is confined in the press. With extruded or calendered pieces the most effective method is to hold them in a steam autoclave that has been purged of air by the steam. Three to five minutes at a pressure of 50 lb is generally adequate. The exact times and pressures will vary with the type of stock used and with the thickness of the piece.

2. Following the precure the piece should be held in the air-circulating oven at a maximum temperature of 250°C (482°F). This aftercure must be carried out in the presence of air. The rate of reaching the peak temperature will vary with the thickness of the piece. Four hours at 250°C (482°F) is generally sufficient to complete the cure. If minimum compression set or better resistance to solvents is required the cure should be extended to 24 hr.

MOLDING, EXTRUDING, OR CALENDERING

Stocks should be milled for a few minutes before molding, extruding, or calendering. A differential-speed two-roll mill is most desirable. Some stocks tend to crumble somewhat before they form a sheet on the rolls. These crumbs should be gathered up and fed into the mill immediately or they should be milled in with the next batch.

Molding

Any steam-heated or electrically heated molding press that operates at temperatures up to 150°C (302°F) can be used in molding silicone rubber. Pressures normally used in molding organic rubbers are suitable. A 5 per cent solution of such synthetic detergents as Dreft, Vel, or Orvus in water prevents the adherence of silicone rubber to the mold. The silicone mold-release agents that are commonly used in the molding of organic rubbers are not effective with the silicone rubbers.

Moldings are formed at a temperature of 115°C (239°F) to 150°C (302°F), depending on the stock used. The time in the mold may be from 3 to 10 min, depending on the thickness of the piece. The mold should be cooled to about 70°C (158°F) before the piece is removed. Thinner pieces or lower molding temperatures may allow removal without mold cooling.

As described earlier, the best properties are developed by the aftercure in the oven.

Extruding

All stocks do not extrude with the same smoothness, and the manufacturer should be consulted as to the best stock for handling in this manner.

In the extruding of a silicone-rubber stock enough heat is generated to make it unnecessary to heat the extruding head or die. The temperature of the extrusion should be about 50°C (122°F). To maintain that temperature it is sometimes necessary to cool the stock by running water through the head of the extruder.

Extrusions are given the initial cure in an autoclave and a final oven cure, as described above.

Calendering

Stock can be sheeted from a two-roll mill or calendered on unheated rolls to form flat sheets. It is easier to handle if it is fed from the calender or taken off the mill and placed on a supporting material such as holland cloth or cellophane. It can also be friction-calendered onto such heat-stable fabrics as Fiberglas, asbestos, or wire cloth to increase tensile strength and tear resistance.

The calendered material may be used to form laminates or can be fabricated into hose and tubing by mandrel wrapping.

The curing cycle is similar to that for extrusions.

SPONGING

The silicone-rubber stocks can be sponged by the use of blowing agents. These products are comparable to organic rubber sponge in uniformity, softness, tensile strength, and resistance to both compression set and flexing. They retain these properties at temperatures within the range of the stocks from which they are made.

The manufacturer should be consulted for the appropriate blowing agent for the stock that is to be used.

USE OF SCRAP WITH STOCK

Clean scrap from flash, trimmings, and rejects can be worked on a warm mill and then combined with fresh stock of the same type. Blending of different types of stock will change the properties of the finished product. The scrap should be milled, with the rolls warmed to about 50°C (122°F) and set as tight as possible, until the scrap sheets smoothly. After the scrap has been milled the rolls should be cooled to room temperature, and new stock should be added gradually until it is thoroughly mixed. Scrap in the proportion of 10 to 30 per cent may be added to new stock.

The addition of scrap may improve the mechanical properties of the completed part. Stocks containing reclaimed material are processed in the same way as new stocks of the same type.

CEMENTING TO CERAMICS, GLASS, METALS

Surfaces to which silicone rubber is to be bonded should be free of all grease and dirt. Metals should be degreased and grit blasted. Different methods are employed, depending on whether the silicone rubber is uncured or cured.

If the Silicone Rubber Is Uncured

METHOD 1. The easiest method for cementing silicone rubber is to mold the unvulcanized stock under heat and pressure in direct contact with the ceramic, glass, or metal. After molding, the normal curing schedule is followed to develop the optimum properties and to give maximum bond strength.

METHOD 2. For cases where it is difficult to secure an adequate bond to metal, special silicone priming resins are available. These are applied to the metal surface and cured with heat. Stocks molded in contact with this surface show good adhesion.

If the Silicone Rubber Is Cured

METHOD 3. The surface of the cured stock should be free of all contamination from dirt, grease, talc, or other contaminants. A sheet of uncured stock about 25 mils thick should be placed between the cured stock and the second bonding surface. The assembly should be molded under heat and pressure, and the normal curing should then be followed.

METHOD 4. A silicone-rubber paste corresponding in composition to the piece to be bonded may be spread on to the contacting surfaces. The procedure then follows that of method 3.

METHOD 5. If good adhesion to metal is not obtained by method 3 or 4, a silicone priming resin should be applied to the initial surface and cured with heat as in method 2. This treatment should be followed by method 3 or 4.

To Cement Cured Rubber to Cured Rubber

The contacting surfaces of two pieces should be cleaned of all dirt, grease, or talc. A sheet of uncured stock about 25 mils thick should be placed between the two pieces, and the assembly should be cured under heat and pressure. A silicone paste may be used in place of a sheet of uncured stock.

USES OF STOCKS

When considering the possible uses of the silicone stocks, or of the dispersions and pastes for that matter, one should keep in mind the properties described in the earlier part of this section: operability at high and low temperatures, oil and chemical resistance, compression set, dielectric properties, ozone resistance, and thermal conductivity. Not all of these properties reach their peak in any one formulation, and the manufacturer should be consulted as to the best material for each application.

Sealing devices such as gasketing, O rings, and push-rod seals made of silicone rubber have much to recommend them. The wider temperature range over which they can be used is an obvious advantage, and the resistance to hot lubricating oil is frequently a characteristic that makes them indispensable. High temperature does not make this rubber sticky, so that valve seats coated with the rubber give quick release. Silicone-rubber gasketing is also used for the sealing of bomb-bay doors, in wind tunnels, searchlights, domestic steam irons, and for the gasketing of ovens, pressure cookers, and autoclaves.

Heating elements embedded in silicone rubber are used as deicing units on the air-intake shut-off doors of jet engines used in B-36 planes. This rubber is used because it is the only resilient material that retains flexibility below −75°C (−103°F). Other applications for this type of silicone-rubber unit include deicing helicopter blades and antenna masts, as well as heating of oil vent lines. Formulations are available that make excellent gaskets for use against Aroclors and chlorinated diphenyls. Silicone rubber has also been used as a sealant in an ozone generator.

The release characteristics are made use of when silicone-rubber-coated rolls are used in the hot and cold dip-coating of fabrics, plastic film, and metal sheeting or foil. The coverings on rolls (or even solid silicone-rubber rolls) are used to prevent sticking in fabricating various pressure-sensitive tapes and in heat-sealing cellophane packages.

A simple and worthwhile application is the coating of a nickel safety disk on a reactor containing ammonia and aldehydes at 100°C (212°F). An unprotected disk lasted about 24 hr, while a coated disk gave good protection for 3 months.

In glass manufacture silicone-rubber wheels are used in the moving of hot tubing. In the fabrication of television tubes the face plate is held by suction to resilient silicone rubber, while the seal is made to the tube itself.

The electrical applications are numerous. Silicone-rubber-coated wire is used as a lead to hot motors, to infrared heating apparatus, and between the heating elements of high-temperature ovens. The application to aircraft antennas reduces static and corona discharge. In addition the dielectric properties are retained, and moisture and foreign matter are excluded after long exposure to outdoor weathering and to the full range of ground and stratospheric temperatures. Silicone-rubber boots for spark plugs on motor boats and automobiles are now used to protect against water and accumulation of dirt.

Coils and solenoids insulated with this material actually operate at lower temperatures than resin-insulated units

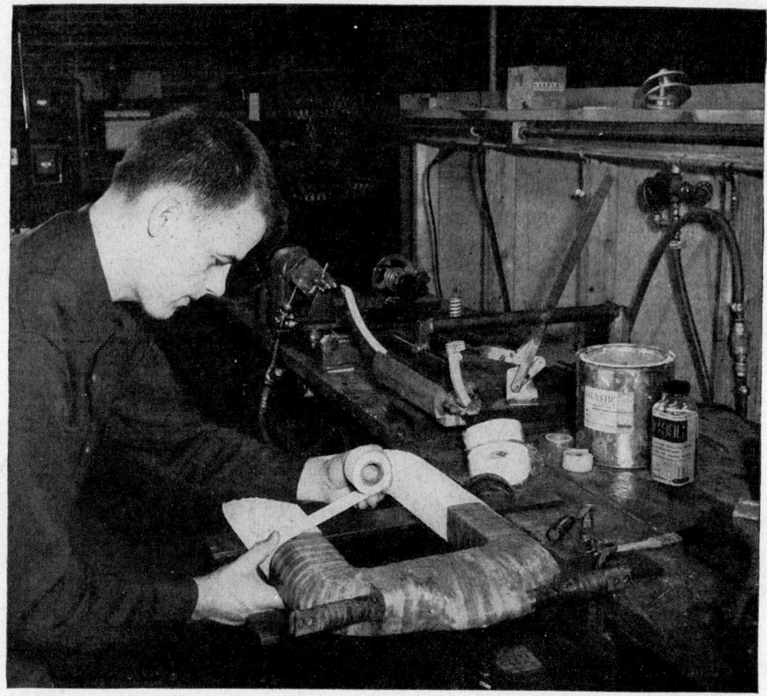

Winding silicone-rubber tape on a coil. This tape gives a resilient, moistureproof jacket with good dielectric properties, is serviceable to 180°C, and dissipates heat more rapidly than any other kind of resinous or mica insulation.

because of the high thermal conductivity of the silicone rubber. Similar effects are obtained when this material is applied to transformers, motors, and other electrical equipment.

It is a remarkable fact that wire coated with certain formulations of silicone rubber will maintain "integrity of circuit" even after exposure to direct flame for 15 min. The high inorganic content (about 90 per cent) of the rubber remains in a sufficiently coherent state to provide electrical insulation even after the organic part has been destroyed.

Silicone rubber that has been sponged has been used as a

cushioning material in the heat sealing of laminated bags, as a ring seal that may be highly compressed to stop leakage, and as a heat-insulating mounting for high-temperature apparatus.

Section 6:

"Bouncing Putty"

One of the first of the silicone products to come to the attention of the general public was "bouncing putty." This is a puttylike material with a peculiar combination of properties, for although it can be molded in the hand like putty, it also has surprising rebound when dropped on a hard surface; although it shows cold flow when left at rest, it can be shattered by a sudden blow; it can be drawn out into long plastic threads. In spite of its unusual combination of properties, however, this material remains relatively unimportant commercially.

"Bouncing putty" is prepared by mixing about 5 per cent of boric oxide with a dimethyl silicone and holding the mixture at 150°C (302°F) to 250°C (482°F) for some hours.[91] Other boron-containing compounds may be used, and fillers may be added to alter the properties.[92]

By adjustment of the amount of boron, the heating schedule, and the amount and type of filler the product may be made hard or soft, with high or low rebound (50 to 90 per cent regain from a drop), or slow or fast flow.

Unlike most of the silicone materials, "bouncing putty" is slowly disintegrated by water. It is slowly dissolved by acetone, low-molecular-weight alcohols, and ether. It swells in chlorinated solvents and in naphthenic hydrocarbons.

Suggested uses for "bouncing putty" include damping devices, sealing and filling compounds, and as an exerciser for crippled muscles. It has been widely distributed as a novelty under such names as "Silly Putty" or "Crazy Clay."

In spite of its lack of wide application at the moment, it would seem that the property of slow flow under mild pressure coupled with resiliency when dropped should find application in some industrial processes in the future.

CHAPTER THREE

Physiological Response to Silicones

Section 1: General Considerations

The growing commercial interest in silicones and their wide variety of applications has raised questions about their possible effect on those who handle them. Studies have been made using rabbits, rats, and guinea pigs to determine the effects of different polymers and intermediates when in contact with the skin or eyes, or when inhaled, ingested, or injected.[93,94]

A. *Polymers*

Following a comprehensive investigation, Rowe, Spencer, and Bass conclude that "the silicones (methyl, and mixed methyl and phenyl polysiloxanes) as a class are very low in toxicity and present no significant handling problems."[93] The validity of this conclusion is amply supported by practical experience. No cases are on record of any permanent physiological disturbance of those handling these materials in research, production, or use.

Silicone fluids representative of all the commercial types have been fed to animals over extended periods and in amounts far beyond any accidental consumption by a human. The only effect noted was a laxative action similar to that of mineral oil. The lack of solubility of the oil-soluble vitamins in the silicones makes them even more innocuous than the mineral oils.[94]

Application to the eye results in temporary irritation such as would be caused by the presence of any insoluble oily foreign body. Persons who have experienced it say that the eyes feel as though they had suffered from wind burn. Relief can be speeded up by washing the eye with water. In any event a night's sleep is usually sufficient to eliminate all discomfort.

No irritation has been noted when silicones have been applied to the skin of animals or humans. Men who have worked with these materials over a period of years report no trouble. Silicone fluids have, in fact, been prescribed as a component of a lotion to protect damaged skin against the action of water.

Many of these materials have been injected into experimental animals. The lack of reaction has been such that the silicone fluids have been suggested as nonaqueous vehicles for intramuscular administration of drugs.[95]

Because of the very high boiling point of most of the silicone polymers the effect of breathing the vapors is almost an academic question. However, some low-boiling siloxanes were investigated. The most volatile of these is hexamethyl disiloxane, $[(CH_3)_3Si]_2O$, with a boiling point of 99.5°C. Rats and guinea pigs exposed repeatedly for 7-hr periods to a concentration of 4,400 ppm showed no signs of discomfort or any aftereffects, although this concentration was distinctly disagreeable to humans. A saturated atmosphere (40,000 ppm) usually caused death in 15 to 20 min; deaths appeared to be due to respiratory failure.[93]

The desirability of using the silicone antifoam material in food products prompted investigations to determine the effect of feeding it to experimental animals.

In one investigation 50 rats were subjected to a 2-year feeding test, the feed containing 0.3 per cent of the silicone antifoam. This is about 1,000 times the average concentration likely to be encountered in ordinary usage. At the end of the experimental period the following conclusions were reached:

> Male and female rats (25 per group) that were maintained for two years on diets containing 0.0 (control) and 0.3 per cent "DC Antifoam A" showed no adverse effects as judged by growth, mortality, gross appearance and behavior, the results of periodic hematologic examinations, blood urea nitrogen, organ weights, hepatic lipid and the results of gross and microscopic examination of the tissues.[96]

A similar investigation was carried out using dogs as the experimental animals. The dogs were fed up to 3 g per kg of "DC Antifoam A" per day over a period of 6 months. The report concludes:

> From the results of this investigation it appears reasonable to assume that the traces of "DC Antifoam A" which may be absorbed from time to time by human subjects should prove to be entirely harmless. "DC Antifoam A" is used as an antifoaming agent in the processing of certain foods, drugs and cosmetics.[97]

B. *Intermediates*

The intermediates used in the preparation of silicones are usually the chlorosilanes or the ethoxysilanes.

The handling of the intermediates is largely the province of the silicone manufacturer, but a word about them may not be amiss.

The chlorosilanes react with water to form hydrochloric acid and can therefore cause extensive damage to parts of the body that are exposed to them. They are, in effect, volatile liquid acids and should be treated as such. Goggles or a face shield should be worn to protect the eyes when these materials are being handled. All handling should be done in hoods with adequate ventilation.

The ethoxysilanes react slowly with water to form ethyl alcohol. The action of these compounds on the skin is not at all comparable to that of the chlorosilanes, although continued application may cause a drying effect, due largely to extraction of fatty materials. The effect on the eye is irritating but transitory.

Although high concentrations of the vapors of the ethoxy compounds for extended periods can cause damage to the kidneys, the concentration required is so high that accidental exposure to dangerous amounts is all but impossible.

References to investigations on the intermediates will be found in the bibliography.[93,95,97–99]

Section 2: Applications in Pharmacy

The lack of physiological response to the silicones as a class has prompted investigations of the pharmaceutical uses of certain silicones, particularly the silicone fluids and compounds.

Consideration of possible uses may be approached from two directions: applications in manufacturing and laboratory procedures; applications to the body as a component of a pharmaceutical or medicinal material. Applications to the body will be discussed in Sec. 3.

Applications in Manufacturing and Laboratory Procedures

In pharmaceutical manufacture and distribution the silicones, because of their long-known water repellency, are now being used on glass ampoules and vials containing penicillin and similar aqueous suspensions or emulsions. The hydrophobic surface produced by the extremely thin layer of methyl silicone allows drainage from the sides of the vial. This results in greater economy and complete use of the penicillin and allows visual determination of the amount left in the container. Glass laboratory apparatus so treated gives better release of liquids, which results in more accurate transfer.[59]

In a similar way glassware for the handling of blood is treated with chlorosilanes to form a silicone surface treatment,[100] or a finished silicone polymer can be applied to the glass.[58,101] The clotting time of blood in treated vessels is considerably increased. This treatment is useful not only in flasks in which blood is handled, but also in glass tubes in which blood is transferred. Artificial kidneys have been constructed using silicone-coated rubber grids for supporting the dialyzing membrane.[102] Silicone rubber itself has also been used. The speed of coagulation of the blood is reduced to the point where large volumes may be passed through without danger to the patient.

The phenyl-methyl silicone fluids that are unusually heat stable have been described earlier (page 80). They have been used in the place of wax as lubricants for syringes. They do not decompose at the temperature of sterilization and the syringe continues to present a clean appearance.[103]

The same fluids are used as heat-transfer media in which surgical instruments can be sterilized and lubricated at the same time. They have very low volatility and so do not smoke at sterilizing temperature.[104]

The use of the dimethyl fluids as release agents in the molding of rubber and plastic articles has been described earlier. The same procedure may be followed in the preparation of hard gelatin capsules. Coating of the mold with the silicone fluid gives easier release with a consequent decrease in the number of rejects.

The resin used for the treatment of bread pans has been used as a coating on trays for drying gelatin and liver extracts. The product comes away from the tray freely.

Silicone-treated paper is available that does not allow adhesion of coated tapes. It may be useful as an interleaving sheet in tape rolls. The same paper has found a use as a "powder paper" for the mixing of finely divided solids. The powder does not stick and so gives better mixing and transfer.

The sterilizing of rubber stoppers often results in the stoppers' sticking together, necessitating separation by hand. A light spray of the fluid on the stoppers before autoclaving eliminates this trouble.

The silicone antifoams have been used with good effect in penicillin and chloromycetin cultures. There is some evidence to the effect that a silicone antifoam in combination with unsaturated acids of the oleic type is effective not only in eliminating the foam but in increasing the yield of penicillin.[105] While there are many compounds that will combat foam there are few, if any, that are active in as small concentrations as the silicone antifoam materials. They thus provide a minimum of contamination.

There are many places in the pharmaceutical laboratory where foam can be controlled successfully with a silicone antifoam agent. Such a simple matter as the distillation in a Kjeldahl determination is a case in point. The addition of a drop of a dilute solution of the silicone often eliminates a foam that otherwise makes the determination difficult. Fractional distillation at atmospheric or reduced pressure can be carried out with a minimum of foaming. The silicone remains with the charge because of its low vapor pressure.

An experimental procedure has been reported in which oxygen has been supplied to the blood artificially. The blood was by-passed through an oxygenator, and excess gas (or foam) which might have caused an embolism was removed by passing the blood through a bed of glass beads coated with a silicone antifoam agent.[106]

Protein extractions are at times very bothersome because of foaming. A drop of silicone antifoam material is often a help. The same principle applies in the homogenization of tissues or foaming material in an apparatus such as a Waring Blendor. In this case a thin smear of the silicone antifoam on the inside of the jar often proves sufficient to control foaming.

Foaming in the aeration of yeast fermentation and bacterial cultures can be controlled similarly.

A simple but effective application is found in the bottling process. Time and material can often be saved if foaming can be controlled.

The use of rubber in pharmaceutical work sometimes poses a problem because of the possible extraction of undesirable materials and also the difficulty of obtaining good heat sterilization. Silicone rubber contains no plasticizers, sulfur, or other materials commonly present in organic rubber. Extraction with solvents yields nothing but a very small quantity of low-molecular-weight silicone polymers. The rubber can be used as a sterilizable tubing or gasketing for bottle stoppers or for diaphragms.

Section 3:
Applications in Medicine

It may seem peculiar that such physiologically inert materials should be considered as useful when incorporated in medicinals or when applied on or in the body. The purpose of the present discussion is to point out where the silicones have been so applied and to draw attention to some peculiarities which have been observed but which have been given little study. One simple application is that of the silicone oil as a base for actors' grease paints. The same consistency is maintained regardless of temperature, so that the warmth of klieg lights does not introduce smearing or running.

Hand lotions containing silicone fluid have been prescribed. These are reported to be useful for those who have their hands in water to any great extent. The silicone does not rapidly emulsify with water and so forms a more permanent water-repellent film.

For a satisfactory "permanent" for the hair of Negroes, the first step is that of straightening. The hair can then be set as desired. But if the hair becomes wet the set is lost. One of the silicone materials originally used for developing water repellency of textiles has proved useful, when properly applied, in straightening hair. After the hair has been washed and dried it is treated with a dilute emulsion of the silicone. Combing with a hot comb brings about the straightening, following which the hair may be set as desired. It then resists the action of water and gives greater permanency to the set.

For the treatment of skin affections by the petrolatum-like silicone compounds, early reports were quite at variance. Some reports suggested that they were superior to petrolatum, while others considered them to be no better and at the same time more expensive. A recent report declares that when a silicone oil was mixed with a petrolatum base the product was effective in controlling a large number of cases that failed to respond to currently accepted forms of therapy. These cases (totaling 61) were colostomy drainage, diaper rash, decubitus ulcer, fissured lips, etc. Of the 61 that failed to respond to other forms of treatment, 58 were controlled by the silicone-petrolatum salve.[107] Further studies of this form of treatment should be rewarding.

In dental work an antibiotic silicone paste for root-canal therapy has been developed by Dr. L. I. Grossman of the School of Dentistry, University of Pennsylvania. A low-viscosity silicone fluid is used as the carrier of the reagents. The low volatility of the silicone oil, its physiological inertness, and its lack of water solubility are factors that are useful in this case and could possibly be of value in more varied applications.[108]

The silicone antifoam has been used as a treatment for "bloat," or tympanites, in cattle. A suspension of the silicone is either injected directly into the rumen or given with water by drench or stomach tube. It is reported to give quick relief by breaking the froth within the ruminal food mass.[73]

The suggestion has been made that the silicone antifoam might be useful in treating extreme cases of lobar pneumonia. In the hope of breaking the tough froth that develops in the lungs, physiological saline solution is sometimes used; it seems possible that the silicone antifoam, which is active in extremely low concentrations, could be helpful in a similar way.[109] An emulsion of silicone antifoam injected into the bronchii of experimental animals has been shown to be remarkably effective in breaking the froth produced during pulmonary edema, and preliminary trials have shown that an antifoam spray may be effective in the treatment of pulmonary edema in patients.[110] There is the possibility that the silicone antifoam could also be introduced as an aerosol in the oxygen being breathed by the patient.

When given orally the silicone fluids appear to be largely recovered in the feces. As they are poor solvents they do not affect the oil-soluble vitamins A, D, E, and K and could serve in lieu of mineral oils.[94]

The most intriguing problem, perhaps because it is the least understood, is that of the action and fate of silicone fluids when they are injected into the body.

The fluids have been injected intradermally, intramuscularly, and intraperitoneally. It is of great interest to note that "intradermal, subcutaneous and intramuscular injections given one of us gave none of the usual stinging or aching sensation at the site of the inoculation."[94] "Certain drugs injected intramuscularly in such fluids exert systemic effects within one minute. Animals injected (0.1 cc./kg.) in a single area three times per week for a period of two months showed no clinical signs of pain or muscle injury."[111] In another case

Subcutaneous injection of seven liquid silicones and one sample of mineral oil in doses of 0.1 ml. were made in designated areas on the back of a rabbit. At autopsy, 13 days after treatment, the treated areas were examined grossly with the following results: (1) The hexamethyldisiloxane (low molecular weight silicone) produced a marked irritation and necrosis; (2) the mineral oil resulted in the formation of a large plaque of connective tissue with slight discoloration but no necrosis; (3) the other six polysiloxanes caused no apparent effects; in fact, there were no remaining indications that the injections had been made.[112]

Intraperitoneal injections of the nonvolatile silicones given rats in doses as high as 10 ml per kg gave a reaction typical of that to a nonirritating foreign body. Nodules containing the fluids appeared in the omental tissue and on the surface of the liver, spleen, and diaphragm. There was no inflammation in any instance.[94]

Concerning intravenous injection the statement is found that "The intravenous administration of such fluids in rabbits sometimes results in death, possibly because of fluid embolism."[111] To quote another case:

Five mice received 13 intravenous injections of 0.5 cc. of a suspension of silicone fluid in a dextrose-acacia solution. None of these animals showed any recognizable evidence of embolism or other adverse reaction. (It has not been fully determined as yet the amount and viscosity of the silicones necessary to induce embolic formation; nor has the fate of the I.V. administered silicone been determined.) The examination of the granulocytes showed no depression, nor jaundice nor other signs of heptatic impairment, the result of siloxemia. However, a curious phenomenon was observed, namely, that the blood cells, in contact with silicone fluid, became completely surrounded by a thin film of the fluid with more or less interference with the rouleaux formation of the RBC; though there does not appear to be any significant interference in their oxygen uptake nor CO_2 release.[94]

Although these latter findings are of great interest, no active investigations are known to be under way to determine their true value. The coating of the blood cells suggests that bacteria and other microorganisms might accept a similar film with unpredictable results.

The findings that have been quoted suggest that there is a very fertile field for further investigation. The use of silicone fluids for the protection and healing of skin has been indicated. Their lack of reaction when injected into the body suggests that they might be useful as carriers for medicinals. An understanding of the action of these low-surface-tension fluids when placed in the blood stream could possibly open up new methods of approach to the treatment of blood disorders.

CHAPTER FOUR

Applications of Silicones to Specific Industries and Cost Considerations

---

The statement has been made earlier that silicones find a use in almost any industry one can name. A complete description of each use would be far beyond the scope of this book, and in fact no attempt has been made to do more than give illustrative examples from different industries. But the question may be raised as to how silicones can be applied to a particular process or industry. To answer this question the following tabulation has been prepared in which industries, together with their known silicone applications, are listed. Industry classifications are arranged alphabetically. Specific silicone applications are then arranged under functional subheadings.

Commercial Applications for Silicones

I. In the Chemical and Allied Industries

A. As additives in

1. Cosmetic creams and hair dressings

2. Paints to prevent flooding
3. Polishes for automobiles, furniture, and glass
4. Various textile chemicals, such as crease-resistant finishes

B. As defoamers in

1. Adhesives and glues
2. Alkyd, phenolic, and urea-formaldehyde resins; rosins and naval stores
3. Cleaners, synthetic detergents, soaps, and glycerin
4. Colors and dyes; inks and pigment grinds
5. Drawing compounds
6. Laboratory distillation and analyses
7. Oils, including cottonseed, linseed, soya, and tall oils, especially during esterification
8. Paints, varnishes, and lacquers
9. Paper chemicals
10. Pharmaceuticals, including chloromycetin, penicillin, streptomycin, and veterinary medicines
11. Photographic solutions
12. Rubbers, especially butadiene-styrene copolymers and both natural and synthetic latices
13. Tannery chemicals and leather dressings
14. Textile chemicals
15. Waxes and wax emulsions
16. Various organic and inorganic chemicals, including antifreeze agents, carboxymethyl cellulose, caustic soda, furfural, sodium bromide, and products of wood distillation

C. As electrical insulating materials for

1. Electric motors exposed to overloads, to high ambient temperatures, or to excessive moisture or corrosive atmospheres. Typical applications: motors driving centrifugal wheels, condensate pumps, cranes and conveyors, fans and blowers, mixing machines, and motors in reversing service

2. Solenoid coils
3. Dry-type distribution transformers
4. Lead wire and cable for electric motors, electric ovens and furnaces, and lighting fixtures exposed to weathering and continuous operation

D. As gaskets, seals, and diaphragms

1. Silicone rubber, unsupported or reinforced with glass cloth or woven wire, is used where resilience and flexibility must be retained at temperatures above or below the limits withstood by organic rubber
2. Silicone-rubber pastes are used as heat-stable and resilient calking and sealing materials

E. As lubricants for

1. Ball bearings in conveyor systems, motors, and process equipment exposed to high or low temperatures
2. Ceramic and glass stopcocks and valves
3. Instruments and gauges under extreme temperature conditions
4. Pressure-lubricated valves and flow-meter bearings operating at high or low temperatures and in contact with a wide variety of corrosive chemicals
5. Studs and bolts to prevent seizure

F. As polishing agents for

Automobiles, furniture, and glass

G. As protective coatings for

1. Stacks and mufflers
2. Boilers, heaters, process equipment, sterilizer racks, ovens, outdoor signs, and other metal surfaces exposed to high temperatures or to humid and corrosive atmospheres

H. As release agents

1. Compounds, fluids, or resins are used to keep materials from sticking to process equipment
2. Applied to paper for use as interleaving sheets and for handling pill powders

I. As vehicles in formulating

1. Heat-stable, weather-resistant coatings
2. Phosphorescent, fluorescent, and silk-screen paints

J. As water repellents for

1. Treating above-grade masonry walls
2. Formulating water-repellent treatments for
   a. Masonry
   b. Leather
   c. Synthetic fabrics and blends
3. Treating glassware, including vials for pharmaceuticals

K. Other applications

1. As dewebbing agents for synthetic latices
2. As a high-temperature bath where maximum stability and life justify a higher initial investment
3. As a high-vacuum diffusion-pump fluid
4. As ointment bases and carriers for medicinals

II. In the Concrete, Cement, and Related Industries

A. As electrical insulating materials

For motors exposed to overloads, to high ambient temperatures, or to excessive moisture or corrosive atmospheres. Typical applications: motors driving crushers, cranes, conveyors

B. As release agents for

1. Ceramic tile
2. Gypsum

C. As water repellents

For above-grade masonry

III. In the Construction Industry

A. As defoamers for

Asphalt applied to highways

B. As electrical insulating materials for

1. Electric motors exposed to overloads, to high ambient temperatures, or to excessive moisture or corrosive atmospheres. Typical applications: crane motors, power-tool motors
2. Lead wire and cable (silicone-rubber insulation)
3. Outdoor switches (silicone compound)

C. As protective coatings for

Weather resistance on exposed wood surfaces

D. As water repellents for

1. Cement-asbestos roofing and siding
2. Masonry constructions
3. Precast concrete slabs
4. Terrazzo floors

IV. In the Electrical and Electronic Industries

A. As coatings to maintain high surface resistivity on

1. Fluorescent light tubes
2. Geophysical instruments
3. Glass and ceramic insulator bodies
4. Resistors

B. As damping media

1. Dashpot fluids for electrical instruments and switches, gauges, phonograph pickups, amplifiers, solenoids, circuit breakers, gyroscopes, and accelerometers
2. Silicone-rubber pistons to damp the operation of ejector mechanisms in electric toasters

C. As defoamers in

1. Insulating resins and varnishes
2. Wiredrawing solutions

D. As electrical insulating materials

1. Bonding resins for electrical components such as
   a. Carbon resistors
   b. Calrod-unit insulation

    c. Flexible and rigid silicone-mica and silicone-mica-glass combinations
    d. Light-bulb bases and sealed-beam headlights
    e. Powdered iron cores in radio and television sets
    f. Printed electronic circuits
    g. Rigid silicone-glass laminates for panel board, slot wedges, cores, tubes, and spacers
2. Coating and impregnating varnishes for
    a. Asbestos paper and cloth
    b. Glass cloth and tape, sleeving and tying cord
    c. Glass-served magnet wire
    d. Capacitors and condensors
    e. Induction-heating coils
    f. Magnets
    g. Motors and generators
    h. Resistors
    i. Solenoids
    j. Transformers
    k. Wire and cable
3. Dielectric sealing compound for
    a. Aircraft engine electrical control systems
    b. Battery terminals
    c. Disconnect junctions in electronic equipment
    d. Geophysical instruments
    e. Ignition systems of aircraft, automobiles, marine and stationary engines, ordnance vehicles
    f. Junction boxes
    g. Switch gear and pole-top disconnect switches
    h. Terminal insulation of high-voltage connections on oscilloscopes and on cathode-ray and television tubes
    i. Variable-inductance rollers on transmitter-receiver sets
    j. Watt-hour meter terminals
4. Liquid dielectrics in
    a. Capacitors

   b. Condensers
   c. Small transformers
   d. Thermostats
5. Molding compounds for
   Brush holders and other electrical parts used in instruments, induction heaters, and switches
6. Silicone rubber for
   a. Bushings for capacitors and transformers
   b. Embedding resistance heating elements, subminiature electronic parts, and printed circuits
   c. Insulated wire and cable for inaccessible or critical exterior lighting fixtures, electric furnaces, motors, naval control systems, transformers, ovens, and other equipment exposed to high ambient or operating temperatures
   d. Paste for potting and calking electrical equipment
   e. Semivulcanized, glass-reinforced tape for winding traction-motor field coils and other coils exposed to high temperatures and excessive vibration, moisture, or contamination

E. As lubricants for

1. Appliances, such as electric clocks and timers, razors, toasters, and dishwashing machines
2. Ball bearings of electric motors
3. Bearings in oven conveyor systems and fans
4. Circuit breakers and other switch gear
5. Electrical instruments, meter bearings and gears, and other measuring devices
6. Gears in carbon arc lamps
7. Impregnating graphite bearings
8. Radio and television antennas and tuners
9. Reducing abrasion and friction in rubber seals
10. Small synchronous motors
11. Solenoids
12. Terminal and junction box threads
13. Valves and regulators

14. Variable condensers
15. Variac transformers

F. As protective coatings for

1. Heaters, ovens, stacks, and stoves
2. Motors and other equipment exposed to high temperatures

G. As release agents for

1. Coil forms
2. Die-cast rotors and other parts
3. Plastic electrical parts and laminates
4. Waffle-iron grids
5. Wire-splicing molds

H. As rubbery gaskets, seals, and mechanical parts for

1. Appliances such as domestic steam irons and toasters
2. Boots to protect automobile spark plugs and aircraft and ordnance switches exposed to extreme operating temperatures
3. Floodlights, searchlights, and sealed-beam lights
4. Use as molds in casting solenoid coils
5. Wipers in tin-plating wire

I. Miscellaneous applications

1. Additive to increase moisture resistance of wax impregnants
2. Diffusion-pump fluids for evacuating radio and television tubes and electron microscopes
3. Fluid as a protective coating for phonograph records
4. Masking compound in soldering joints
5. Rubber to cushion radio and television tubes

V. In the Fabricated Products Industries

A. As defoamers in

1. Caustic solutions for reclaiming tin
2. Cutting and cooling oils
3. Paint spray booths
4. Plating solutions

B. As electrical insulating materials for

1. Electric motors exposed to overloads, high ambient temperatures, and excessive moisture or corrosive atmospheres. Typical examples: lift-truck motors, machine- and hand-tool motors
2. Lead wire and cable on motors and equipment described in (1) above

C. As lubricants for

1. Can-soldering equipment
2. Conveyor systems
3. Oven fans
4. Pump packing for chemical service
5. Regulators and switches
6. Valves on chemical, steam, and gas service

D. As protective coatings for

1. Radiant-heating panels
2. Space heaters
3. Stoves

E. As release agents for

1. Shell process
2. Casting ferrous and nonferrous metals
3. Bakery pans, cooking utensils, and waffle grids

F. As rubber gaskets, seals, and diaphragms for

1. Calking commercial refrigeration units
2. Processing equipment
3. Shell dump box
4. Valves

G. Miscellaneous

1. As soldering flux
2. As nonadhesive resilient rolls

VI. In the Food and Related Industries

A. As defoamers in

1. Flavor concentrates, wines, and beverages
2. Brine used for cooling

3. Dehydrating foods
4. Edible oils
5. Molasses and sugar
6. Preserves and confections
7. Rendering animal fats
8. Vacuum evaporation of milk

B. As electrical insulating materials for

1. Electric motors and solenoid coils exposed to overloads or high ambient temperatures and to excessive moisture or corrosive atmospheres
2. Lead wire and cable for electric motors and ovens

C. As lubricants for

1. Ball bearings in motors, oven conveyor systems, and process equipment, such as bottling machines, where the cost of relubrication and down time justifies the higher initial cost of silicone lubricants
2. Ceramic and glass stopcocks and valves
3. Packing glands on tanks and kettles
4. Pressure-lubricated valves operating at high or low temperatures and in contact with such materials as hot extracts, vegetable oils, hot water and steam at sterilizing temperatures
5. Wheels of dollies handling cans in cooking ovens

D. As protective coatings for

Boilers, heaters, process equipment, stacks, sterilizer racks, ovens, and other metal surfaces exposed to high temperatures or to humid and corrosive atmospheres or outdoor weathering

E. As release agents

1. In the form of resins for glazing
   a. Bread, bun, and cake pans
   b. Meatloaf pans
   c. Trays for frozen foods
2. In the form of fluids or compounds for coating
   a. Containers and conveyors used in the process-cooking and drying of foods and confections

b. Heat-sealing bars and irons

3. In the form of treated paper for

a. "Brown-and-serve" rolls

b. Confections

c. Sweet rolls

VII. In the Leather Industry

A. As additives

In shoe dressing

B. As defoamers

For adhesives, dyes, and finishes

C. As impregnants and coatings to

1. Increase the mar resistance of luggage
2. Improve the heat resistance of gaskets and diaphragms

D. As release agents for

1. Shoe soles and heels
2. Vinyl leather coatings

E. As water repellents

VIII. In the Mining Industry

A. As electrical insulating materials for

Electric motors exposed to overloads, high ambient temperatures, and excessive moisture or corrosive atmospheres. Typical applications: crane and hoist motors, conveyor motors, and other motors used in mines

B. As lubricants for

Electric-motor ball bearings

C. As dielectric, water-repellent compounds for

1. Equipment exposed to high humidity
2. Geophysical equipment and oil-well instruments

IX. In the Nonelectrical Machinery Industry

A. As damping media in

1. Aircraft, automobile, tractor instruments

2. Draft injectors
3. Scales and balances
4. Automotive torsional vibration dampers
5. Aircraft motor-cooling fins

B. As defoamers for

Lubricating oils

C. As electrical insulating materials for

1. Electric motors exposed to overloads, high ambient temperatures, and excessive moisture or corrosive atmospheres. Typical applications: lift-truck motors and motors driving grinders, tapping machines, boring machines, thread cutters, electric hammers, drilling machines, turret lathes, sanders, welders
2. Induction-heating coils

D. As lubricants for

1. Bearings in motors driving machinery exposed to high ambient temperatures or humid or corrosive atmosphere
2. Conveyors
3. Impregnating gaskets and packing
4. Oil-field equipment
5. Oven-door hinges
6. Oven fans
7. Steam swivel joints
8. Textile machinery
9. Valves and fittings

E. As protective coatings for

Equipment exposed to high temperatures. Typical applications: conveyors, space heaters, furnaces, and ovens

F. As gaskets and seals for

1. Chemical-processing equipment
2. Compressors
3. Valves (diaphragms)

G. Miscellaneous

1. As sight-glass fluids

2. As pressure plates on heat-sealing equipment
3. To prevent oxidation of solder

X. In the Paper Industries

A. As a nonstick coating for

1. Fabricated paper products
2. Paper and fiber board used in handling and packaging such items as adhesive tape, baked sweet goods, asphalt and tar, wax and rubber
3. Heat-sealing irons, calender rolls, and pulp shredders

B. As defoamers for

1. Glues, sizes, and coatings
2. Pulp slurries and black waste liquor
3. Printing inks, carbon-paper coatings, and hot melt-wax coatings

C. As lubricants for

Bond-sealing machines and chain drives

D. As protective coatings for

Flues and stacks exposed to corrosive gases

E. As water repellents for

Paper and fabricated paper products

F. Miscellaneous

As pressure pads on heat-sealing equipment

XI. In the Petroleum and Coal Industries

A. As defoamers for

1. Oils and greases
2. Asphalt and tars
3. Waxes
4. Petrochemicals

B. As instrument-damping media for

Galvanometers, geophones, and other geophysical instruments

C. As protective coatings for

Stacks, exhausts, storage tanks, and refinery flues

D. As release agents for

1. Treating paper liners used in packaging asphalt, waxes, and greases
2. Manufacturing asphalt tile

E. Miscellaneous

As a compound dielectric and water repellent for seismographic equipment

XII. In the Primary Metal Industries

A. As defoamers in

1. Galvanizing tanks
2. Pickling solutions

B. As electrical insulating materials for

1. Motors driving rolling mills
2. Cupola hoists
3. Cranes
4. Blowers
5. Grinders
6. Other electric motors exposed to high ambient temperatures and excessive moisture or corrosive atmospheres

C. As lubricants for

1. Conveyors
2. Electric-furnace sliding guides
3. Motor bearings
4. Pump and valve packing

D. As protective coatings for

1. Aluminum foil
2. Fabricated metal structural pieces
3. Identification markings on welding rod

E. As release agents for

1. Centrifugal casting
2. Die-casting
3. "Lost-wax" process
4. Pattern-wash additives
5. Precision-investment casting

6. Sand cores
7. Saws used in cutting magnesium
8. Shell process

F. Miscellaneous

As an adhesive for metal foil

XIII. In the Printing and Publishing Industries

A. As defoamers for

1. Paper coatings
2. Printing inks

B. As release agents for

Engraving and printing plates

C. Miscellaneous

To prevent blocking of printing inks

XIV. In the Professional and Scientific Instruments Industry

A. As lubricants for

1. Glass joints of laboratory equipment
2. Hydrometer bearings
3. Precision instruments
4. Surgical and dental instruments
5. Watches, clocks, and timers

B. Miscellaneous

1. To damp engineering instruments
2. As diffusion-pump oils
3. To fill sight gauges
4. As oil sterilizer, temperature-bath fluids
5. As gaskets and seals

XV. In the Rubber Industry

A. As defoamers in

1. The manufacture of "cold" rubber
2. Latex
3. Foam-rubber salvage and other rubber-reclaiming processes

4. Cleaners and soaps

B. As lubricants for

1. Steam-line valves
2. Neoprene and rayon cord driers
3. Vulcanizer cart wheels
4. Press hold-down bolts
5. Tire bags and molds

C. As electrical insulation for

Class H motors on tread cutters, Banbury mixers, and scrap cutters

D. As release agents for

1. Molded goods, tires, tile, shoe soles and heels, and foam rubber
2. Mandrel-wrapped hose and tubing
3. Mills, calender rolls, Bag-O-Matic presses
4. Hot rolls handling rubberized fabrics
5. Recapping molds

E. As stocks in

1. The fabrication of silicone-rubber parts
2. Coating wire, cable, and fabrics
3. The production of electrical insulating tape and cloth

F. Miscellaneous

1. As antiwebbing agents
2. As plasticizers for natural and synthetic rubber
3. As coating for fabricated parts to provide weather resistance and improve appearance
4. As impregnating fluids for press pads
5. As a nonstick coating for interleaving paper

XVI. In the Stone, Clay, Glass, and Glass-product Industries

A. As lubricants for

1. Glass-handling equipment, *e.g.*, oven conveyors, lehrs, burn-off machines
2. Impregnating asbestos packing and gaskets

3. Joints of glass laboratory equipment
4. Pottery-kiln carts

B. As protective coatings for

1. Flat glass
2. Fluorescent tubes

C. As release agents for

1. Ceramic tile
2. Clay sewer pipe from forming machines
3. Glass cloth laminates
4. Glass cloth from mandrels
5. Glass molding
6. Gypsum molds
7. Pottery from plaster molds
8. Treating glass containers for antibiotics and other medicinals and glass medical equipment

D. As water repellents for

1. Ceramic insulators
2. Glass block mortar joints
3. Glass cloth and fibers
4. Monuments
5. Outdoor reflector signs

E. Miscellaneous

1. As diffusion-pump fluids for evacuating radio and television tubes
2. As polishing agents for glass
3. As impregnants for graphite glass-tube flaring wheels
4. To bond glass cloth to glass radiant-heater panels
5. In handling hot glass during fabrication, *e.g.*, "up-draw" wheels, chucks, gripper fingers, tubing, coated gloves, conveyor parts
6. As an interleaver to prevent grinding wheels from sticking together during curing

XVII. In the Textile Industry

A. As coatings in the manufacture of

1. Weather-resistant awnings

2. Tent sections to be used adjacent to stove pipes
3. Conveyor belts operating at high temperatures and handling sticky materials

B. As defoamers for

1. Bleaching solutions
2. Latex coatings
3. Printing pastes
4. Textile-finishing agents
5. Vat dyes
6. Washing solutions

C. As electrical insulation for

1. Spinner-bucket motors
2. Dye-house motors

D. As lubricants for

1. Extruding and sewing synthetic threads
2. Nylon parachute cloth
3. Processing equipment—tenter frames, drying cans, sanforizing equipment, motors, and fans (operating near ovens)

E. As water repellents in

1. Formulations
2. Treating synthetic fabrics such as acetates, nylon, Orlon, Dacron, dynel, rayon, and synthetic mouton

F. Miscellaneous

1. As slip agents for cotton yarns
2. As nonstick agents for textile-coating equipment

XVIII. In the Transportation, Public Utilities, and Communication Industries

A. As damping media for

1. Instruments
2. Torsional vibration dampers
3. Aircraft-engine-cooling fins

B. As defoamers in

1. Asphalt distillation

2. Sewage disposal plants
3. Hydraulic, transmission, and lubricating oils

C. As dielectric and water-repellent media or treatment for

1. Aircraft, automotive ignition systems, and electronic equipment
2. Aircraft-fuel-transmitter head gauges
3. Glass and ceramic insulators
4. Junction boxes

D. As electrical insulation for

1. Ignition wire and Navy cable
2. Motors, generators, and transformers for aircraft and shipboard use
3. Induction-heating coils
4. Diesel-electric locomotive-motor armatures and coils
5. Aircraft communication equipment
6. Power equipment, motors, generators, transformers

E. As gaskets and seals on

1. Automotive fluid-drive transmissions
2. Diesel cylinder liners, waterports, and air coolers
3. Ordnance vehicle carburetors and air cleaners
4. Jet engines
5. Aircraft-engine rocker boxes and push rods
6. Oil separators on spark plugs and instruments
7. Truck and bus tire valves

F. As lubricants on

1. High-temperature conveyors
2. Motors in aircraft and on shipboard
3. Fan motors operating at high temperatures
4. Automobile door and trunk locks
5. Automobile speedometer cables
6. Switch gears, bomb-bay rack mechanisms, and gyrobearings
7. Automobile-starter ignition switches, radio antennas
8. Rubber seals and instruments

9. Control valves
10. Automobile window channels
11. Synchronous motors and control devices

G. As protective coatings for

1. Ship stacks and boilers
2. Jet-engine turbine blades
3. Automotive and aircraft exhausts
4. Strain gauges

H. As water repellents for

1. Masonry buildings
2. Outdoor reflector signs
3. Treating lineman's "hot sticks," gloves, belts, etc.

I. Miscellaneous

1. As polish agents
2. In automotive polishes
3. As antisqueak coatings for rubber parts on automobile bodies
4. As scuff preventives in planishing operations
5. As antiseize materials for magnesium assemblies and on automotive and aircraft head bolts
6. To improve weather resistance of automotive weather stripping and other exposed rubber parts

XIX. In the Wood Industry

A. As defoamers for

1. Pentachlorophenol wood preservative, creosote, and oil
2. Wood-tar distillation
3. Glues and waste liquors
4. Paint spray booths

B. As electrical insulation

For power tools and kiln motors

C. As lubricants

For kiln carts

D. As polishing agents

Used on finished furniture

E. As release agents

1. On cauls, loaders, gluers, splicers, and saws
2. On press platens for plywood and hardwood

XX. In Miscellaneous Manufacturing Industries

A. As defoamers for

Calcium chloride brine-circulating system in ice plants

B. As lubricants for

1. Clocks and timers
2. Diastats
3. Electric razors
4. Electric-sign controls
5. Fishing reels
6. Hypodermic needles
7. Movie film
8. Movie projectors and cameras
9. Parking meters
10. Plastic extruders
11. Recording instruments

C. As release agents for

1. Die-cast costume jewelry
2. Glass fishing rods and laminates
3. Plastic calender and embossing rolls
4. Plastic moldings

D. As water repellents for

1. Fish flies and lines
2. Furs and mouton
3. Plastic aeration tubes

E. Miscellaneous

1. As constant-temperature-bath fluids
2. As diffusion-pump fluids
3. As instrument bubble-chamber fluids

4. As belts for handling plastic in vacuum-forming operation
5. As gaskets, diaphragms, and seals for instruments, gauges, regulators
6. As rubber molds for casting resins
7. As rubber press pads for forming decorative plastic laminates

Cost Considerations

In comparison with most materials used by industry, silicones are high in price per pound, but the fact that the market for them is constantly expanding is evidence that their use brings about more economical operation. The increased volume of production, coupled with improved methods of manufacture, has resulted in a steady decline in price since silicones were first introduced. Figure 19 shows the price of a basic silicone material, dimethyl siloxane fluid, over the period 1942 to 1952. For comparison, curves for the percentage change in the price of all commodities and for chemicals alone are shown for the same period. It will be noted that the price of the silicone fluid dropped from $6.80 per pound in 1942 to $3.80 in 1952. The price of $3.80 may be considered as a median price for all silicone products, with a low of about $2 and a high of about $6 per pound.

There is reason to believe that the slope of this price curve will continue, and that constantly lower prices will obtain even if the general price level should continue to rise.

In attempting to decide if the use of a silicone would be economical in a certain application there are three points that are helpful to bear in mind:

1. In some cases a silicone can do a job that no other material can do: *e.g.*, it provides a rubbery material that is

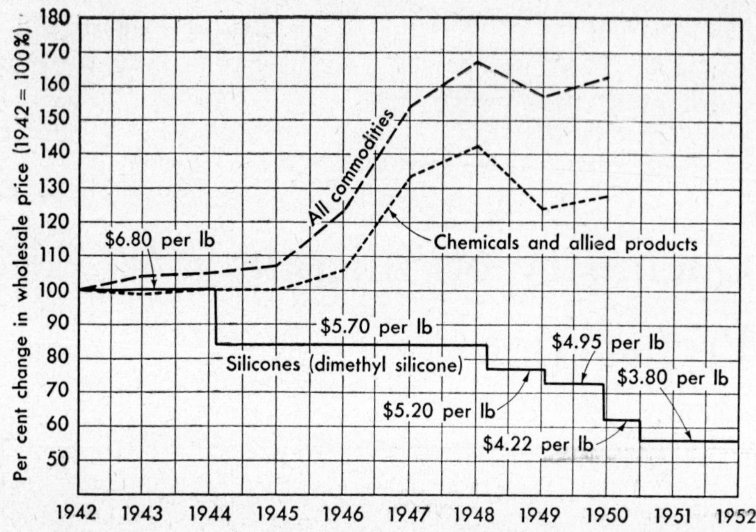

FIGURE 19 Per cent change in wholesale prices, 1942–1952.

flexible and stable at both −75°C (−100°F) and 250°C (482° F).

2. Silicones often provide much longer life than other available materials: *e.g.*, silicone electrical insulation (class H) gives 10 to 100 times the life of class B insulation.

3. Only small amounts of silicone may be required: *e.g.*, silicone antifoams are required in such small amounts that they frequently show the lowest cost per gallon defoamed.

The use of a silicone will not necessarily be indicated for all problems for which it may be considered. But it will frequently be found that the cost of the silicone is inconsequential in view of the better or more continuous operation possible, the small amount required, or the improved design that can be used.

CHAPTER FIVE

Chemistry of Silicone Preparation

Section 1: Definitions and Nomenclature

A silicone may be defined for the purposes of this book as a compound containing the elements silicon and oxygen and organic groups, the silicon being present in sufficient amount to affect the properties measurably. Of course, there are borderline cases where the effect of silicon is small, but the discussion of such cases may be left for more academic treatises. By and large the above definition suffices for our present purpose.

The word "silicone" originally meant a compound in which silicon was present and in which each silicon atom was surrounded by two oxygens and two carbon groups. As the study of these materials expanded, the word gradually took on a wider meaning, becoming a generic term rather than a specific one.

A nomenclature has been developed to simplify the naming of silicon-containing compounds, and an understanding of the method of naming the smaller units will greatly simplify the further discussion.

All compounds containing only one silicon atom can be described as "silanes" of some sort. If only hydrogens are present on the silicon, giving SiH_4, the compound is known simply as "silane." If one chlorine is present in place of one of the hydrogens to give SiH_3Cl the compound is known as "chlorosilane." The presence of four chlorine atoms results in $SiCl_4$ or "tetrachlorosilane."

If two silicons are united in a molecule, such as $H_3Si—SiH_3$, the compound is known as a "disilane." Similarly we may have trisilanes, tetrasilanes, etc., or polysilanes.

Now, if two or more silicons are present in a molecule and they are separated from one another by some other atom, the name "silane" is altered to describe the character of this new linkage. If the silicons are separated by an oxygen

$$\begin{array}{ccccc} & | & & | & \\ — & Si & —O— & Si & — \\ & | & & | & \end{array}$$

the compound is known as a "sil-ox-ane." This, by the way, is the characteristic structure found in most silicones. Other types are as follows:

$$\begin{array}{ccccccc} & | & & | & & | & \\ — & Si & — & N & — & Si & — \\ & | & & & & | & \end{array} \qquad \text{Sil-az-ane}$$

$$\begin{array}{ccccccc} & | & & | & & | & \\ — & Si & — & C & — & Si & — \\ & | & & | & & | & \end{array} \qquad \text{Sil-carb-ane}$$

The type that will interest us most is that of the siloxanes. Nomenclature here is similar to that of the silanes, for if two silicons are separated by an oxygen

$$\begin{array}{ccccc} & | & & | & \\ — & Si & —O— & Si & — \\ & | & & | & \end{array}$$

the compound is known as a "disiloxane." Where three silicons are similarly separated

$$-\overset{|}{\underset{|}{\mathrm{Si}}}-\mathrm{O}-\overset{|}{\underset{|}{\mathrm{Si}}}-\mathrm{O}-\overset{|}{\underset{|}{\mathrm{Si}}}-$$

the compound is known as a "trisiloxane." Where there are many such groupings present the compound is known as a "polysiloxane."

The silicones of commerce—the fluids, greases, resins, and rubbers—are polysiloxanes. The nature of the silicone is dependent on the types of silanes used. The silanes, in turn, have the properties they possess as a result of the types of groupings that have replaced the hydrogens in silane, SiH_4. So if we are to understand how the silicones are made or why they act as they do, we must first see how the silanes are made

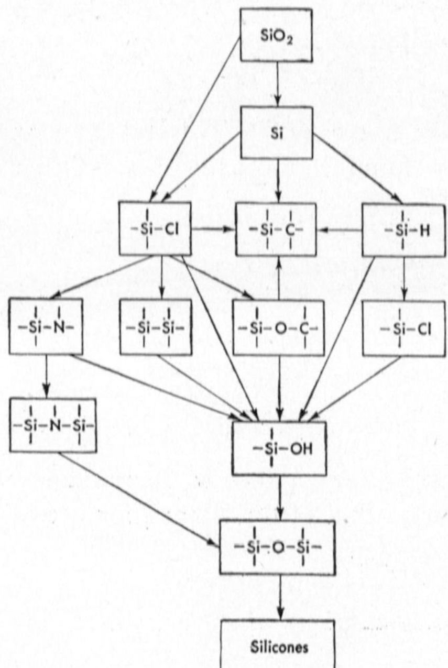

FIGURE 20
Steps in silicone preparation.

and what properties are conferred by different groupings present. The methods of preparation and the properties of the groupings on silicon comprise the subject matter of this chapter.

The "flow sheet" (Fig. 20) is a diagrammatic outline of the method that will be followed in the discussion. It will be noted that the starting point is silicon dioxide, SiO_2. Reaction to convert this into a volatile and reactive compound containing chlorine, hydrogen, or carbon is necessary to obtain materials that can be further reacted to the point where they show properties that are of commercial significance. Halogens other than chlorine would react equally well in most cases, but they are more expensive and have little or no advantage.

Section 2:

Synthesis of Intermediates

A. Preparation and Properties of Silicon

The first step toward the formation of a silicone is the preparation of elemental silicon.

Silicon itself never occurs free in nature but is commonly found in the form of its oxide, SiO_2, as sand, or as a constituent of quartz rock. The oxide is reduced to elemental silicon by being heated in the presence of carbon in an electric furnace:

$$SiO_2 + 2C \rightarrow Si + 2CO$$

With an excess of carbon, silicon carbide or Carborundum is formed:

$$SiO_2 + 3C \rightarrow SiC + 2CO$$

Silicon is generally seen as a gray-black solid with a metallic luster. It has a density of 2.42 and melts at 1,420°C.

Although very inert at ordinary temperatures, it combines with oxygen readily at elevated temperatures. For this reason it is widely used in the steel industry as a deoxidizer. As an alloying additive it imparts corrosion-resistant properties to iron and to aluminum.

The so-called "amorphous" silicon, actually a very finely divided crystalline brown powder, is prepared by heating sand and magnesium powder, the products being silicon, magnesium silicide, Mg_2Si, and magnesium oxide. The latter two compounds may be removed by treatment with acid.

B. Silicon Compounds Containing Chlorine

1. Preparation

After the preparation of silicon the next step toward the formation of a silicone is that of converting the element to a compound containing chlorine.

There are two methods of doing this, the first of which may use silicon dioxide rather than silicon. This method provides compounds that contain only chlorine and silicon. The second method produces compounds containing hydrogen and carbon as well as chlorine and silicon. Each method has its advantages, depending on the type of product to be produced finally.

The first commercial method results in the formation of silicon tetrachloride, $SiCl_4$. This compound was first prepared by Berzelius in 1824 shortly after his isolation of silicon. Passing a current of chlorine through heated silicon resulted in the formation of a condensible gas which was identified as the chloride of silicon.[6]

Substantially the same process is in commercial use today, although for reasons of economy silica, SiO_2, is generally used in place of silicon metal. When silica is used a reducing agent such as carbon is added to the charge. The mixture is heated to about 1,000°C, and chlorine is passed through:

$$SiO_2 + 2C + 2Cl_2 \rightarrow SiCl_4 + 2CO$$

Heat is developed in the reaction, and chlorine addition is maintained at a rate that will hold the temperature within the necessary limits.

The product is a gas which condenses to a liquid, boiling at 57.6°C. It has a freezing point of −70°C and a specific gravity of 1.48. It gives off copious fumes of hydrochloric acid when exposed to moist air:

$$SiCl_4 + 2H_2O \rightarrow SiO_2 + 4HCl$$

The second commercial method of preparing chlorine-containing silanes is an historical descendant of methods developed by Wöhler and by Combes.

Wöhler in 1857 found that by passing hydrochloric acid over a heated mixture of silicon and carbon a volatile product was formed. Analysis showed that it contained silicon, chlorine, and hydrogen. The product appears to have been largely "trichlorosilane," $HSiCl_3$, or silicochloroform.[10]

In 1896 Combes reported that better yields of silicochloroform were obtained if copper powder was added to the silicon.[23]

In 1945 patents were issued to E. G. Rochow, covering a process wherein methyl chloride, CH_3Cl, is passed over a heated charge of silicon to which copper powder had been added.[113] The product is a mixture of volatile compounds containing chlorine, hydrogen, carbon, and silicon. This method of forming a

$$-\overset{|}{\underset{|}{Si}}-Cl$$

grouping is important commercially; but as even greater interest is attached to its reaction in forming, at the same time, a

$$-\overset{|}{\underset{|}{Si}}-C$$

grouping, it is described in detail in that section (see page 245).

2. Reactions of the Silicon Chlorides

The silicon-chlorine bond is stable to heat, but it is highly reactive toward ammonia, water, alcohol, organic acids, and other hydroxyl-containing reagents. It is readily replaced by organic groups by the use of reagents such as sodium, and organometallic compounds. In fact, its high reactivity, coupled with its ease of availability, is the reason for its great value in silicone synthesis.

To Form Si—N (*Silazanes*)

Chlorine attached to silicon is readily replaced by ammonia:

$$SiCl_4 + 8NH_3 \rightarrow Si(NH_2)_4 + 4NH_4Cl$$

Silicon tetrachloride is pumped into an excess of dry ammonia in a pressure reactor. Both the silazane and the ammonium chloride are soluble in the excess ammonia, but when the latter is allowed to evaporate the salt precipitates. The silazane may be extracted with organic solvents. As will be seen below the tetramino silane, $Si(NH_2)_4$, readily gives off ammonia, forming higher-molecular-weight compounds.

The silicon-nitrogen bonding has two outstanding characteristics: it is very stable to heat when hydrogen is not attached to the nitrogen but it is easily hydrolyzed in water. If any hydrogens are attached to nitrogen, ammonia will be eliminated on heating. Thus when the product $Si(NH_2)_4$ is heated the first reaction is

$$2Si(NH_2)_4 \rightarrow (NH_2)_3Si - NH - Si(NH_2)_3 + NH_3$$

On continued heating this reaction continues until all the hydrogen has been eliminated as NH_3 and we have the compound Si_3N_4. This is the compound apparently prepared by Vigoroux and Hugot in 1903. They reported it to be very stable, even at the melting point of glass.[114]

Methods of preparing polymers containing silicon and nitrogen have been described.[115] Elimination of ammonia by heat results in polymerization by the reaction described above.

Substituted ammonias, RNH_2, react similarly:

$$-\overset{|}{\underset{|}{Si}}Cl + RNH_2 \rightarrow -\overset{|}{\underset{|}{Si}}NHR + HCl$$

These silazanes, as they are called, are extremely sensitive to moisture. An amino silane reacts as follows:

$$-\overset{|}{\underset{|}{Si}}(NH_2) + H_2O \rightarrow -\overset{|}{\underset{|}{Si}}(OH) + NH_3$$

The very heat-stable material prepared by Vigoroux and Hugot reacts thus:

$$Si_3N_4 + 12H_2O \rightarrow 3Si(OH)_4 + 4NH_3$$

Alcohols react readily with the $-SiNH_2$ group:

$$-\overset{|}{\underset{|}{Si}}NH_2 + C_2H_5OH \rightarrow -\overset{|}{\underset{|}{Si}}OC_2H_5 + NH_3$$

This is an excellent method for preparing silicon "esters."

The statement of reactivity toward water and alcohols can be made as a generalization covering all hydroxyl-containing compounds.

To Form $-\overset{|}{\underset{|}{Si}}-OH$ (*Silanols*)

Chlorine attached to silicon reacts vigorously with water:

$$-\overset{|}{\underset{|}{Si}}Cl + H_2O \rightarrow -\overset{|}{\underset{|}{Si}}(OH) + HCl$$

In most cases the —OH group does not remain as such but reacts with other —OH groups:

$$-\overset{|}{\underset{|}{Si}}OH + HO\overset{|}{\underset{|}{Si}}- \rightarrow -\overset{|}{\underset{|}{Si}}-O-\overset{|}{\underset{|}{Si}}- + H_2O$$

This is the basis of silicone polymerization.

If the organic groups on silicon are sufficiently large the silanol can be prepared by dissolving the halide, *e.g.*, $(C_6H_5)_3$-SiCl, in ether and then slowly adding aqueous ammonia until the neutral point is reached:

$$(C_6H_5)_3SiCl + NH_4OH \rightarrow (C_6H_5)_3SiOH + NH_4Cl$$

The ether layer, containing the product, is separated and the silanol is obtained upon evaporation of the ether.

Sauer describes the preparation of the relatively unstable trimethyl silanol, $(CH_3)_3SiOH$. Trimethyl chlorosilane, $(CH_3)_3SiCl$, in dry ether is first treated with anhydrous ammonia to obtain hexamethyl disilazane:

$$2(CH_3)_3SiCl + 3NH_3 \rightarrow (CH_3)_3SiNHSi(CH_3)_3 + 2NH_4Cl$$

This product is then titrated with dilute hydrochloric acid:

$$(CH_3)_3SiNHSi(CH_3)_3 + 2H_2O + HCl \rightarrow 2(CH_3)_3SiOH + NH_4Cl$$

The product is obtained by evaporation of the ether layer.[116]

In commercial silicone materials the amount of hydroxyls on silicon is generally vanishingly small. The presence of this grouping usually is an indication that polymerization has not been completed.

The ease with which this condensation takes place is influenced by a number of factors, but there is one point about it that does not vary. This is that the condensation always takes place between hydroxyls on different silicons and never between hydroxyls on the same silicon. If this were not so we would, at times, find the structure

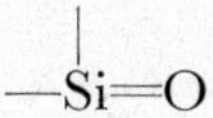

$$\begin{array}{c} | \\ -\mathrm{Si}{=}\mathrm{O} \end{array}$$

resulting from

$$\begin{array}{c} | \\ -\mathrm{Si(OH)_2} \end{array} \rightarrow \begin{array}{c} | \\ -\mathrm{Si}{=}\mathrm{O} \end{array} + H_2O$$

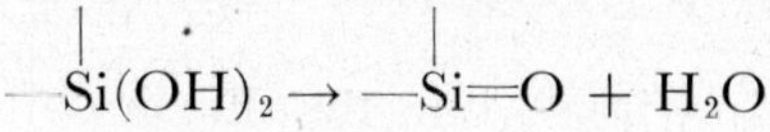

but this structure has never been found.

In spite of the ease with which hydroxyls on silicon condense, some considerable number of compounds have been isolated which contain either one or two of these units. For instance, trimethyl silanol, $(CH_3)_3SiOH$, is a liquid boiling at 98.6°. It is not stable indefinitely, for on standing at room temperature it will gradually split out water with the formation of a siloxane

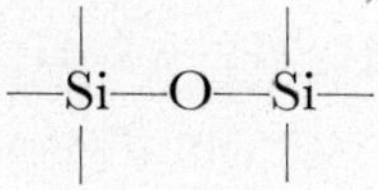

$$\begin{array}{ccccc} & | & & | & \\ - & \mathrm{Si} & -\mathrm{O}- & \mathrm{Si} & - \\ & | & & | & \end{array}$$

linkage. But as the organic groups become larger, the compound becomes more stable. Tripropyl silanol, $(C_3H_7)_3$-$SiOH$, melts at 21° and has a boiling point of 207°, while triphenyl silanol, $(C_6H_5)_3SiOH$, is a solid melting at about 150° and boiling at about 350° at 50 mm Hg without decomposition.

The presence of two hydroxyl groups results in a higher boiling point but also in greater readiness of condensation. No compounds have been surely isolated in which three hydroxyls are present on one silicon.

The two most evident effects of hydroxyl groups on silicon are a raising of the boiling point of the compound and an increased solubility in water. It is difficult to make use of either of these factors commercially, for even the most stable of the silanols will undergo condensation, quickly or slowly, if subjected to heat and acid or base catalysis.

To Form $-\overset{|}{\underset{|}{Si}}-O-\overset{|}{\underset{|}{C}}-$ (*Silicon "Esters"*)

Chlorine attached to silicon reacts with alcohols:

$$SiCl_4 + 4C_2H_5OH \rightarrow Si(OC_2H_5)_4 + 4HCl$$

The alcohol is dripped into the silicon chloride while the mixture is stirred. The acid is evolved as a vapor and is led to a trap or discarded. When the reaction is concluded the product is blown with dry air to remove dissolved acid and is then distilled.

While this is a straightforward operation another reaction can take place, as well, which lowers the yield. As the amount of hydrochloric acid increases it may react directly with the alcohol:

$$HCl + C_2H_5OH \rightarrow C_2H_5Cl + H_2O$$

The water which is formed will then react:

$$-\overset{|}{\underset{|}{Si}}Cl + H_2O \rightarrow -\overset{|}{\underset{|}{Si}}OH + HCl$$

As a result of these side reactions important amounts of both the alcohol and the silicon chloride fail to take part in the desired reaction.

To obtain the best yield it is necessary to keep both the temperature and the acid content low. This may be done by blowing dry air through the cooled reaction mixture as the alcohol is added or by adding an acid acceptor, such as pyridine, to combine with the acid as formed. Precautions of this type are particularly necessary when methyl alcohol is used. To get complete reaction in this case it is necessary, as a final step, to add sodium methylate, CH_3ONa.

This is a general reaction which applies to all hydroxyl-containing organic compounds, *e.g.*, phenols, castor oil, etc.

Another reagent that may be used is a cyclic organic oxide:[117]

$$-\overset{|}{\underset{|}{Si}}Cl + \overset{O}{CH_2-CH_2} \rightarrow -\overset{|}{\underset{|}{Si}}OCH_2CH_2Cl$$

Here, it will be noted, no acid is given off, but the chlorine is transferred to the organic part of the molecule.

A product of this type is generally referred to as an "organosilicon ester" because it can be considered as the reaction product of an alcohol and an acid. The acid in this case is considered to be silicic acid, $Si(OH)_4$. There are valid objections, which will be mentioned shortly, to describing these compounds as "esters," but as this is the common commercial method of referring to them, the name will be retained here.

The "esters" of all but the high-molecular-weight alcohols and the phenols are liquids with a mild pleasant odor. They are insoluble in water but are soluble in a large number of common organic solvents. They are all subject to attack by water, *e.g.*,

$$-\overset{|}{\underset{|}{Si}}OC_2H_5 + H_2O \rightarrow -\overset{|}{\underset{|}{Si}}OH + C_2H_5OH$$

but the reaction is slower as the size of the organic groups increases. This reaction is considerably slower than when the halides are used.

The best known and most widely used of the "esters" is ethyl silicate, $Si(OC_2H_5)_4$, more properly called "tetraethoxysilane." It is a colorless liquid with a boiling point of 168.1°C, a mild, pleasant odor, and a slightly oily feel.

The complexity as well as the size of the organic group affects the stability toward water. For instance the reaction of 1 mol of tertiary butyl alcohol with a silicon chloride gives a product which has the structural formula

$$\begin{array}{c} CH_3 \\ | \\ CH_3\text{—}C\text{—}CH_3 \\ | \\ O \\ | \\ R\text{—}Si\text{—}R \\ | \\ R \end{array}$$

The three methyl groups might be considered as an "umbrella" protecting the oxygen from reaction with water. While this way of looking at it is somewhat pictorial, it is adequate for our purpose, for large or complicated organic structures attached to the oxygen stabilize this bonding to a remarkable degree.

The action of water on the esters can be speeded up by the addition of catalytic amounts of acid. The silicon-containing products of hydrolysis are the same as those of the halides. There can be a certain advantage in the use of the esters, for the by-product is a neutral alcohol, rather than acid as with the halides, or ammonia as with the silazanes.

While both esters and halides give the same end products on hydrolysis, the two can take part in an interesting reaction. If these two types are heated together in the presence of ferric chloride the following reaction takes place:

$$\begin{array}{c}|\\ \text{—}SiCl\\ |\end{array} + \begin{array}{c}|\\ \text{—}SiOR\\ |\end{array} \xrightarrow{FeCl_3} \begin{array}{c}|\\ \text{—}Si\\ |\end{array}\text{—}O\text{—}\begin{array}{c}|\\ Si\\ |\end{array} + RCl$$

It will be noted that this provides a means of carrying out a polymerization without the generation of either acid or alkali.[118]

It will be noted in the next section that when a

$$\begin{array}{c}|\\ \text{—}Si\text{—}Cl\\ |\end{array}$$

bonding is treated with sodium, the chlorines are removed, giving a

$$-\overset{|}{\underset{|}{Si}}-\overset{|}{\underset{|}{Si}}-$$

bonding. An ester group on silicon fails to react in this way. In fact, ethyl silicate, $Si(OC_2H_5)_4$, can be held in contact with molten sodium over a period of hours without any observable change. But sodium can bring about a reaction if an organic halide is present. This is apparently because the sodium first reacts with the organic halide to give an organosodium product:

$$C_6H_5Cl + 2Na \rightarrow C_6H_5Na + NaCl$$

The organosodium product will react with an ester group

$$-\overset{|}{\underset{|}{Si}}OR + C_6H_5Na \rightarrow -\overset{|}{\underset{|}{Si}}(C_6H_5) + NaOR$$

So it is possible by this slightly round-about method to obtain reaction with sodium although direct reaction does not occur. By this method it is possible to replace an ester group by an organic group, but an ester group cannot be replaced by

$$-\overset{|}{\underset{|}{Si}}-$$

to give a

$$-\overset{|}{\underset{|}{Si}}-\overset{|}{\underset{|}{Si}}-$$

bonding as the halides can. A peculiarity of this reaction is that organic groups are likely to replace ester groups on those compounds which already have organic groups, so that the product of the reaction contains mostly highly substituted and unsubstituted products, rather than those with only one or two substitutions.

To substitute only an intermediate number of groups, the use of organomagnesium compounds (or Grignard reagents) is much more satisfactory:

$$-\underset{|}{\overset{|}{\mathrm{Si}}}\mathrm{OR} + \mathrm{RMgX} \rightarrow -\underset{|}{\overset{|}{\mathrm{Si}}}\mathrm{R} + \mathrm{Mg(OR)X}$$

This reaction is described later on pages 246–249.

Another method of establishing a

$$-\underset{|}{\overset{|}{\mathrm{Si}}}-\mathrm{O}-\underset{|}{\overset{|}{\mathrm{C}}}-$$

bond is that of reacting a silicon chloride with an organic acid:

$$-\underset{|}{\overset{|}{\mathrm{Si}}}\mathrm{Cl} + \mathrm{CH_3COOH} \rightarrow -\underset{|}{\overset{|}{\mathrm{Si}}}-\mathrm{O}\overset{\overset{\mathrm{O}}{\|}}{\mathrm{C}}-\mathrm{CH_3} + \mathrm{HCl}$$

The procedure in this reaction is similar to that with the alcohols. The organic acid is added to the silicon compound, and hydrochloric acid is evolved. When low-molecular-weight acids are used the product is a liquid, but with the higher-molecular-weight acids the products are solids.

The products are soluble in organic solvents. The products from the lower-molecular acids are soluble in water as well, but they slowly hydrolyze to regenerate the organic acid and a hydroxylated silicon compound:

$$-\underset{|}{\overset{|}{\mathrm{Si}}}\mathrm{O}\overset{\overset{\mathrm{O}}{\|}}{\mathrm{C}}-\mathrm{CH_3} + \mathrm{H_2O} \rightarrow -\underset{|}{\overset{|}{\mathrm{Si}}}\mathrm{OH} + \mathrm{CH_3}\overset{\overset{\mathrm{O}}{\|}}{\mathrm{C}}-\mathrm{OH}$$

Continued heating results in reaction to form the anhydride of the acid and a

$$-\underset{|}{\overset{|}{\mathrm{Si}}}-\mathrm{O}-\underset{|}{\overset{|}{\mathrm{Si}}}-$$

bonding:

$$2\,\overset{|}{\underset{|}{\mathrm{Si}}}\mathrm{O}\overset{\mathrm{O}}{\overset{\|}{\mathrm{C}}} - \mathrm{CH_3} \rightarrow -\overset{|}{\underset{|}{\mathrm{Si}}}-\mathrm{O}-\overset{|}{\underset{|}{\mathrm{Si}}}- + (\mathrm{CH_3}\overset{\mathrm{O}}{\overset{\|}{\mathrm{C}}})_2\mathrm{O}$$

The compounds just described are more entitled to the name of "ester" than those described earlier. Where exactness of nomenclature is necessary to avoid confusion, it is preferable to use the terms "methoxy," "ethoxy," etc., to designate the —OR part of the molecule in compounds such as

$$-\overset{|}{\underset{|}{\mathrm{Si}}}\mathrm{OCH_3},\ -\overset{|}{\underset{|}{\mathrm{Si}}}\mathrm{OC_2H_5}\ \cdots$$

This is generalized to the term "alkoxy" where the organic group is linear, or "aroxy" where the organic group is benzoid in nature. The name "ester" should properly be reserved for the reaction product of an organic acid and a silicon chloride. The true esters, however, will enter into this discussion so infrequently later that it will actually be less confusing to continue the use of the incorrect term "ester" when referring to structures of the type

$$-\overset{|}{\underset{|}{\mathrm{Si}}}\mathrm{OC_2H_5}$$

Momentarily, at least, it is the term used commercially.

To Form $-\overset{|}{\underset{|}{\mathrm{Si}}}-\overset{|}{\underset{|}{\mathrm{Si}}}-$ (*Silane Bonding*)

The

$$-\overset{|}{\underset{|}{\mathrm{Si}}}-\overset{|}{\underset{|}{\mathrm{Si}}}-$$

bond is not commonly found in commercial silicones, but its use has been suggested for certain purposes. The methods of preparation and the properties are of interest.

One method of forming compounds with Si—Si bondings is that of treating magnesium silicide, Mg_2Si, with an acid. This results in the formation of silane, SiH_4, and some of the higher homologues, such as $H_3Si—SiH_3$, $H_3Si—SiH_2—SiH_3$, etc.:

$$Mg_2Si + 4HCl \rightarrow SiH_4 \cdots + 2MgCl_2$$

Where all the substituents on silicon are hydrogen, high-molecular-weight materials are not formed. In fact no compounds larger than Si_4H_{10} have been isolated in pure form.

By far the most practical method of preparation is to treat with metallic sodium a compound which has at least one chlorine atom attached to silicon:

$$2R_3SiCl + 2Na \rightarrow R_3Si—SiR_3 + 2NaCl$$

This is most readily done by first melting the sodium in an inert organic liquid, such as toluene or xylene, heated above the melting point (100°C) of the sodium. At this temperature the silicon chloride may be slowly added to the molten sodium to react according to the equation shown above. On completion of the reaction the sodium chloride may be filtered off and the product may be recovered from the filtrate.

It may be stated as a general rule that the larger the number of halogens attached to silicon the more vigorous the reaction with sodium. Compounds with one halogen and three organic groups, R_3SiX, react very slowly; those with two halogens and two organic groups, R_2SiX_2, are not so sluggish but often require long periods for complete reaction; compounds with three halogens and one organic group, $RSiX_3$, react with good speed; compounds with four halogens, SiX_4, react vigorously. Like all good rules this one has exceptions, for the type of substituent on silicon has an effect. For example, a compound with two methyl groups and two chlorines, $(CH_3)_2SiCl_2$, reacts slowly with sodium, but one with a phenyl and a methyl group and two chlorines, $(CH_3)(C_6H_5)SiCl_2$, reacts vigorously. Not much has been published on the effect of various groups on this reaction, but a study of it could be rewarding academically. The result could possibly throw new light on the chemistry of silicon.

The

$$\begin{array}{ccccc} & | & & | & \\ - & \text{Si} & - & \text{Si} & - \\ & | & & | & \end{array}$$

bond (or silane bonding) as in silicon itself, is not resistant to oxidation at elevated temperature. When this bonding is present in a silicone the resistance to oxidation is variable, depending on the other groups attached to the silicons. If the other groups are small or few in number, oxidation may take place at room temperature and the

$$\begin{array}{ccccc} & | & & | & \\ - & \text{Si} & - & \text{Si} & - \\ & | & & | & \end{array}$$

bonding becomes

$$\begin{array}{ccccccc} & | & & & & | & \\ - & \text{Si} & - & \text{O} & - & \text{Si} & - \\ & | & & & & | & \end{array}$$

If large organic groups are attached to the silicon atoms the compound may be heated to over 200°C for some period of time before complete oxidation takes place.

This bonding is not generally stable in aqueous alkalies, for the following reaction takes place:

$$\begin{array}{cccccccccc} & | & & | & & & & & | & \\ - & \text{Si} & - & \text{Si} & - & + \; 2\text{NaOH} \rightarrow & 2 & - & \text{SiONa} & + \; \text{H}_2 \\ & | & & | & & & & & | & \end{array}$$

In fact a method for the quantitative analysis for the amount of silane bonding is based on the measurement of the volume of hydrogen produced from a given weight of a silane in aqueous or alcoholic alkali.

The reactivity of compounds of this type in aqueous alkalies varies, as does the resistance toward oxidation, and is apparently governed by the nature of the groups attached to silicon. For instance Kipping found difficulty in breaking open with alkali a

$$-\overset{|}{\underset{|}{Si}}-\overset{|}{\underset{|}{Si}}-$$

bonding in which silicon had three organic groups (ethyl, propyl, phenyl).[39]

The

$$-\overset{|}{\underset{|}{Si}}-\overset{|}{\underset{|}{Si}}-$$

bonding is inert in water and acids.

C. Silicon Compounds Containing Hydrogen

1. Preparation

The silicon-hydrogen bonding is present in some commercial polymers. Hydrogen attached to silicon is also useful as an intermediate in the formation of a silicon-carbon bonding, as is described in a later section (pages 249–250).

There are at least four methods of preparing compounds having silicon-hydrogen bondings, only one of which has commercial significance. The other three are useful for preparation of specific materials in the laboratory.

The commercial method is similar to that developed by Wöhler in 1857[10] and improved by Combes,[23] who in 1896 added copper powder as a catalyst. This method consists of passing dry hydrochloric acid through a bed of silicon and copper powder heated to about 300°C. Ideally the reaction would be

$$Si + 2HCl \rightarrow H_2SiCl_2$$

As a practical matter, the product formed in largest amount is $HSiCl_3$ (silicochloroform). This is a gas which condenses to a liquid with a boiling point of 32°C. The chlorine present causes it to fume in moist air.

Methyl chloride, CH_3Cl, reacts similarly under similar conditions, forming CH_3SiCl_3, $(CH_3)_2SiCl_2$, etc.[113] This reaction generally provides a certain amount of silicochloroform as a side reaction. The amount of the latter product can be increased by using a copper halide, *e.g.*, CuCl, in place of metallic copper.[119]

One of the early laboratory methods of preparing compounds having an —Si—H bonding is that of treating magnesium silicide, $SiMg_2$, with hydrochloric acid:[120]

$$SiMg_2 + HCl \rightarrow SiH_4, Si_2H_6, Si_3H_8 \cdots + MgCl_2$$

The product is always a mixture which is difficult to separate cleanly into its component parts. Yields are low.

Much-improved yields are obtained by the method developed by Johnson and Isenberg.[152] Magnesium silicide suspended in liquid ammonia is treated with ammonium bromide

$$Mg_2Si + 4NH_4Br \xrightarrow{\text{liquid } NH_3} SiH_4 + 2MgBr_2 + 4NH_3$$

This method presents some mechanical difficulties, which no doubt could be mastered if the economics of the process should prove satisfactory.

A third laboratory method that has wider application is the treatment of a silicon chloride, *e.g.*, R_3SiCl, with lithium aluminum hydride, $LiAlH_4$:

$$4R_3SiCl + LiAlH_4 \rightarrow 4R_3SiH + LiCl + AlCl_3$$

The reaction is carried out in a flask from which moisture is excluded. The required amount of powdered lithium aluminum hydride is covered with dry ether. Into this is slowly dripped the organosilicon chloride, R_3SiCl. After some heating to make sure that the reaction has gone to completion, the ether and the product can be distilled off. This is a splendid laboratory method for the preparation of specific hydrides, but the cost of lithium aluminum hydride makes it an impossible commercial procedure at the present time.

2. Stability

The silicon-hydrogen bond varies in its stability toward oxygen of the air, depending upon the number and type of other groups attached to silicon. When four hydrogens are attached to silicon, the product takes fire upon exposure to air and may even react with explosive violence. Moissan and Smiles[26] suggest that this product is stable if it is not contaminated with products containing an —Si—Si— bonding. Whatever may be the truth of this, the fact is that silane, SiH_4, as commonly prepared, oxidizes readily upon exposure to air.

$$SiH_4 + 2O_2 \rightarrow SiO_2 + 2H_2O$$

It should be handled with caution.

The substitution of one hydrogen by a larger organic group such as phenyl or amyl brings about better stability. Compounds such as phenyl silane, $C_6H_5SiH_3$, and amyl silane, $C_5H_{11}SiH_3$, may be boiled to dryness from an open beaker without apparent decomposition. A small organic group such as methyl does not confer stability of this order, for even dimethyl silane, $(CH_3)_2SiH_2$, may take fire spontaneously in contact with air. The presence of halogens is a stabilizing influence comparable to that of small organic groups.

Compounds containing the

$$-\overset{|}{\underset{|}{Si}}-H$$

bonding may be distilled and may be used as chemical

reagents. If there is any question of their stability, they should be distilled in a stream of inert gas such as nitrogen.

3. Reactions

The silicon-hydrogen bond is not rapidly affected by water but is readily broken by alkalies according to the equation

$$2\text{—}\overset{|}{\underset{|}{\mathrm{Si}}}\text{—H} + 2\mathrm{NaOH} \rightarrow 2\text{—}\overset{|}{\underset{|}{\mathrm{Si}}}\mathrm{ONa} + \mathrm{H_2}$$

The hydrogen in these compounds is readily replaced by halogens:

$$\text{—}\overset{|}{\underset{|}{\mathrm{Si}}}\text{—H} + \mathrm{Cl_2} \rightarrow \text{—}\overset{|}{\underset{|}{\mathrm{Si}}}\mathrm{Cl} + \mathrm{HCl}$$

As the number of hydrogens on silicon increases the reaction with halogens becomes more vigorous. Silane, SiH_4, and the halogens react with explosive violence. Even such organic substances as carbon tetrachloride, CCl_4, and chloroform, $CHCl_3$, will react violently:

$$\text{—}\overset{|}{\underset{|}{\mathrm{Si}}}\mathrm{H} + \mathrm{CCl_4} \rightarrow \text{—}\overset{|}{\underset{|}{\mathrm{Si}}}\mathrm{Cl} + \mathrm{CHCl_3}$$

$$\text{—}\overset{|}{\underset{|}{\mathrm{Si}}}\mathrm{H} + \mathrm{CHCl_3} \rightarrow \text{—}\overset{|}{\underset{|}{\mathrm{Si}}}\mathrm{Cl} + \mathrm{CH_2Cl_2}$$

The preparation of compounds containing both hydrogen and chlorine can be controlled if aluminum chloride is added to the hydride and the mixture is then treated with hydrochloric acid. By this method it is possible to prepare materials such as SiH_3Cl, SiH_2Cl_2, etc.

Hydrogens on silicon are less reactive than the halogens to certain reagents. For example water will remove a halogen without affecting a hydrogen:

$$\mathrm{SiH_3Br} + \mathrm{H_2O} \rightarrow \mathrm{SiH_3(OH)} + \mathrm{HBr}$$

An organic group can replace a halogen:

$$2SiH_3Cl + Zn(CH_3)_2 \rightarrow 2SiH_3(CH_3) + ZnCl_2$$

Ammonia can replace a halogen without affecting hydrogen:

$$H_3SiCl + 2NH_3 \rightarrow H_3SiNH_2 + NH_4Cl$$

Compounds containing a

$$-\overset{|}{\underset{|}{Si}}-H$$

grouping can react, under appropriate conditions, to give a

$$-\overset{|}{\underset{|}{Si}}-C$$

grouping, *e.g.*,

$$CH_2{=}CH_2 + HSiCl_3 \rightarrow CH_3CH_2SiCl_3$$

This is described in more detail under The Olefin Addition Method, pages 249-250.

Readers who would like a more complete description of the hydrides should consult Stock's "Hydrides of Boron and Silicon."[120]

D. Silicon Compounds Containing Carbon

The silicon-carbon bond is one of the distinguishing marks of a true silicone and is responsible for many of the striking differences between silica and silicones. For one thing, as long as a silicon atom retains a carbon it is axiomatically barred from reverting to silica. The organic substituent brings to the molecule certain properties of organic compounds, such as solubility in organic solvents and ability to be handled and reacted by known organic techniques.

1. Preparation

There are four commercial methods for attaching a carbon group to a silicon atom:

1. The "direct process"
2. The Grignard method
3. The olefin addition method
4. The sodium method

THE DIRECT PROCESS

The "direct process" is so called because it converts elemental silicon in one operation into a silane containing both an organic group and chlorine. The method was patented by E. G. Rochow in 1945.[113,121]

The operation is carried out by first mixing powdered silicon with about 10 per cent copper powder (or the mixture may be sintered under hydrogen). This is then placed in a tube or tumbler and heated to about 300°C while methyl chloride gas is passed through. The exit gases are condensed. The composition of the exit gases may be controlled within satisfactory limits by regulation of temperature, rate of gas flow, and amount of catalyst. Naturally there is a mixture of products which must be separated by distillation.

The condensate generally contains compounds as shown in Table 32.

TABLE 32

Compound	*Boiling Point, °C*
$(CH_3)SiCl_3$	65.7
$(CH_3)_2SiCl_2$	70
$(CH_3)HSiCl_2$	41
$(CH_3)_3SiCl$	57
$SiCl_4$	57.6
$HSiCl_3$	32

The most useful of these products from the commercial

standpoint is dimethyl dichlorosilane. The reaction can be regulated to give a preponderance of this material.

The copper present in the mixture, although in rather large amount, is a true catalyst. Its function is to form the unstable copper methyl, $CuCH_3$, which then decomposes to give methyl free radicals, which react with the silicon.[122]

While the process may be operated with many different organic halides, provided the proper catalyst is used in each case, its actual use is largely restricted to the preparation of methyl silicon chlorides.

There are at least two reasons for this limitation. First, the catalyst (copper) used in conjunction with the methyl halides is not as effective with other organic groups. Better catalysts have been found for these other groups, but they are more expensive and give rather low yields of product. Secondly, the larger groups show some decomposition at the reaction temperature so that the amount of desired product is further reduced. In spite of these present difficulties it is not too much to expect that further research will open up a way to make this method more widely applicable.

The method has many obvious advantages but requires auxiliary methods of synthesis if the total product is to be used to the best advantage. Although it is possible to direct the synthesis to a high yield of one particular compound, all possible substitutions of organic and halogen groups are found to some extent; in addition some hydrogen is found as a substituent, *e.g.*, $RHSiCl_2$.

This method lacks the versatility of the more classical methods in that it is economically applicable to only a few types of substitution, but fortunately the methyl group with which it is most effective is the group that has the widest commercial demand at this time.

THE GRIGNARD METHOD

The Grignard method was devised about the beginning of the twentieth century for use in organic synthesis and was first applied to organosilicon compounds by F. S. Kipping in 1906. The method has been of prime importance in organosilicon investigations and for many years was considered as applicable only to laboratory work. Its first large industrial application was in the synthesis of organosilicon compounds by the Dow Corning Corporation.

The problem that this method solves is that of substituting an organic group for one or more of the chlorines on silicon tetrachloride, or to form from $SiCl_4$ compounds of the types $RSiCl_3$, R_2SiCl_2, R_3SiCl, or R_4Si.

In the Grignard method of accomplishing this there is first formed what is called the "Grignard reagent." To prepare this, magnesium chips or shavings are covered with dry ether or other suitable solvent in a flask, kettle, or reactor equipped with a stirrer and a condenser. The reaction should be protected against moisture from the air. A halogenated organic compound, for example a liquid such as butyl chloride, C_4H_9Cl, is then allowed to drip into the mixture. An intriguing reaction takes place in that the solvent begins to boil and the magnesium begins to disappear. Finally the magnesium is completely consumed, and if the proper solvent has been used there will be a clear solution. The reaction, stripped of theoretical complications that need not concern us, may be described as

$$C_4H_9Cl + Mg \rightarrow C_4H_9MgCl$$

We are now prepared to react this with silicon tetrachloride. This is done by dissolving silicon tetrachloride in ether and slowly adding, with stirring, the Grignard reagent just described. A certain amount of heat is evolved and at the same time a precipitate of magnesium chloride forms. The reaction taking place is

$$SiCl_4 + C_4H_9MgCl \rightarrow C_4H_9SiCl_3 + MgCl_2$$

This means simply that there has been an exchange of the butyl group for one of the chlorines on silicon. It is possible to exchange all the chlorines on silicon by adding enough Grignard reagent.

Of course, there are many other compounds similar to butyl chloride that can be used, but as this is a liquid it is a simple compound for demonstration purposes. One of the most common and useful groups used in silicon work is the methyl group. Although methyl chloride is a gas (boiling point, $-20°C$) the course of the reaction is just the same as with butyl chloride. Naturally the reaction should be carried out in a pressure vessel to retain the gas until it reacts, but otherwise the general procedure is the same.

As in many other chemical reactions, not all the molecules react in precisely the same fashion; some molecules of silicon tetrachloride take up only their fair share of the Grignard reagent, while others act like the less-admired members of the human race and take more than they are supposed to take. This means that some may not have a chance to react at all. Because of this perverseness or antisocial behavior, they have to be separated by distillation.

The reaction mixture is first filtered to remove the solid magnesium chloride. The filtrate is then distilled to remove the ether and separate the other products into those having one, two, three, or four of the organic groups and to recover any unreacted silicon tetrachloride.

Each of these products is generally a liquid, the properties of which depend on the number and type of organic groups added. They are the basic materials required for the preparation of silicones.

The two steps of preparing the Grignard reagent and then reacting it with silicon tetrachloride can be converted into one step by a variant that has both advantages and disadvantages. The alternative method is based on the use of ethyl silicate. Instead of the magnesium chips being covered with ether, they are covered with the amount of ethyl silicate required for the reaction. The appropriate organic chloride is slowly added to this mixture. The Grignard reagent will form readily in this solvent and will also react with it:

$$Si(OC_2H_5)_4 + RMgCl \rightarrow RSi(OC_2H_5)_3 + MgCl(OC_2H_5)$$

The result is that both steps go forward at once. When the reaction is completed the magnesium salts may be filtered off and the filtrate distilled to obtain the various reaction products.[123]

It will be seen that there is only one operation required. Further, no other solvent is needed, so that smaller reaction vessels may be used to prepare a given amount of product.

If ethyl silicate is used there is no danger of hydrochloric acid being formed and corroding pipe lines. For laboratory work this method is often convenient and timesaving, and for plant procedures it is at times an economical method to use.

But while this method presents some economy of operation, the economy may prove more apparent than real unless the whole process is carefully analyzed. As a matter of fact it is really a two-step process, for, although the Grignard reagent does not have to be prepared separately, the ethyl silicate does. Then there is the practical matter of using large quantities of ethyl alcohol. The careful accounting required when this reagent is used entails such careful recovery and such meticulous record keeping that those in charge of production may feel they would prefer to turn out product rather than keep books. Still, it is not a method to be overlooked for certain purposes.

THE OLEFIN ADDITION METHOD

Silicochloroform, $HSiCl_3$ (boiling point, 32°), is the reagent commonly used in the olefin addition method. This is placed in a bomb or reactor to which is added an unsaturated organic compound. The mixture, with or without peroxide catalyst, is heated to some temperature between 45 and 400°, the temperature depending on the reactants being used and the presence or absence of catalyst. The following reaction takes place:

$$RCH{=}CH_2 + HSiCl_3 \rightarrow RCH_2{-}CH_2{-}SiCl_3$$

In this way aliphatic groups containing two or more carbon atoms may be attached to silicon.[124]

A modification of the above method has been described by which disubstitution can be obtained.[125] So far as is known this modification is not in commercial use.

The olefin addition method has the advantage of using cheap starting materials, and it can be used to bond many different organic groups to silicon. It suffers from the disadvantages that it cannot be used to prepare a methyl-silicon bonding nor is it yet commercially applicable to bringing about the addition of more than one organic group.

THE SODIUM METHOD

This method could be described as "alkali metals," for the other alkali metals, such as potassium or lithium, could also be used. But the cost of these other metals is so much in excess of that of sodium that they are rarely considered in production processes.

The sodium method depends on the following reaction:

$$SiCl_4 + 4C_4H_7Cl + 8Na \rightarrow Si(C_4H_9)_4 + 8NaCl$$

The procedure in this case is to add metallic sodium to toluene or xylene in a flask or kettle fitted with a condenser, and heat until the sodium melts. Then, while stirring vigorously, add the desired amount of a solution of organic chloride and silicon tetrachloride. The reaction gives off a large amount of heat and the temperature can be regulated by the speed of addition of the reagents. With the addition of the first small amount of charge the solution becomes deep purple, and this color persists throughout the reaction time.

This reaction is similar in many ways to the Grignard in the end result, although the mechanism of the reaction is undoubtedly different. But the end result is not precisely the same, for this reaction generally gives poorer distributions of the organic groups on silicon than the Grignard gives. With the Grignard method the use of sufficient organic chloride to replace two chlorines on each silicon generally gives a preponderance of disubstituted product. With the sodium method the amount of more highly substituted silanes is greater, and correspondingly larger amount of unsubstituted silicon tetrachloride is left.

Under certain conditions the sodium may react solely with chlorines on silicon, adding a silicon to a silicon

$$-\overset{|}{\underset{|}{\mathrm{Si}}}-\overset{|}{\underset{|}{\mathrm{Si}}}-$$

instead of a carbon to a silicon

$$-\overset{|}{\underset{|}{\mathrm{C}}}-\overset{|}{\underset{|}{\mathrm{Si}}}-$$

Although this type of product has its uses, its presence is a complicating factor when the carbon-silicon bonding is desired.

Another disadvantage of the method is the precautions necessary in the handling of the sodium itself and of the residues which may contain small amounts of unreacted sodium. Nevertheless with experience this becomes a useful reagent, and for certain reactions, such as replacing a final chlorine on silicon with an organic group, it is at times preferred to the Grignard method.

Schumb and Saffer[126] have pointed out that better distribution of substituents may be obtained by a simple change in procedure. They suggest first melting the sodium in toluene or xylene and then adding the organic chloride, RCl, only. A reaction takes place which may be shown as

$$\mathrm{RCl} + 2\mathrm{Na} \rightarrow \mathrm{RNa} + \mathrm{NaCl}$$

This reaction product is then added to a solution of silicon tetrachloride with the result

$$RNa + SiCl_4 \rightarrow RSiCl_3 + NaCl$$

Of course, other substitution products are formed as well, but the method, although a bit more cumbersome than the first described, does give less multisubstitution. In any case the precipitated salts must be filtered off and the products separated by distillation.

Another type of silicon-carbon bond, where carbon is present between two silicons

$$-\overset{|}{\underset{|}{Si}}-\overset{|}{\underset{|}{C}}-\overset{|}{\underset{|}{Si}}-$$

can be formed through this type of reaction. First, an organic group already on silicon must be halogenated:

$$-\overset{|}{\underset{|}{Si}}-CH_3 + Cl_2 \rightarrow -\overset{|}{\underset{|}{Si}}CH_2Cl + HCl$$

This grouping has some of the properties of an organic halide and may be reacted with a silicon halide, (SiCl), in the presence of sodium.[127]

$$-\overset{|}{\underset{|}{Si}}CH_2Cl + Cl\overset{|}{\underset{|}{Si}}- + 2Na \rightarrow -\overset{|}{\underset{|}{Si}}CH_2-\overset{|}{\underset{|}{Si}}- + 2NaCl$$

This reaction is described in more detail later (see p. 280).

The bonding of organic groups to silicon is one of the most important and expensive steps in the preparation of silicones. A great deal has been done to improve the present methods and to develop better ones. We have looked at the four methods now in commercial use: the direct process, the Grignard method, the olefin addition method, and the sodium method. No one of them is completely satisfactory. Each has its points of superiority.

In spite of this present lack of a completely satisfactory overall method one can afford to indulge in a certain amount of optimism. The commercial development of these materials is about 10 years old, and the early part of this development was carried out when there was pressure for production of specific materials for military purposes. Little time was available for attack on problems that did not promise an early solution. In spite of that the methods of production have improved and some new ones have been devised. It is not too much to expect that progress will continue and that more economical methods will continue to be developed for carrying out this essential step.

2. Stability

The properties of a carbon on silicon vary, depending on the chemical structure of which the carbon is a part. The carbon may have three hydrogens (methyl group) or it may be part of a long chain or part of a cyclic radical. All these and many other structures affect the stability or reactivity of the carbon.

The oxidation stability of a carbon chain on silicon becomes less as the chain length increases. In the alkyl series (methyl, ethyl, propyl, etc.) the oxidation stability falls off rapidly beyond methyl, and by the time a five-carbon chain (amyl) is reached, the oxidation resistance is little better than that of an organic compound. Some idea of the relative values may be obtained when it is stated that under conditions where a methyl group on silicon will show evidences of oxidation at 200°C an ethyl group will show comparable oxidation at 140°, a butyl group at 120°, and an amyl group at 113°. The cyclic phenyl, —C_6H_5, group is definitely more resistant to oxidation than the methyl group although no comparable figures are at hand.

3. Reactions

If the carbon attached to silicon is part of a linear radical, the bonding is more stable to aqueous acids than if it is part of a phenyl radical. The cleavage of the phenyl radical is the result of hydrolysis catalyzed by the acid:

$$-\overset{|}{\underset{|}{Si}}C_6H_5 + H_2O \rightarrow -\overset{|}{\underset{|}{Si}}OH + C_6H_6 \text{ (benzene)}$$

The stability of an organic group on silicon is affected by the nature of the other groups on silicon. Concentrated sulfuric acid cleaves a phenyl (or aryl) group from silicon.[36] If linear (or alkyl) groups are the organic substituents on silicon this effect is not observed if there is at least one halogen or oxygen or other negative group present. But if all the substituents on silicon are linear organic groups concentrated sulfuric acid at 100° will remove one of them, *e.g.*,

$$(CH_3)_4Si + H_2SO_4 \rightarrow CH_4 + (CH_3)_3SiHSO_4$$

The negative sulfate group immediately stabilizes the molecule against this reaction, with the result that only one group is removed.[128]

This variable stability is shown if the linear alkyl-substituted compounds are reacted with halogens. Exposure to chlorine in the presence of light results in exchange of one or more of the hydrogens on carbon:

$$-\overset{|}{\underset{|}{Si}}CH_3 + Cl_2 \rightarrow -\overset{|}{\underset{|}{Si}}CH_2Cl + HCl$$

$$-\overset{|}{\underset{|}{Si}}CHCl_2$$

$$-\overset{|}{\underset{|}{Si}}CCl_3$$

If the other three substituents on silicon are organic or positive groups the whole molecule is about as stable as an analogous organic compound. But if one of the substituents on silicon is a negative group the chlorinated group may be split from the silicon with aqueous alkali. This instability increases as the number of chlorines on carbon and the number of negative groups on silicon increase. This reaches the point where, with three chlorines on carbon and three chlorines on silicon, the organic radical is cleaved by the action of water alone.[129]

$$Cl_3SiCCl_3 + 4H_2O \rightarrow Si(OH)_4 + CHCl_3 + 3HCl$$

The chlorinated organic group may contain more than one carbon, and in that case other peculiarities present themselves. If the chlorine (or other negative group) is on the carbon attached to silicon

$$-\overset{|}{\underset{|}{Si}}CHClCH_3$$

the stability is similar to that described above. But if the chlorine is on the second carbon atom

$$-\overset{|}{\underset{|}{Si}}CH_2CH_2Cl$$

the organic group is much more loosely held to silicon. If the other three valences of silicon are satisfied by negative groups, *e.g.*, $Cl_3SiCH_2CH_2Cl$, even cold dilute alkali is sufficient to rupture the silicon-carbon bond:[130]

$$-\overset{|}{\underset{|}{Si}}CH_2CH_2Cl + NaOH \rightarrow -\overset{|}{\underset{|}{Si}}OH + CH_2{=}CH_2 + NaCl$$

As the number of negative groups on silicon is decreased the stability of the silicon-carbon bond increases until, in the total absence of negative groups, the compound is similar in stability to that of an organic compound.

The same general principles apply if the halogen is on a third carbon

$$-\overset{|}{\underset{|}{Si}}CH_2CH_2CH_2Cl$$

but the stability of this silicon-carbon bond is intermediate between that found when the chlorine is on the first or the second carbon.[131]

If the chlorine is on the fourth carbon, or further removed from silicon, this cleavage effect is not found. The group acts as it would in an organic compound.

The vinyl ($-CH{=}CH_2$) and allyl ($-CH_2-CH{=}CH_2$) radicals on silicon are not as stable to oxidation as ethyl ($-CH_2-CH_3$) or propyl ($-CH_2-CH_2-CH_3$) but are of interest because of their potentialities of polymer formation by means of the double bonds.[132]

For many years practically all the work done in attaching carbon to silicon involved only "nonfunctional" organic groups: that is, hydrocarbon groups, such as methyl, ethyl, propyl, phenyl, etc. Recently considerable work has been reported covering the "functional" groups such as alcohols,[133] ketones,[128,134] acids,[135] amines,[136] etc. The discussion of these results is beyond the scope of this book but these papers should be consulted by those who are interested in the wider development of organosilicon chemistry.

E. Silicon Compounds Containing Siloxane Bondings

The siloxane bonding is the distinguishing mark of all commercial silicones. Certain structures that do not contain this bonding may be considered, by a generous definition, as silicones, but in by far the most cases the

$$-\overset{|}{\underset{|}{Si}}-O-\overset{|}{\underset{|}{Si}}-$$

bonding is present.

1. Preparation

There are four main methods of establishing a siloxane bonding, of which the first described is by far the most important:

1. By condensation of hydroxyls on silicon:

$$-\overset{|}{\underset{|}{Si}}OH + HO\overset{|}{\underset{|}{Si}}- \rightarrow -\overset{|}{\underset{|}{Si}}-O-\overset{|}{\underset{|}{Si}}- + H_2O$$

The speed of this reaction varies depending on the number and type of the other substituents on silicon. For as complete reaction as possible it is generally necessary to use heat and catalytic quantities of acid or base.

2. By reaction of a silicon chloride with a silicon ester using ferric chloride as a catalyst:[118]

$$-\overset{|}{\underset{|}{Si}}Cl + -\overset{|}{\underset{|}{Si}}OC_2H_5 \xrightarrow{FeCl_3} -\overset{|}{\underset{|}{Si}}-O-\overset{|}{\underset{|}{Si}}- + C_2H_5Cl$$

The chloride, ester, and iron chloride are heated under anhydrous conditions and the course of the reaction may be followed by determining the amount of ethyl chloride evolved.

3. By oxidation of an organic group on silicon:

$$2-\overset{|}{\underset{|}{Si}}-CH_3 + 2O_2 \rightarrow -\overset{|}{\underset{|}{Si}}-O-\overset{|}{\underset{|}{Si}}- + 2CH_2O + H_2O$$

The organosilicon compound is heated while air or oxygen is bubbled through it. The linear organic groups (methyl, ethyl, propyl, etc.) are oxidized more readily than the cyclics (phenyl); the longer the linear group, the more readily is it oxidized.

4. By hydrolysis of an organic group on silicon:

$$-\overset{|}{\underset{|}{Si}}-R + H_2O \rightarrow -\overset{|}{\underset{|}{Si}}-OH + RH$$

The organosilicon compound is heated in the presence of water and a strong acid catalyst. Under these conditions a cyclic group such as phenyl (—C_6H_5) is removed more readily than a linear (CH_3—, C_2H_5—).

For practical purposes by far the most important of these reactions is the first one shown. The others find use at times, but perhaps the biggest advantage in knowing of them is to recognize conditions to be avoided if this reaction is not desired.

REACTIONS OF —Si—O—Si—

The silicon-oxygen-silicon (or the siloxane) bonding is one of the most common marks of a true silicone. It is the same structure found in silica or quartz, and the great heat resistance of the latter is definitely reflected in the silicones themselves. This is not to say that the silicones are as heat-resistant as quartz, for there are two factors that reduce the stability at high temperature. One of them is the presence of at least one organic radical on silicon which is susceptible of oxidation, and if oxidation takes place the silicone structure is disrupted. The other factor is that in a silicone there are not more than three oxygen-silicon groups attached to any one silicon, and in many cases there are only two or one:

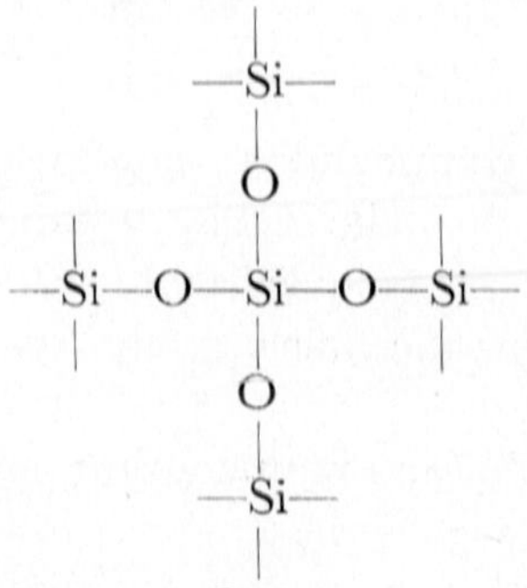

```
              |
            —Si—
              |
              O
      |       |       |
    —Si—O—Si—O—Si—
      |       |       |
              O
              |
            —Si—
              |
```

Quartz

```
       R                    R                       R
  |    |    |          |    |    |                  |      |
—Si—O—Si—O—Si—      —Si—O—Si—O—Si—          R—Si—O—Si—
  |    |    |          |    |    |                  |      |
       O                    R                       R
       |
     —Si—
       |
```

Silicones

The reduction in the number of silicon-oxygen-silicon bondings results in less rigidity in a silicone product, and it is physically possible for the molecules to move about, contact one another, and rearrange into different structures. Quartz cannot do this, partly because of its rigidity and high softening point and partly because, having all the same type of units attached to silicon, no rearrangement would give any different products.

To anticipate some statements in the section on Polymerization we may consider a large silicone molecule having many siloxane bondings and two organic groups on each silicon:

```
     R      R      R      R      R      R
     |      |      |      |      |      |
—O—Si—O—Si—O—Si—O—Si—O—Si—O—Si—
     |      |      |      |      |      |
     R      R      R      R      R      R
```

Under conditions of high temperature (350°C) or alkaline catalysts this polymer may rearrange into two smaller cyclic polymers:

```
   R      R      R              R      R      R
   |      |      |              |      |      |
O—Si—O—Si—O—Si—          O—Si—O—Si—O—Si—
|  |      |      |  |       |  |      |      |  |
|  R      R      R  |       |  R      R      R  |
|___________________|       |___________________|
```

The products formed upon rearrangement differ, depending

on the type of polymer in which the siloxanes are present, and will be described in more detail in Sec. 3.

The siloxane bonding can be split by water, alkalies, and acids under certain severe conditions.

Water in the form of high-pressure steam can react:

$$-\overset{|}{\underset{|}{\mathrm{Si}}}-\mathrm{O}-\overset{|}{\underset{|}{\mathrm{Si}}}- + \mathrm{H_2O} \rightarrow -\overset{|}{\underset{|}{\mathrm{Si}}}\mathrm{OH} + \mathrm{HO}\overset{|}{\underset{|}{\mathrm{Si}}}-$$

This reaction is not peculiar to silicones, for it is possible to hydrate glass and even silica by the same general method.

Alkalies react similarly:

$$-\overset{|}{\underset{|}{\mathrm{Si}}}-\mathrm{O}-\overset{|}{\underset{|}{\mathrm{Si}}}- + \mathrm{NaOH} \rightarrow -\overset{|}{\underset{|}{\mathrm{Si}}}\mathrm{ONa} + \mathrm{HO}\overset{|}{\underset{|}{\mathrm{Si}}}-$$

This is, of course, the same reaction which is used to solubilize glass and silica. The reaction takes place more readily with silicones, for their physical form as liquids or resins makes them more open to attack.

Anhydrous acids can split the siloxane bonding:

$$-\overset{|}{\underset{|}{\mathrm{Si}}}-\mathrm{O}-\overset{|}{\underset{|}{\mathrm{Si}}}- + \mathrm{HCl} \rightarrow -\overset{|}{\underset{|}{\mathrm{Si}}}\mathrm{OH} + \mathrm{Cl}\overset{|}{\underset{|}{\mathrm{Si}}}-$$

Water will form as a result of condensation of —SiOH groups and the reaction quickly comes to equilibrium unless the water is continuously removed. The reaction may be carried to completion if the silicone is dissolved in sulfuric acid and equivalent amounts of sodium or ammonium halide are added. Low-boiling products may be distilled directly from the mixture.

Concentrated sulfuric, phosphoric, and boric acids also split the siloxane bonding. The products, sulfates, phosphates, and borates, are quite unstable to moisture, and on the addition of water the siloxane bonding is regenerated.

Section 3:

Polymerization

Having discussed the methods of forming the different silicon-containing units, it should be of interest to see how they are tied together into those immense molecules known as "siloxane polymers" or "silicones."

We are accustomed now to see and use articles made of Bakelite, nylon, Vinylite, and similar synthetic materials. These materials are known technically as "high polymers" or more generally as "plastics." It is hard to realize that it is scarcely 40 years since the first serious study of the preparation of these materials was commenced. Indeed most of these materials have been developed within the past 30 years, and the most rewarding studies have been carried out within that same period. General principles were deduced, and laws governing polymerization were found. These findings have been of the utmost importance in hastening the understanding of polymer chemistry.

In the polymerization of silicones the same laws apply as in the polymerization of organic compounds, and the same nomenclature is used. Definitions of the commonly employed terms will be of help in the discussion which follows.

"Polymer" Definitions

To define the term "polymer" itself, we can state that a polymer is a compound in which some chemical unit is continuously repeated in the structure. The term "mer" is sometimes used in referring to one unit in a compound. The molecular unit used to prepare the polymer is known as a "mono-mer." We can have "di-mers," or compounds containing only two units. Similarly, we may have "tri-mers" or "tetra-mers." When a great many units are present the compound is referred to as a "poly-mer."

If more than one distinct type of unit is present, the compound is sometimes referred to as a "mixed polymer," or more commonly as a "copolymer."

The terms "high polymer" and "low polymer" are simply terms of convenience to indicate that there is a high or low number of "mers" in the compound.

Thermoplastic and Thermoset

In the description of polymers there are two terms used to describe their behavior to heat. These terms are "thermoplastic" and "thermoset." As the name suggests, "thermoplastic" means nothing more nor less than that the material becomes plastic or soft on the application of heat. Most of the commercial organic thermoplastic polymers show this property to more or less degree at about the boiling point of water. In general they can be pressed and formed at about 110°C; on cooling they show the properties that are desired in that particular material and retain these properties over a useful temperature range.

"Thermoset" means that under the application of heat the polymers go through a reaction at some temperature that causes them to set to a firm solid. A later application of heat does not cause them to become plastic. A truly thermoset material may decompose at some elevated temperature but will not soften. Of course, there are some materials described as "thermoset" that soften to a certain extent, but no thermoset material worthy of the name can be remolded after the secondary or "setting" reaction has taken place.

Functionality

Another definition required for ease of discussing polymerization and polymers is that of "functionality." This refers to the number of groups in the molecule that can function in tying that molecule to some other. In silicone polymerization the functional group is the hydroxyl on silicon, —Si—OH, which can condense with another similar group to give the siloxane bonding

$$-\overset{|}{\underset{|}{Si}}OH + HO\overset{|}{\underset{|}{Si}}- \rightarrow -\overset{|}{\underset{|}{Si}}-O-\overset{|}{\underset{|}{Si}}- + H_2O$$

Any group that can give rise to a hydroxyl group on silicon under the conditions imposed is also considered as a functional group.

It is evident that if a molecule has no functional group at all—no group that can react with any other group that may be brought into the system—it can be of no interest whatever from the standpoint of polymerization. If it has only one functional group we are not much better off, for when that group reacts the product becomes nonfunctional:

$$(CH_3)_3SiOH + HOSi(CH_3)_3 \rightarrow (CH_3)_3Si-O-Si(CH_3)_3 + H_2O$$

No hydroxyl group is left and it is, therefore, dead for this type of reaction.

But when we have two functional groups (or a difunctional molecule) we can have hopes for a continuing reaction, for as two molecules react to form a larger one, one end of each remains functional. Thus we still have a difunctional molecule, but a larger one.

$$HO-\overset{CH_3}{\underset{CH_3}{Si}}-OH + HO-\overset{CH_3}{\underset{CH_3}{Si}}-OH \rightarrow HO-\overset{CH_3}{\underset{CH_3}{Si}}-O-\overset{CH_3}{\underset{CH_3}{Si}}-OH + H_2O$$

Of course, there is the possibility that the two ends of an identical molecule will react. If this occurs all functionality is lost and the resulting compound, although a polymer, has no ability to grow further. There are ways of encouraging this if low polymers are desired and ways of avoiding it if high polymers are sought. It is generally possible to retain a larger proportion of the reactants in a difunctional state and so to continue the polymerization to some high degree that is commercially useful. Theoretically the difunctional compounds should continue adding or condensing until the final product is one huge molecule. For two reasons this does not take place. As reaction continues, fewer and fewer functional groups are present, and so there are fewer chances for them to meet and react. Secondly, the product becomes more viscous, and the reduced movement is a deterrent to reaction.

There are situations, though, where smaller polymers are wanted. There are different ways of stopping the reaction. One is to neutralize or remove the necessary catalyst or to lower the temperature of reaction. Another method is to add at the beginning of the reaction or later a certain number of monofunctional groups. As these react with the end of a polymer, they block the functionality there, and it is possible to work out in some cases just the proper quantities of monofunctional material to be added to bring the reaction to some desired point and have it stop there.

The reaction of difunctional molecules can build up nothing but cyclic or linear polymers. The linear polymers are chains which, although they may become tangled, have no firm union or chemical bonding with one another. If they are heated the thermal agitation allows them to move about more freely and finally to flow. They are thermoplastic. And it should be noted that all thermoplastic polymers are formed from difunctional molecules.

We are now in a position to realize what happens when we

use trifunctional molecules. If we mix molecules of this type with difunctional molecules we have the possibility of the third function reaching across from one chain to a similar neighboring one and so making a firm chemical bonding. This will slow up the freedom of movement on heating, for the chains are tied together here and there. The viscosity is higher, partly because of the increase in molecular weight; but of more importance is the interference to flow caused by this cross linking. As the number of trifunctional groups is increased the stiffness increases, and finally we come to the point where no amount of heat will be enough to cause flow. The material has thermoset.

Molecules with higher functionality than three can, of course, be used. They, too, will cause thermosetting, and considerable variation in final properties can be obtained by judicious combination of molecules having two, three, and more functionalities.

What we have done, then, in this section, has been to define the terms "monomer," "polymer," "copolymer," "thermoplastic," "thermoset," and "functionality." Understanding of the meaning of these terms is necessary for any consideration of polymerization. We should now be in a position to look at the polymerization of silicones and see how these large molecules are constructed.

A. *Silicone Polymerization*

The foregoing definitions should be helpful in discussing silicone polymerization and silicone polymers. But one peculiarity should be pointed out. There are no thermoplastic silicone polymers that have shown any practical usefulness as solid materials. This is due not to lack of difunctional intermediates (the necessary type for formation of thermoplastics) but rather to the fact that silicones show relatively small change of viscosity with temperature. An organic polymer formed from difunctional units, such as vinyl acetate or styrene, is quite workable at 125°C and yet at room temperature it is tough and nontacky. But most silicone polymers formed from difunctional units that show only enough flow to be workable at 125°C are still likely to be somewhat soft and plastic at room temperature. Thus when we discuss useful silicone polymers we have to consider largely liquids and thermoset solids.

It was pointed out in a previous chapter that the reaction in the polymerization of a silicone is the elimination of water between hydroxyl groups on different silicon atoms:

$$-\overset{|}{\underset{|}{Si}}OH + HO\overset{|}{\underset{|}{Si}}- \rightarrow -\overset{|}{\underset{|}{Si}}-O-\overset{|}{\underset{|}{Si}}- + H_2O$$

The hydroxyl group is present as the result of the action of water on a hydrolyzable group attached to silicon, *e.g.*,

$$-\overset{|}{\underset{|}{Si}}Cl + H_2O \rightarrow -\overset{|}{\underset{|}{Si}}OH + HCl$$

$$-\overset{|}{\underset{|}{Si}}OC_2H_5 + H_2O \rightarrow -\overset{|}{\underset{|}{Si}}OH + C_2H_5OH$$

$$-\overset{|}{\underset{|}{Si}}NH_2 + H_2O \rightarrow -\overset{|}{\underset{|}{Si}}OH + NH_3$$

As these hydrolyzable groups are so readily transformed into hydroxyls that can condense with one another, we may consider them as functional groups. And if we choose we may have the four valences of silicon occupied by these groups, which will result in the high functionality of four. Or we can exchange one or more of these groups for nonhydrolyzable groups, such as organic radicals, so that the functionality can be decreased to 3, 2, 1, or 0. This flexibility of functionality makes possible a wide variation of properties without the addition of plasticizers and fillers, so that the term "tailoring the molecule" becomes in the case of the silicones something more than an empty phrase.

Condensation of Monofunctional Compounds

To get an exact picture of the polymerization of the silicones we should look first at monomers containing only one functional group. Let us assume we are handling a compound such as trimethyl chlorosilane, $(CH_3)_3SiCl$. This is a liquid, boiling at 57C°, which fumes in the air, giving off hydrochloric acid.

This liquid is dripped into about its own volume of water, vigorous stirring accompanying the mixing. The silicone polymerization goes forward readily, being catalyzed by the acid formed:

$$(CH_3)_3SiCl + H_2O \rightarrow (CH_3)_3SiOH + HCl$$
$$2(CH_3)_3SiOH \rightarrow (CH_3)_3Si{-}O{-}Si(CH_3)_3 + H_2O$$

The charge is heated and stirred for perhaps an hour to ensure completion of the reaction. The fluid product rises to the top. The acid-water lower layer is withdrawn, and the product is washed with water to remove traces of hydrochloric acid. The product can be distilled (boiling point, 99.5°C) if high purity is needed and is then ready for such uses as its properties may indicate.

The reaction described goes quite readily but can be speeded up, if desired, by the addition of some alcohol to the water. The function of the alcohol is to make the unreacted material more soluble in the aqueous layer. The greater ease of physical contact with the water hastens the hydrolysis of the chlorines. Condensation of hydroxyls then completes the reaction.

If the monomer used should be trimethyl ethoxysilane, $(CH_3)_3SiOC_2H_5$, catalytic quantities of acid should be added to the water. The alcohol formed on hydrolysis may be distilled off during the reaction or may be washed out later with water.

As far as monofunctional units are concerned, the one in which the three nonfunctional units are all methyl groups shows the most rapid reaction. As larger organic groups are used the condensation of the hydroxyls becomes more difficult, and in some cases the hydroxyls become so stable that considerable heating may be required to bring about condensation.

It will be recalled that in the description of the preparation of the

$$-\overset{|}{\underset{|}{Si}}-\overset{|}{\underset{|}{C}}-$$

bond, the point was made that aryl groups such as phenyl, $—C_6H_5—$, are rather readily split from the silicon by hot acid. This should tell us that in condensing a monofunctional unit in which phenyl is one of the organic constituents strong acid should not be used as a catalyst. Catalytic quantities of alkali should be used under such circumstances.

Condensation of Difunctional Compounds

The method for carrying out the condensation or polymerization of difunctional compounds is the same as that for the monofunctional. Of course, the products are of a different type, for here we meet up with the possibility of making truly large polymers.

One of the most important difunctional monomers in the preparation of commercial silicones is dimethyl dichlorosilane, $(CH_3)_2SiCl_2$. This is a liquid, boiling at 70°C, which fumes in moist air, giving off hydrochloric acid. We may use it as an example of the polymerization of all difunctional silanes.

All that is required to polymerize this material is that it be exposed to sufficient moisture to hydrolyze all the chlorines. It may be exposed to moist air, or treated with steam, or thrown into water or aqueous solvents. In all cases polymerization will occur, but the type of final product is dependent on the method of treatment.

There are two main types of polymer obtainable, cyclic polymers and linear polymers. Cyclic polymers are those in which the two ends of the same polymer condense to form a closed ring.

```
        CH3                CH3
        |                  |
O-------Si--------O--------Si--------O →
 \      |                  |        /
  \     CH3                CH3     /
   \                              /
CH3—Si—CH3          CH3—Si—CH3
     |                   |
     O[H                HO]

              CH3                   CH3
              |                     |
        CH3—Si----------O----------Si—CH3 + H2O
              |                     |
              O                     O
              |                     |
        CH3—Si—CH3         CH3—Si—CH3
               \                  /
                \                /
                 \              /
                        O
```

The two functional groups have been eliminated by condensation with one another, and further growth of the polymer by this mechanism is impossible.

Linear polymers are those which have escaped this "head-to-tail" condensation and have continued to react with other polymers to form:

$$
\begin{array}{ccccccc}
 & CH_3 & & CH_3 & & CH_3 & \\
 & | & & | & & | & \\
HO- & Si & -O- & Si & -O- & Si & -OH- \cdots \\
 & | & & | & & | & \\
 & CH_3 & & CH_3 & & CH_3 &
\end{array}
$$

As long as the two hydroxyls remain, growth can be, theoretically, unlimited.

Both cyclic and linear polymers have their own spheres of usefulness, and polymerization may be carried out in such a fashion that either one or the other is formed, as desired.

PREPARATION OF CYCLIC POLYMERS

As a general statement it may be said that cyclic polymers will be formed preferentially if the catalyst is strong and if solvent is present. For instance if dimethyl dichlorosilane is dripped into about 3 volumes of water and stirred vigorously, about 50 per cent of the product will be cyclic polymers. On completion of the reaction the product may be washed free of acid, dried, and distilled. It will be found that about half of the product is distillable, and that the distillate can be separated into fractions. The smallest unit, boiling at 170°C, is the cyclic tetramer, $[(CH_3)_2SiO]_4$; it will comprise about 50 per cent of the distillate. The remainder will be found to be cyclic pentamer, hexamer, heptamer, and so on, the amount obtainable decreasing as the molecular weight or boiling point increases.

A larger proportion of cyclics will be formed if the dimethyl dichlorosilane is first dissolved in a solvent such as ether and is then stirred or shaken vigorously with excess water.[137]

These methods, though simple, do not give as pure a product as might be desired. Small polymers which are not cyclic may distill over with the cyclics and act as contaminants.

One method of avoiding this difficulty is to heat the hydrolyzed product, prior to distillation, with 20 per cent hydrochloric acid.[138] This brings about further condensation of the noncyclic compounds and their boiling point becomes too high to permit of distillation. So the pure cyclics may be distilled away without contamination, leaving the high polymers as a residue in the flask.

Another method is to heat the hydrolyzed product with about 0.1 per cent sodium hydroxide.[139] This has the effect, first of all, of polymerizing the noncyclic material; but as the pot temperature is raised to the neighborhood of 200°C the reverse effect takes place and the alkali acts as a depolymerizer of the higher polymers, converting them to cyclic polymers. The result is that the entire charge becomes converted into cyclics and may be distilled away. It should be pointed out that, because of the high boiling point of some of the materials, the distillation should be carried out in the absence of oxygen, for at these high temperatures some oxidation can take place in the vapor state.

The same result can be obtained without alkali, but a temperature of between 350° and 400°C is required if the rearrangement into cyclics is to take place at a satisfactory rate. Table 33[48] gives some of the physical properties of the cyclic dimethyl siloxanes that have been separated.

TABLE 33

Formula	Boiling point, °C	Melting point, °C	Viscosity, cs at 25°C	Refractive index, n_D^{25}
$[(CH_3)_2SiO]_3$	133	64.5		
$[(CH_3)_2SiO]_4$	171	17.4	2.30	1.3935
$[(CH_3)_2SiO]_5$	204.5	−44	3.87	1.3958
$[(CH_3)_2SiO]_6$	236	−3	6.62	1.3996
$[(CH_3)_2SiO]_7$	147 at 20 mm Hg	−32	9.47	1.4018
$[(CH_3)_2SiO]_8$	168 at 20 mm Hg	31.5	13.23[a]	1.4039

[a] Determined on the supercooled liquid.

The same general principles apply to the preparation of cyclics other than those of dimethyl siloxanes. As the organic groups become larger the boiling points of the cyclics rise, and it becomes difficult to isolate the higher cyclics as satisfactorily as those of the dimethyl siloxanes. In addition they may be less heat stable, and pyrolysis may destroy them before they can be captured.

PREPARATION OF LINEAR POLYMERS

The linear polymers with their great range of molecular sizes or viscosities have much more commercial interest than the cyclic polymers. Their wide industrial uses are described in Chapter 2.

The dimethyl siloxane polymers are the most widely used of the linear polymers, and the method of polymerizing them sets the pattern for most of the others.

The simplest way to make these linear polymers is to stir the dichloride with excess water. As described in the previous section both cyclic and linear molecules are formed. The cyclic compounds can be distilled off, leaving the linears as residue. This method, though simple, has two disadvantages. Only part of the product is recovered as linear polymers; and they are of low viscosity.

Both the yield of linear polymers and the viscosity can be increased by a method that calls for the use of dimethyl diethoxysilane, $(CH_3)_2Si(OC_2H_5)_2$, rather than the dichloride, $(CH_3)_2SiCl_2$. Equal volumes of 20 per cent hydrochloric acid and 95 per cent alcohol are mixed. To this mixture an equal volume of the diethoxy compound is added, and the charge is refluxed for some hours. Although the solution is homogeneous at the start, there is a separation as the reaction proceeds, the silicone polymer forming the top layer. At the conclusion the water layer is drawn off and the polymer is washed to free it from alcohol and acid. By this method the cyclic polymers are reduced to between 15 and 20 per cent. The viscosity of the polymer as prepared is generally about 25 centistokes.

This can be increased to about 200 centistokes by distilling off cyclic compounds and then holding the residue for some hours at about 200°C under nonoxidizing conditions.[138]

Another method that has been reported is that of pouring the dichlorosilane onto solid powders of hydrated inorganic salts, such as copper hydroxide, ferric sulfate, sodium sulfate, etc. The water in these hydrated compounds acts as the hydrolyzing medium and the metal salt acts as a condensing agent, withdrawing the water of condensation. Very viscous polymers can be prepared by this method.[140]

A still different method is described. This requires that the hydrolyzable groups should be both ethoxy and chloride in substantially equal proportion. When ferric chloride is added to such a mixture the following reaction takes place:[118]

$$-\overset{|}{\underset{|}{Si}}OC_2H_5 + -\overset{|}{\underset{|}{Si}}Cl \xrightarrow{FeCl_3} -\overset{|}{\underset{|}{Si}}-O-\overset{|}{\underset{|}{Si}}- + C_2H_5Cl$$

In some specific cases this turns out to be a useful method of polymerization.

It will be noted that nearly all the methods described yield low-viscosity fluids. And if the monomers used are quite pure it will be found that the fluids do not have stable viscosity but show a slow increase with time. The reason is that these linear molecules are still terminated by hydroxyl groups which can condense further, although this condensation is sluggish in the absence of a strong catalyst.

Strong catalysts which can promote further condensation are available. By their use it is possible to increase polymer size or viscosity to the point where flow is scarcely observable. These catalysts can, for the most part, be classed as strong alkalies or strong acids.

There is an apparent paradox about their catalytic ability, for they bring about both polymerization and depolymerization. The mechanism that predominates can be governed by amount of catalyst, temperature, and pressure. Increased amount of catalyst, high temperature, and low pressure are factors which promote depolymerization, while the reverse favors polymerization.

The very high polymers are not generally made directly from the monomers. This is because of the difficulty of obtaining difunctional monomers which are substantially free from monofunctional and trifunctional monomers. If a monofunctional monomer should react with a polymer end, all further growth in that direction is stopped:

$$(CH_3)_3SiOH + HO\overset{\displaystyle CH_3}{\underset{\displaystyle CH_3}{\overset{|}{\underset{|}{Si}}}}—O—\overset{\displaystyle CH_3}{\underset{\displaystyle CH_3}{\overset{|}{\underset{|}{Si}}}}OH \rightarrow$$

$$(CH_3)_3Si—O—\overset{\displaystyle CH_3}{\underset{\displaystyle CH_3}{\overset{|}{\underset{|}{Si}}}}—O—\overset{\displaystyle CH_3}{\underset{\displaystyle CH_3}{\overset{|}{\underset{|}{Si}}}}OH$$

If a trifunctional monomer should react it will destroy the complete linearity of the molecule and will promote gel formation.

A method commonly used to obtain pure difunctional units is first to convert the monomer to cyclics by one of the methods described in the previous section. The cyclics, which, of course, are made up of nothing but difunctional units, can be distilled away from polymers of other types which may contain mono- or trifunctional units. Then the strong catalysts, with their Dr. Jekyll and Mr. Hyde type of action, can open up or depolymerize the cyclics and at the same time convert the product to a large linear polymer.

One procedure for this is to add to a charge of pure cyclics about 0.1 to 1 per cent of 97 per cent sulfuric acid and stir vigorously. The viscosity very quickly starts to rise. When the reaction has proceeded to the desired extent the acid is washed out with water. If the viscosity is very high it may be necessary to dissolve the product in some solvent such as benzene to facilitate washing.[141]

An alkali such as sodium hydroxide may be used in a similar fashion. About 0.1 per cent sodium hydroxide is added to the charge of cyclics, and the same procedure is followed with substantially the same result. A great deal, if not all, of the alkali may be removed by treating the product with CO_2. The alkali is converted to the carbonate which may be removed by filtration.[142]

The highest polymers to be made by these methods are those in which only methyl groups are attached to silicon. These products may be so viscous that they can be cut into chunks and handled like solids. Nevertheless they show true flow and are completely soluble in organic solvents.

The viscosity of these high polymers remains stable, for the potentially condensable hydroxyl groups that remain are relatively few in number and their mutual contact is inhibited because of the high viscosity. But if low-viscosity fluids are prepared they will be found to be less stable because the reactive hydroxyl groups are more numerous and the lower viscosity permits easier physical contact.

There is a very simple and effective method of stabilizing the low-molecular-weight polymers. It has frequently been pointed out that monofunctional units should be absent if large polymers are hoped for. They stop the growth of the polymer. So to obtain polymers which will not grow larger, or which, in other words, will have a stable viscosity, it is only necessary to add some monofunctional material. A common additive for this purpose is hexamethyl disiloxane, $(CH_3)_3SiOSi(CH_3)_3$, which was described under "monofunctional compounds." This compound will be opened up or depolymerized by the catalyst, and can then condense again with a polymer end. It will be evident that as increasing amounts of this material are added the average size of the molecules will decrease and the viscosity will become lower. It is possible to construct a table showing the amount of this material to be added in order to end up with a given viscosity for the final product. Even after a high polymer has been prepared its viscosity can be reduced by heating it with a monofunctional compound and catalyst. Not only does the average molecular size become smaller but, as the reaction continues, the monofunctional units become more evenly distributed, resulting in a more uniform molecular size throughout the charge. The adjustment to more uniform distribution is often referred to as "equilibration." By the means described, viscosity-stable polymers of almost any desired viscosity can be prepared.[137,143]

Such illustrations as have been given have referred to methyl-substituted materials. Of course, any other type may be used, depending on the properties desired in the final product. It will be recognized that as bigger alkyl groups, such as ethyl, propyl, butyl, etc., are used, it becomes more difficult to make very large polymers, for condensation is more sluggish. These substituents bring about less stability toward oxidation and a greater change in viscosity with change of temperature. But they have better compatibility with purely organic materials, and they show better lubricating properties. The use of aryl groups, such as phenyl, naphthyl, etc., brings about some of these advantages and in addition, the resistance to oxidation is improved rather than lessened. It is, however, difficult to polymerize these to very high polymers. Acid catalysts are liable to cause cleavage of the aryl groups from silicon, so that it is advisable to use an alkaline catalyst.

Condensation of Trifunctional Compounds

The mechanism of the reaction in the condensation of trifunctional compounds is exactly the same as for the mono- and difunctional compounds. But for practical purposes the entire reaction should not take place too quickly. The end products of polymerization of these materials are infusible and insoluble resins, and if the entire reaction was carried out at once, it would be impossible to handle the product satisfactorily. So in actual practice the desired monomer or mixture of monomers is hydrolyzed and heated just as with the difunctional monomers. Heating is continued until some predetermined viscosity is reached and the product is then cooled and diluted with solvent. The lower temperature and the presence of solvent hinder further polymerization. The solution can then be used as a paint vehicle, a coating, or an impregnant. When it has been applied, it is again heated, and the reaction that had previously been stopped picks up where it left off and continues to completion. The end product is a thermoset resin possessing properties that depend in part on the nature of the monomer, the catalyst used, the amount of heating, and various other factors.

A variant of the procedure has been described.[144] In this method difunctional units only are used as starting materials. The organic groups attached to silicon may be alkyls, such as methyl, ethyl, etc., or aryls, such as phenyl, tolyl, etc. The product of hydrolysis consists largely of cyclic groups, mostly trimer and tetramer. By heating to 200–300° and bubbling air through the mass it is possible to oxidize some of the alkyl groups, or by treating with acid at about 170–180°C the aryl groups may be removed by hydrolysis. Regardless of which method is chosen (and both may be used in conjunction), an organic group is removed from the ring and replaced by a hydroxyl group. The hydroxyl groups may then condense, and the product is a chain of cyclics. The treatment may be continued to the point where other organic groups in this chain are removed. This provides a point for cross linking, and resinous properties then appear. This treatment is continued until the viscosity has reached a point where the product is tacky and semiresinous. Solvent is added and the material is ready for application. Cure can be completed *in situ*. This principle operates whether the original product of hydrolysis is cyclic or linear.

Few, if any, silicone resins are prepared from trifunctional materials only, for the final products are too brittle for practical use. To confer some flexibility it is generally advisable to add some difunctional units to dilute the number of cross links. The amount of difunctional units required to prepare a resin to definite specifications must be arrived at empirically, and experience is about the only guide.

The resin properties will depend not only on the average functionality but also on the type of the organic substituents on silicon. The substituents play a double role, for they can be used to alter the physical properties, such as flexibility, hardness, or heat stability, and they also determine to a considerable degree the ease with which hydroxyls on silicon condense, or, in other words, the speed of cure. And the speed of cure must lie between the limits of being slow enough to have good shelf life and fast enough that it can be cured in reasonable time.

It should be clear that the formulation of a resin is as much an art as a science. No simple rules can be given that will be a guide to good resin manufacture, although some general statements can be made to indicate the directions in which to turn if certain properties are wanted.

Flexibility can be obtained by the use of increasing amounts of difunctional units, and conversely hardness (which also may mean brittleness) can be obtained by the use of trifunctional units. Phenyl substituents on silicon contribute to toughness and hardness of film more than short-chain alkyls, such as methyls, do. But the presence of aryl substituents, such as phenyl groups, brings about slower cure. This is an advantage as far as shelf life is concerned but may be a detriment in application. So a balance must be struck between all these factors while at the same time obtaining the properties required in the specifications.

Other factors may also enter into both the preparation of a resin and the final cure. If acid hydrolysis is resorted to it will be found that high acid strength provides a resin of slow cure, while low acid strength generally results in a resin with fast cure. Hydrolysis and condensation can be carried out in solvents, and the final properties may be affected as a result of the solvent used. The presence of ketones as solvent is advocated as a help in combatting gel formation during polymerization.[145] Heat resistance is reported to be improved by heating a solution of a resin with a hydrated salt, such as ferric chloride or copper sulphate.[146] The speed of final cure is improved by the addition of a metallic oxide, such as those of lead or cobalt. The naphthenates may also be used.[147]

B. *Other Types of Polymers Containing Silicon*

The foregoing discussion relates to the formation of those polymers that contain silicon-oxygen-silicon bonds. Other types of polymers may be prepared in which the silicons are bridged by carbon

$$\begin{array}{ccccc} & | & & | & & | & \\ — & Si & — & C & — & Si & — \\ & | & & | & & | & \end{array}$$

or by nitrogen

$$\begin{array}{ccccccc} & | & & | & & | & \\ — & Si & — & NH & — & Si & — \\ & | & & & & | & \end{array}$$

instead of by oxygen. Neither of these types is in commercial production, but both are potentially useful and deserve at least passing reference. Still other types are the so-called "modified" silicones in which the functional groups are supplied by both silicon-containing compounds and organic compounds. Lastly, the organic substituents on silicon may be such that they can react with organic reagents, such as vinyl and allyl compounds, and so superimpose an organic polymerization on the silicone polymer.

Academically these compounds have no right to the name of silicone. But the same intermediates are used in their formation as are used in forming the silicones, and it is quite likely that if they become of commercial significance, they will be referred to as silicones. They may be considered as foster children who have acquired the name by adoption.

CARBON BRIDGES $\left(-\overset{|}{\underset{|}{Si}}-\overset{|}{\underset{|}{C}}-\overset{|}{\underset{|}{Si}}-\right)$

As has been suggested, we can call these polymers "silicones" if we are generous in our interpretation of the term. But to refer to them as "sil-ox-anes" is altogether too magnanimous. If we wish to be specific, the best name is "sil-carb-anes." This designation may be further broken down into "sil-methylenes" if the bridging group is methylene $-CH_2-$, or "sil-ethylenes" if it is ethylene, $-CH_2-CH_2-$, etc.

The methods for preparing simple compounds of this type have been described (page 252). The same methods may be used to prepare higher-molecular-weight polymers. It will be recalled that the first step in the preparation is that of chlorinating an organic group on silicon:

$$Cl-\overset{\overset{\large R}{|}}{\underset{\underset{\large R}{|}}{Si}}-CH_3 + Cl_2 \rightarrow Cl-\overset{\overset{\large R}{|}}{\underset{\underset{\large R}{|}}{Si}}-CH_2Cl + HCl$$

The product can be polymerized by either the Grignard or the sodium method (pages 246 and 250).

With the Grignard method the reactions are

$$\mathrm{Cl{-}}\underset{\textstyle \mathrm{R}}{\overset{\textstyle \mathrm{R}}{\mathrm{Si}}}\mathrm{{-}CH_2Cl} + \mathrm{Mg} \rightarrow \mathrm{Cl{-}}\underset{\textstyle \mathrm{R}}{\overset{\textstyle \mathrm{R}}{\mathrm{Si}}}\mathrm{{-}CH_2MgCl}$$

$$\mathrm{Cl{-}}\underset{\textstyle \mathrm{R}}{\overset{\textstyle \mathrm{R}}{\mathrm{Si}}}\mathrm{{-}CH_2}\boxed{\mathrm{MgCl} + \mathrm{Cl}}\mathrm{{-}}\underset{\textstyle \mathrm{R}}{\overset{\textstyle \mathrm{R}}{\mathrm{Si}}}\mathrm{{-}CH_2MgCl} \rightarrow$$

$$\mathrm{Cl{-}}\underset{\textstyle \mathrm{R}}{\overset{\textstyle \mathrm{R}}{\mathrm{Si}}}\mathrm{{-}CH_2{-}}\underset{\textstyle \mathrm{R}}{\overset{\textstyle \mathrm{R}}{\mathrm{Si}}}\mathrm{{-}CH_2MgCl} + \mathrm{MgCl_2}$$

With the sodium method the reaction is

$$\mathrm{Cl{-}}\underset{\textstyle \mathrm{R}}{\overset{\textstyle \mathrm{R}}{\mathrm{Si}}}\mathrm{{-}CH_2}\boxed{\mathrm{Cl} + 2\mathrm{Na} + \mathrm{Cl}}\mathrm{{-}}\underset{\textstyle \mathrm{R}}{\overset{\textstyle \mathrm{R}}{\mathrm{Si}}}\mathrm{{-}CH_2Cl} \rightarrow$$

$$\mathrm{Cl{-}}\underset{\textstyle \mathrm{R}}{\overset{\textstyle \mathrm{R}}{\mathrm{Si}}}\mathrm{{-}CH_2{-}}\underset{\textstyle \mathrm{R}}{\overset{\textstyle \mathrm{R}}{\mathrm{Si}}}\mathrm{{-}CH_2Cl} + 2\mathrm{NaCl}$$

In both cases the reaction can, theoretically, continue indefinitely.

The point to note in the reaction in both cases is that it takes place between the chlorine on carbon and the chlorine on silicon. With the sodium method there is some reaction between two chlorines attached to silicon and also between two chlorines attached to carbon, but this is generally in minor amount.

Polymers prepared with this type of bonding have many of the properties of the siloxane type for they are heat-resistant (although less so than the siloxanes), water-repellent, and inert to many reagents. The —Si—C—Si— bonding is not as susceptible to rearrangement as the —Si—O—Si—. That means that the heating of high-molecular-weight materials is less likely to result in breakdown and rearrangement to low-boiling cyclic compounds. It also means that there is greater difficulty in polymerizing the low-molecular-weight cyclic compounds to high-molecular-weight linear polymers.

The chemistry and preparation of compounds of this type are described in a number of publications.[148]

NITROGEN BRIDGES $(-\overset{|}{\underset{|}{Si}}-NH-\overset{|}{\underset{|}{Si}}-)$

If we wish to be specific in the naming of polymers having nitrogen bridges between silicons we should refer to them as "sil-az-anes."

Methods of preparing the $-Si-NH_2$ bonding were described in a previous section (see page 228).

Polymers may be prepared from compounds containing the $-SiNH_2$ grouping simply by allowing them to stand at room temperature in the absence of moisture:

$$H_2N-\overset{R}{\underset{R}{Si}}-NH_2 + NH_2-\overset{R}{\underset{R}{Si}}-NH_2 \rightarrow$$

$$H_2N-\overset{R}{\underset{R}{Si}}-NH-\overset{R}{\underset{R}{Si}}-NH_2 + NH_3$$

Application of heat speeds up the reaction.[115] On exposure to moisture they may be converted to siloxanes with the elimination of ammonia:

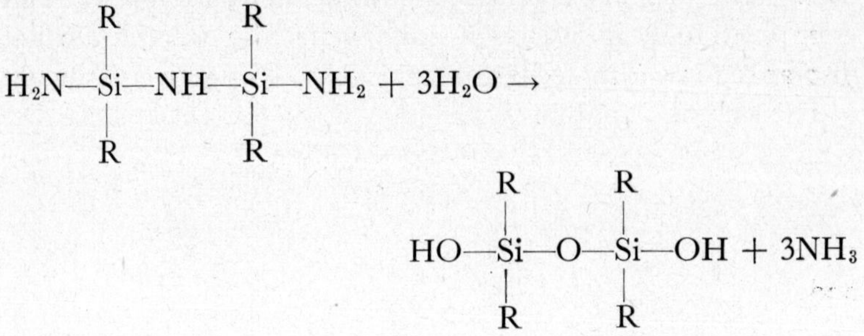

$$\begin{array}{ccccc} & R & & R & \\ & | & & | & \\ H_2N- & Si & -NH- & Si & -NH_2 + 3H_2O \rightarrow \\ & | & & | & \\ & R & & R & \end{array}$$

$$\begin{array}{ccccc} & R & & R & \\ & | & & | & \\ HO- & Si & -O- & Si & -OH + 3NH_3 \\ & | & & | & \\ & R & & R & \end{array}$$

Polymers of this type are not in commercial use.

"MODIFIED" SILICONES

The so-called "modified" silicone polymers are prepared by reacting a silicone intermediate with an organic compound containing more than one hydroxyl group, such as a glycol, $HO-(CH_2)_x-OH$, or glycerol $HOCH_2-CH(OH)-CH_2OH$. The reaction is generally carried out by using a silicone "ester" as the intermediate. The reaction with glycerol is shown:

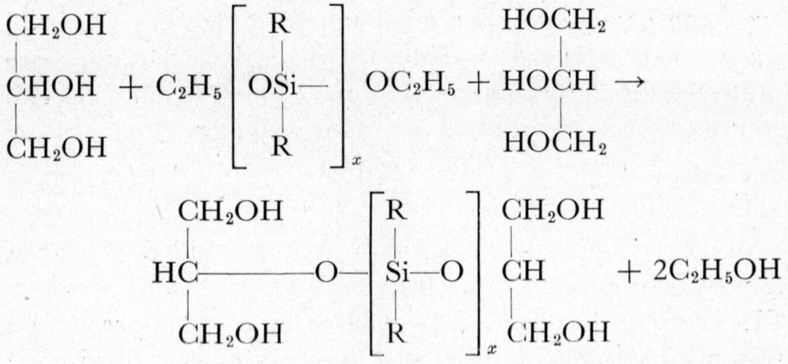

$$\begin{array}{l} CH_2OH \\ | \\ CHOH \\ | \\ CH_2OH \end{array} + C_2H_5\left[\begin{array}{c} R \\ | \\ OSi- \\ | \\ R \end{array}\right]_x OC_2H_5 + \begin{array}{l} HOCH_2 \\ \;\;\;\;| \\ HOCH \\ \;\;\;\;| \\ HOCH_2 \end{array} \rightarrow$$

$$\begin{array}{l} CH_2OH \\ | \\ HC \text{———} O- \\ | \\ CH_2OH \end{array}\left[\begin{array}{l} R \\ | \\ Si-O \\ | \\ R \end{array}\right]_x \begin{array}{l} CH_2OH \\ | \\ CH \\ | \\ CH_2OH \end{array} + 2C_2H_5OH$$

The siloxane part of the molecule may be large or small, and the reaction with the glycerol may give high- or low-molecular-weight polymers, as desired. The final product can then be reacted with fatty acids and phthalic anhydride to give an alkyd type of polymer containing more or less siloxane groupings. The original reaction is nothing more or less than an ester exchange in which a high-molecular-weight alcohol displaces a lower-molecular-weight alcohol attached to silicon.

The polymer contains both

$$-\overset{|}{\underset{|}{Si}}-O-\overset{|}{\underset{|}{Si}}-$$

and

$$-\overset{|}{\underset{|}{Si}}-O-C-$$

bondings. Although the point has been made that silicon "esters"

$$-\overset{|}{\underset{|}{Si}}-O-\overset{|}{\underset{|}{C}}-$$

are unstable to moisture, the instability decreases as the size of the organic group increases. So polymers of this type which are large enough to have good film-forming properties will show good moisture stability, particularly when they are protected by large organic groups. The siloxane linkages contribute heat stability to the whole polymer.[149]

VINYL-TYPE POLYMERS

Another type of polymerization may be added to that of siloxane formation if unsaturated radicals such as vinyl, $CH_2{=}CH-$, or allyl, $CH_2{=}CH-CH_2-$, are present on silicon. Polymers of this type have been described.[132,150] The siloxane polymerization is carried out first by the usual methods. Additional polymerization may then take place through the unsaturated radicals by the use of peroxides. A silicone the organic radicals of which are all unsaturated does not have good heat resistance and the most promising use of these materials appears to be as copolymers with the usual type of siloxane or organic polymers. The addition of 15 to 20 per cent of these units speeds up the setting of siloxane resins and increases the hardness. When added to organic polymers the craze resistance is improved.

They have been employed with good effect as a primer on glass fabric which is used to prepare laminates with organic resins.[151]

LITERATURE CITED

1. Quoted by Mellor, J. W., "A Comprehensive Treatise on Inorganic and Theoretical Chemistry," Vol. VI, p. 135, Longmans, Green & Co., Inc., New York, 1925.
2. "Chymia," Vol. 2, p. 77, University of Pennsylvania Press, Philadelphia, 1949.
3. Quoted by Mellor, J. W., "A Comprehensive Treatise on Inorganic and Theoretical Chemistry," Vol. VI, p. 136, Longmans, Green & Co., Inc., New York, 1925.
4. *Ibid.*, p. 136.
5. Berzelius, J. J., *Pogg. Ann.*, *1*, 169, 1824.
6. Berzelius, J. J., *ibid.*, p. 219, 1824.
7. Persoz, M., *Ann. Chim. et phys.* (2), *44*, 315, 1830.
8. Ebelman, J. J., *Compt. rend.*, *19*, 398, 1844.
9. Wöhler, F., and H. Buff, *Ann.*, *103*, 218, 1857.
10. Buff, H., and F. Wöhler, *ibid.*, *104*, 94, 1857.
11. Deville H., and F. Wöhler, *ibid.*, *110*, 248, 1859.
12. Wöhler, F., *ibid.*, *127*, 257, 1863.
13. Wöhler, F., *ibid.*, *127*, 268, 1863.
14. Schiel, J., *ibid.*, *120*, 94, 1861.
15. Friedel, C., and J. M. Crafts, *Compt. rend.*, *56*, 592, 1863.
16. Friedel, C., and J. M. Crafts, *Ann.*, *136*, 203, 1865.
17. Friedel, C., and J. M. Crafts, *ibid.*, *138*, 19, 1866.
18. Friedel, C., and A. Ladenburg, *ibid.*, *143*, 118, 1867.
19. Friedel, C., and A. Ladenburg, *Compt. rend.*, *68*, 923, 1869.
20. Friedel, C., and A. Ladenburg, *Ann.*, *159*, 259, 1871.
21. Ladenburg, A., *ibid.*, *164*, 300, 1872.
22. Ladenburg, A., *ibid.*, *173*, 143, 1874.
23. Combes, C., *Compt. rend.*, *122*, 531, 1896.
24. Stock, A., and C. Massenez, *Ber.*, *45*, 3539, 1912.
25. Stock, A., and C. Somieski, *Ber.*, *49*, 111, 1916.
26. Moissan, H., and S. Smiles, *Compt. rend.*, *134*, 569, 1902.
27. Stock, A., and C. Somieski, *Ber.*, *50*, 1739, 1917.

28. Stock, A., and C. Somieski, *ibid.*, *52*, 695, 1919.
29. Nebergall, W. H., *J. Am. Chem. Soc.*, *72*, 4702, 1950.
30. Schumb, W. C., J. Ackerman, and C. M. Saffer, *ibid.*, *60*, 2486, 1938.
31. Bygden, A., *Ber.*, *44*, 2640, 1911; *45*, 707, 1912.
32. Blix, M., and W. Wirbelauer, *Ber.*, *36*, 4220, 1903.
33. Schlenk, W., J. Renning, and G. Racky, *ibid.*, *44*, 1178, 1911.
34. (a) Andrianov, K. A., *J. Gen. Chem.* (*U.S.S.R.*), *8*, 1255, 1938.
(b) Dolgov, B. A., and Y. Volnov, *ibid.*, *1*, 91, 1931.
(c) Koton, M. M., *ibid.*, *12*, 1435, 1939.
35. Kipping, F. S., *J. Chem. Soc.*, *101*, 2125, 1912.
36. Kipping, F. S., *ibid.*, *91*, 209, 1907.
37. Kipping, F. S., *ibid.*, *130*, 104, 1927.
38. Kipping, F. S., and J. E. Hackford, *ibid.*, *99*, 138, 1911.
39. Kipping, F. S., *ibid.*, *119*, 647, 1921.
40. Kipping, F. S., *Proc. Roy. Soc. 159A*, 131, 1937.
41. Williams, C. G., *ibid.*, *10*, 516, 1860.
42. Pickles, S. S., *J. Chem. Soc.*, *97*, 1088, 1910.
43. Staudinger, H., *C. A.*, *14*, 3423, 1920; *Ber. 53B*, 1073, 1920.
44. Staudinger, H., *Ber.*, *59*, 3079, 1926.
45. U.S. Patents 2,389,802 to 2,389,807 to R. R. McGregor and E. L. Warrick.
46. Atkins, D. C., C. M. Murphy, and C. E. Saunders, *Ind. Eng. Chem.*, *39*, 1395, 1947.
47. Collyer, H. J., and E. M. Dannenberg, paper presented before Cleveland Meeting, Rubber Division, American Chemical Society, May 27, 1947.
48. Hunter, M. J., J. F. Hyde, E. L. Warrick, and H. J. Fletcher, *J. Am. Chem. Soc.*, *68*, 667, 1946.
49. Wilcock, D. F., *ibid.*, *68*, 691, 1946.
50. Hunter, M. J., E. L. Warrick, J. F. Hyde, and C. C. Currie, *ibid.*, *68*, 2284, 1946.
51. Bridgman, P. W., *Proc. Am. Acad. Arts Sci.*, *77*, 115, 1949.
52. Currie, C. C., and B. F. Smith, *Ind. Eng. Chem.*, *42*, 2457, 1950.
53. Fitzsimmons, V. G., D. L. Pickett, R. O. Militz, and W. A. Zisman, *Trans. ASME*, *68*, 365, 1946.
54. Bates, O. K., *Ind. Eng. Chem.*, *41*, 1966, 1949.
55. Wright, N., and M. J. Hunter, *J. Am. Chem. Soc.*, *69*, 803, 1947.

56. Burkhard, C. A., and E. H. Winslow, *ibid.*, *72*, 3276, 1950.
57. Weissler, A., *ibid.*, *71*, 93, 1949.
58. Johannson, O. K., and J. J. Torok, *Proc. IRE*, *34*, 296, 1946.
59. Gilbert, P. T., *Science*, *114*, 637, 1951.
60. Norton, F. J., *Gen. Elec. Rev.*, August, 1944, pp. 6–16.
61. U. S. Patent 2,547,396 to M. A. Joanen.
62. U. S. Patents 2,416,503 and 2,416,504 to C. E. Troutman and H. A. Ambrose.
63. U. S. Patent 2,585,522 to E. V. Watts and B. Folda.
64. O'Connor, B. E., *SAE Journal*, *54*, 389, 1946.
65. Fitzsimmons, V. G., D. L. Pickett, R. O. Militz, and W. A. Zisman, *Trans. ASME*, *68*, 361, 1946.
66. Morris, A. L., *Proc. Inst. Elec. Engrs.* (*London*), *96* (Part III), 279, 1949.
67. U. S. Patents 2,588,365 and 2,588,366 to F. L. Dennett.
68. Smith, J. E., *Chem. Eng. News*, *29*, 551, 1951.
69. Private Communication from F. L. Dennett, Dow Corning Corporation.
70. U. S. Patent 2,588,367 to F. L. Dennett.
71. U. S. Patent 2,428,608 to S. L. Bass.
72. Lehman, A. J., *Bull. Assoc. Food & Drug Officials of the U. S.*, *14*, No. 3, 89, July, 1950.
73. Quin, A. H., J. A. Austin, and K. Ratcliff, *J. Am. Vet. Med. Assoc.*, *114*, 313, 1949.
74. Grant, G., and C. C. Currie, *Mech. Eng.*, *73*, 311, 1951.
75. Brophy, J. E., R. O. Militz, and W. A. Zisman, *Trans. ASME*, *68*, 355, 1946.
76. Brophy, J. E., J. Larson, and R. O. Militz, *ibid.*, *70*, 929, 1948.
77. Johnson, R. L., D. Godfrey, and E. E. Bisson, *Nat. Advisory Comm. Aeronaut. Technical Notes*, 2076, April, 1950.
78. (a) U. S. Patents 2,584,340 to 2,584,344 to J. T. Goodwin and M. J. Hunter.
    (b) U. S. Patent 2,584,351 to M. J. Hunter and L. A. Rauner.
    (c) U. S. Patent 2,587,295 to C. D. Doyle and H. C. Nelson.
    (d) U. S. Patent 2,589,243 to J. T. Goodwin and M. J. Hunter.
79. Arntzen, C. E., and R. D. Rowley, *Materials & Methods*, *35*, 82, 1952.
80. Bromstead, E. J., and M. A. Glaser, *Org. Finishing*, *9*, No. 3, 21, 1948.

81. (a) Staff Report, *Modern Plastics*, *29*, 106, April, 1952.
(b) Hoffman, K. R., *ibid.*, *30*, 146, November, 1952.
82. Axilrod, B. M., and M. A. Sherman, *J. Research Nat. Bur. Standards*, *45*, 65, 1950.
83. Walker, H. P., *Elec. Mfg.*, *46* (No. 6), 115, 1950.
84. U. S. Patent 1,561,988 to A. P. Laurie.
85. Anderegg, F. O., *Progressive Architecture*, *32*, 94, 1951.
86. Anderegg, F. O., *ASTM Bull.*, No. 171, p. 51, 1951.
87. Moses, G. L., *Westinghouse Engr.*, *9*, 168, 1949.
88. Grant, G., T. A. Kauppi, G. L. Moses, and G. P. Gibson, *Trans. Am. Inst. Elec. Engrs.*, *68*, Part 2, 1133, 1949.
89. Dow Corning Corporation, *Silastic Facts*, No. 10, p. 7, September, 1950.
90. (a) U. S. Patent 2,448,565 to J. G. E. Wright and C. S. Oliver.
(b) U. S. Patent 2,460,795 to E. L. Warrick.
(c) U. S. Patent 2,541,137 to E. L. Warrick.
(d) U. S. Patent 2,560,498 to E. L. Warrick.
91. U. S. Patent 2,431,878 to R. R. McGregor and E. L. Warrick.
92. U. S. Patent 2,541,851 to J. G. E. Wright.
93. Rowe, V. K., H. C. Spencer, and S. L. Bass, *J. Ind. Hyg. Toxicol.*, *30*, 332–352, 1948.
94. Barondes, R. de R., W. D. Judge, C. G. Towne, and M. L. Baxter, *Military Surgeon*, *106*, 379–387, 1950.
95. McNamara, B. O., E. A. McKay, and M. M. Quille, *Federation Proc.*, *9*, 301, 1950.
96. Rowe, V. K., H. C. Spencer, and S. L. Bass, *Arch. Ind. Hyg. and Occupational Med.*, *1*, 539, 1950.
97. Child, G. P., H. O. Paquin, and W. B. Deichmann, *ibid.*, *3*, 479, 1951.
98. Smyth, H. F. Jr., and Jane Seaton, *J. Ind. Hyg. Toxicol.*, *22*, 288–296, 1940.
99. Badinand, A., and M. Barlier, *Excerpta Med.*, *2*, No. 9, Sec. 2, Item 4961, 1949.
100. Clark, L. C., F. Gollan, and V. B. Gupta, *Science*, *111*, 85, 1950.
101. Moe, G. K., S. D. Malton, B. R. Rennick, and W. A. Freyburger, *J. Pharmacol. Exp. Therap.*, *94*, 319, 1948.
102. Skeggs, L. T., and J. R. Leonards, *Science*, *108*, 212, 1948.
103. Darling, G. H., and J. G. O. Spencer, *Brit. Med. J.*, *300*, 1951.
104. Crowley, M., and F. J. Ostrander, *Science*, *111*, 542, 1948.

105. Koffler, H., and M. C. Goldschmidt, *Ind. Eng. Chem.*, *42*, 1819, 1950.
106. Clark, L. C., V. B. Gupta, and F. Gollan, *Proc. Soc. Exp. Biol. Med.*, *74*, 468–71, 1950.
107. Talbot, J. R., J. K. MacGregor, and F. W. Crowe, *J. Invest. Dermatol.*, *17*, 125–126, 1951.
108. Grossman, L. I., *J. Am. Dental Assoc.*, *43*, 265, 1941.
109. Private communication from Dr. A. J. Lehman, head of the Department of Pharmacology of the Federal Food and Drug Administration, Washington, D.C.
110. Private Communication from Dr. Leland C. Clark, Fels Research Institute, Antioch College, Yellow Springs, Ohio.
111. McNamara, B. P., E. A. McKay, and M. M. Quille, *Federation Proc.*, *9*, 301, 1950.
112. Rowe, V. K., H. C. Spencer, and S. L. Bass, *J. Ind. Hyg. Toxicol.*, *30*, 332–352, 1948.
113. U. S. Patent 2,380,995 to E. G. Rochow.
114. Vigoroux, E., and Hugot, *Compt. rend.*, *136*, 1670, 1903.
115. U. S. Patents 2,579,416 to 2,579,418 to N. D. Charonis.
116. Sauer, R. O., *J. Am. Chem. Soc.*, *66*, 1707, 1944.
117. U. S. Patent 2,381,137 to W. I. Patnode and R. O. Sauer.
118. U. S. Patent 2,485,928 to P. C. Servais.
119. U. S. Patent 2,447,873 to E. G. Rochow.
120. Stock, A., "Hydrides of Boron and Silicon," Oxford University Press, New York, 1933.
121. Rochow, E. G., *J. Am. Chem. Soc.*, *67*, 963, 1945.
122. Rochow, E. G., "An Introduction to the Chemistry of the Silicones," 2d ed., John Wiley & Sons, Inc., New York, 1951.
123. U. S. Patent 2,380,057 to R. R. McGregor and E. L. Warrick.
124. (a) Sommer, L. H., E. W. Pietrusza, and F. C. Whitmore, *J. Am. Chem. Soc.*, *69*, 188, 1947.
(b) Burkhard, C. A., and R. H. Krieble, *ibid.*, *69*, 2687, 1947.
(c) Barry, A. J., L. DePree, J. W. Gilkey, and D. E. Hook, *ibid.*, *69*, 2916, 1947.
125. U. S. Patent 2,532,493 to D. B. Hatcher.
126. Schumb, W. C., and C. M. Saffer, *J. Am. Chem. Soc.*, *63*, 93, 1941.
127. Goodwin, J. T., W. E. Baldwin, and R. R. McGregor, *ibid.*, *69*, 2247, 1947.

128. Sommer, L. H., N. S. Marans, G. M. Goldberg, and J. Rockett, *ibid.*, *73*, 882, 1951.
129. Krieble, R. H., and J. R. Elliott, *ibid.*, *67*, 1810, 1945.
130. Sommer, L. H., and F. C. Whitmore, *ibid.*, *68*, 485, 1946.
131. Sommer, L. H., E. Dorfman, G. M. Goldberg, and F. C. Whitmore, *ibid.*, *68*, 488, 1946.
132. Hurd, D. T., and G. F. Roedel, *Ind. Eng. Chem.*, *40*, 2078, 1948.
133. Speier, J. L., *J. Am. Chem. Soc.*, *74*, 1003, 1952.
134. U. S. Patent 2,591,736 to L. H. Sommer.
135. Sommer, L. H., J. R. Gold, G. M. Goldberg, and N. S. Marans, *J. Am. Chem. Soc.*, *71*, 1509, 1949.
136. (a) Noll, J. E., J. L. Speier, and B. F. Daubert, *ibid.*, *73*, 3867, 1951.
(b) Benkeser, R. A., and P. E. Brumfield, *ibid.*, *74*, 253, 1952.
137. Patnode, W., and D. F. Wilcock, *ibid.*, *68*, 358, 1946.
138. U. S. Patent 2,439,856 to R. R. McGregor and E. L. Warrick.
139. U. S. Patent 2,438,478 to J. F. Hyde.
140. U. S. Patent 2,452,416 to J. G. E. Wright.
141. U. S. Patent 2,469,883 to J. Marsden and G. F. Roedel.
142. U. S. Patent 2,542,334 to J. F. Hyde.
143. Hurd, C. B., *J. Am. Chem. Soc.*, *68*, 364, 1946.
144. U. S. Patent 2,371,050 to J. F. Hyde.
145. U. S. Patent 2,390,378 to J. Marsden.
146. U. S. Patent 2,389,477 to J. G. E. Wright.
147. U. S. Patent 2,516,047 to J. B. DeCosta.
148. (a) U. S. Patent 2,381,002 to W. I. Patnode and R. W. Schiessler.
(b) U. S. Patent 2,383,817 to E. G. Rochow.
(c) U. S. Patent 2,452,895 to B. A. Bluestein.
(d) U. S. Patent 2,507,512 to J. T. Goodwin.
(e) Goodwin, J. T., *J. Am. Chem. Soc.*, *69*, 2247, 1947.
(f) Bluestein, B. A., *ibid.*, *70*, 3068, 1948.
149. (a) U. S. Patents 2,584,340 to 2,584, 344 to J. T. Goodwin and M. J. Hunter.
(b) U. S. Patent 2,584,351 to M. J. Hunter and L. A. Rauner.
(c) U. S. Patent 2,587,295 to G. D. Doyle and H. C. Nelson.
(d) U. S. Patent 2,589,243 to J. T. Goodwin and M. J. Hunter.
150. (a) U. S. Patent 2,532,430 to C. O. Strother and G. H. Wagner.
(b) U. S. Patent 2,532,583 to L. W. Tyran.

(c) U. S. Patents 2,595,727 and 2,595,730 to J. Swiss and C. E. Arntzen.

151. (a) Arne, F., ed., *Chem. Eng.*, *58*, 198, September, 1951.
(b) *Proc. 6th Annual Tech. Session, Reinforced Plastics Div., Soc. of the Plastics Industry, Inc.*, Sec. 12, p. 1., Feb. 28, 1951.
(c) Bjorksten, J., and L. L. Yaeger, *Modern Plastics*, *29*, 124, July, 1952.
(d) Jellinek, M. H., *ibid.*, *30*, 150, November, 1952.

152. Johnson, W. C., and S. Isenberg, *J. Am. Chem. Soc.*, *57*, 1349, 1935.

INDEX